A Second Course in

Complex Analysis

A Second Course in

Complex Analysis

William A. Veech

University of California, Berkeley

W. A. BENJAMIN, INC.

New York   Amsterdam

1967

To my Mother and Father
and to Kay

A Second Course in Complex Analysis

Copyright © 1967 by W. A. Benjamin, Inc.

All rights reserved

Library of Congress Catalog Card Number 67-20771

Manufactured in the United States of America

The manuscript was put into production on November 17, 1966;
this volume was published on June 30, 1967

W. A. Benjamin, Inc.
New York, New York 10016

Preface

It would be possible to guess with a fair degree of accuracy the contents of a book entitled *A First Course in Complex Analysis*. Not so however with one entitled *A Second Course in Complex Analysis*, and this is one of the pleasant aspects of the subject. With a working knowledge of the elements the curious student may proceed in a number of directions, any one of which will be richly rewarding. In the following we have chosen one of these directions.

This book is intended for the student, graduate or undergraduate, who (a) has had previous experience with complex analysis, (b) is well grounded in (plane) point-set topology, and (c) has sufficient background to understand not only a mathematical proof but also the development of a mathematical theory.

Our goal has been to present an integrated theory, and the tone, if not the pace, of the presentation is that of a modern research paper. It appears in retrospect that our goal has been more successfully approached with the closely related Chapters 1–4 than it has with Chapters 5 and 6 which are of a different character. For an undergraduate course we would, therefore, suggest the first four chapters be taken as a one-semester unit, while at a "quarter system" school the entire book could be covered in the second two terms of a three-term sequence. In a graduate course, where it should be possible to move rapidly through the first two chapters, much of the book can be covered in one semester.

It is my hope and intention that this book will be consulted as frequently by students engaged in independent study as by students actually enrolled in a "second course in complex analysis." Indeed, the choice of topics and manner of presentation has been greatly influenced by my own experience with such independent study.

The topics herein being for the most part classical, we have not attempted to cite chapter and verse of the literature for specific results. The bibliography contains many books which have directly influenced this work, and foremost among these are the books of Carathéodory.

v

The geometric flavor of Chapters 2–4 is one manifestation of the Carathéodory influence.

There are a number of people to whom thanks are due in connection with this work, and not the least of these are the many undergraduates at Princeton University who, over a period of three years, were subjected to the material at various stages of its development. I would also like to thank: Robert C. Gunning, who suggested such a text might be useful and who specifically suggested the inclusion of the Prime Number Theorem; the Mathematics Department of Princeton University, not only for its delightful atmosphere, but also for affording me the opportunity to teach the relevant course; the secretarial staff at Princeton, and particularly Patricia Clark, who did such excellent work in typing the manuscript; and finally my wife, Kay, who with patience and encouragement was behind me all the way.

WILLIAM A. VEECH

Berkeley, California
March 1967

Contents

CHAPTER 6   THE PRIME NUMBER THEOREM   200

chapter 1

Analytic Continuation

1. The Exponential Function and the Logarithm

The exponential function is defined by the power series

$$(1.1) \qquad e^w = \sum_{n=0}^{\infty} \frac{w^n}{n!}$$

which converges for each w. This function's usefulness stems from its being a solution to the differential equation

$$(1.2) \qquad \frac{dy}{dw} = y$$

as one sees through term-by-term differentiation.

To illustrate the importance of (1.2) we derive the relation

$$(1.3) \qquad e^{-w} = \frac{1}{e^w}$$

as follows. Set up the function $h(w) = e^{-w}e^w$ and differentiate using (1.2). The result is $h'(w) = -h(w) + h(w) \equiv 0$, meaning that h is constant. To calculate the constant set $w = 0$ and observe directly from (1.1) that $h(0) = 1$. Thus $h(w) \equiv 1$, and (1.3) is obtained. Notice we have also proved $e^w \neq 0$ for any w.

By a similar application of (1.2) one sees for fixed z that, as a function

1

of w, $e^{z+w}e^{-w} \equiv e^z$. In view of (1.3) the formula

(1.4)
$$e^{z+w} = e^z e^w$$

holds for all w. Letting z vary, it also holds for all z.

Equations (1.3) and (1.4) are basic to what follows.

Lemma 1.1.   If $w = u + iv$, where u and v are real numbers, then

(1.5)
$$|e^w| = e^u.$$

Furthermore, $|e^w| = 1$ if and only if $u = 0$; i.e., if and only if $w = iv$.

Proof.   We have $e^w = e^u e^{iv}$, and therefore

(1.6)
$$|e^w| = |e^u|\,|e^{iv}|.$$

We compute separately the factors on the right of (1.6). First $|e^{iv}|$:

If n is an integer, then because v is real, $\overline{(iv)^n} = (-iv)^n$, where $\overline{}$ denotes complex conjugation. Substituting $w = iv$ into (1.1) we see that $\overline{e^{iv}} = e^{-iv}$. Thus

(1.7)
$$
\begin{aligned}
|e^{iv}|^2 &= e^{iv}\overline{e^{iv}} \\
&= e^{iv}e^{-iv} \\
&= 1.
\end{aligned}
$$

As for $|e^u|$, we claim if $u > 0$ that

(1.8)
$$1 < e^u < \infty$$

and

(1.9)
$$0 < e^{-u} < 1.$$

The first inequality is immediate from (1.1) while the second is a consequence of the first. Since $e^0 = 1$, (1.5) and the second statement of our lemma now follow from (1.6)–(1.9).

The *logarithm* will be introduced as the inverse function to the exponential function. Before we make this introduction, it is necessary (a) to determine the range of e^w and (b) to devise a procedure for computing the inverse function. Toward (a) and (b) we establish the following statements:

(A) If $z \neq 0$, then $z = e^w$ for some w.

(B) Let U be an open disk which does not contain zero. If z_0, w_0 are such that $z_0 \in U$ and $e^{w_0} = z_0$, it is possible to define on U an analytic function φ having the properties

$$e^{\varphi(z)} = z, \quad z \in U$$

and

$$\varphi(z_0) = w_0.$$

We will observe that (B) implies (A), and then we will prove (B). Let z be a nonzero complex number. We assume for the moment that z does not lie on the negative real axis. There is, as the reader can show, an open disk U containing z and 1 but not zero. According to (B), z belongs to the range of e^w because 1 does. Thus all nonzero complex numbers, except possibly those which are real and negative, belong to the range of the exponential. If z is real and negative, let U be an open disk which contains z but not 0. U contains a point z_0 which is not real, and by what we have just seen, z_0 belongs to the range. Invoking (B) once more, z must belong to the range of e^w, and (A) is proved.

Now to prove (B). Suppose $z_0 = e^{w_0}$, and let U be an open disk which contains z_0 but does not contain zero. For each $z \in U$ let γ_z be the line segment from z_0 to z parametrized by $z(t) = z_0 + t(z - z_0)$, $0 \leq t \leq 1$. Define

(1.10)
$$\varphi(z) = w_0 + \int_{\gamma_z} \frac{d\zeta}{\zeta}.$$

Of course φ is well defined; one can compute directly (Problem 4) that φ is analytic with derivative $1/z$. Alternatively, one can call upon the following fact from the elementary theory:

Theorem. *Suppose f is analytic on a disk U, and let z_0 be a fixed point of U. For each $z \in U$ join z_0 to z by a differentiable arc γ_z. The function*

$$F(z) = w_0 + \int_{\gamma_z} f(\zeta)\, d\zeta$$

is analytic on U and satisfies $F'(z) = f(z)$.

Continuing with (1.10) we set up an auxiliary function, h, defined by

$$h(z) = \frac{e^{\varphi(z)}}{z}.$$

Using the relation $\varphi'(z) = 1/z$, we find

$$h'(z) = \frac{ze^{\varphi(z)}\varphi'(z) - e^{\varphi(z)}}{z^2}$$

$$= \frac{e^{\varphi(z)} - e^{\varphi(z)}}{z^2}$$

$$= 0.$$

Thus h is constant on U. To determine which constant, set $z = z_0$. Since $\varphi(z_0) = w_0$, we have $h(z_0) = (e^{w_0}/z_0) = 1$. It follows that $e^{\varphi(z)} = z$ for all z, and (B) is established.

Having satisfied ourselves that the equation $e^w = z$, $z \neq 0$, has at least one solution w for each z, we will now look for *all* solutions. The problem becomes simpler if we first find all solutions to

(1.11) $e^w = 1.$

For if w_1 and w_2 are solutions to $e^w = z$, then $w_2 - w_1$ is a solution to (1.11). Therefore knowing all solutions to (1.11) and one solution to $e^w = z$, one knows all solutions to the latter.

According to Lemma 1.1 the solutions to (1.11) have the form $w = iv$ for certain real numbers v. Let E be the set of real numbers

$$E = \{t \mid e^{it} = 1\}.$$

E is closed because e^{it} is continuous in t. Furthermore E contains together with any pair of numbers the sum and difference of that pair.

We will show that E contains a positive number. By statement (A) there exists a number w such that $e^w = -1$. Lemma 1.1 tells us that $w = is$ for some real number s. Since of course $s \neq 0$, one of the numbers $2s$ or $-2s$ is positive. Whichever it is, let t be that number. Since $e^{is} = -1 = e^{-is}$, we have $e^{it} = e^{is}e^{is} = 1$, meaning $t \in E$.

Because E contains positive numbers, the number

$$T = \inf\{t \in E \mid t > 0\}$$

is well defined. By definition $T \geq 0$, and since E is closed, $T \in E$[1]. Our object is to show $T > 0$.

If there is a $\delta > 0$ such that the interval $0 < t < \delta$ contains no elements of E, then by definition $T \geq \delta$. The existence of such a δ is a consequence

---

[1] This is a fact about the real numbers. The set E intersected with the interval $[0, \infty)$ is closed. Therefore any nonempty subset has a greatest lower bound which belongs to E.

of the "uniqueness theorem" for analytic functions (Problem 7); we include the following direct proof.

Lemma 1.2. There exists $\delta > 0$ such that if $0 < |w| \leq \delta$, then $e^w \neq 1$.

Proof. By (1.1) $e^w - 1 = wh(w)$, where h is the power series $h(u) = \sum_{n=1}^{\infty} (w^{n-1}/n!)$. Now h is continuous, and $h(0) = 1$. Therefore, there exists $\delta > 0$ such that if $|w| \leq \delta$, then $|h(w)| \geq \frac{1}{2}$. Clearly, if $0 < |w| \leq \delta$, $wh(w) \neq 0$, and *a fortiori* $e^w \neq 1$. The lemma is proved.

As we have remarked before Lemma 1.2, it follows that $T > 0$. If ζ is a complex number of absolute value 1, we shall denote by E_ζ the set

$$E_\zeta = \{s \mid e^{is} = \zeta\}.$$

If $\zeta = 1$, we continue to write $E = E_1$. Notice if s is one solution to $e^{is} = \zeta$, then

(1.12) $$E_\zeta = \{s + t \mid t \in E\}.$$

Lemma 1.3. The set E is generated by T in the sense that

(1.13) $$E = \{nT \mid n = 0, \pm 1, \ldots \}.$$

Proof. Naturally $nT \in E$ for each integer n. If t is an arbitrary element of E, we will use the definition of T to show that $t = nT$ for some n. To this end let n be an integer (positive, negative, or zero) such that $nT \leq t < (n + 1)T$. The number $t - nT$ belongs to E, and by our choice of n, $0 \leq t - nT < T$. Since T is the smallest *positive* element of E, we have $t - nT = 0$ or $t = nT$. This completes the proof.

Equations (1.12) and (1.13) combine to imply for each number ζ of absolute value 1 the existence of exactly one element of E_ζ in the interval $[0, T)$. What is the same, the function $z(t) = e^{it}$ maps $[0, T)$ in a one-to-one fashion onto the unit circle.

Similarly, for any real number v_0, $z(t) = e^{it}$ maps $[v_0 - T/2, v_0 + T/2)$ in a one-to-one fashion onto the unit circle.

Denote by γ the unit circle with parametrization $z(t) = e^{it}, 0 \leq t \leq T$. The length of γ is

$$\int_\gamma |dz| = \int_0^T |ie^{it}| \, dt$$

$$= T.$$

Define π to be the real number $T/2$. By definition the unit circle has length 2π.

REMARK.   Throughout this book we are assuming the *Cauchy integral formula*, at least for circles. If f is analytic inside and on a neighborhood of a circle γ, then

$$f(z) = \frac{1}{2\pi i} \int_\gamma \frac{f(\zeta)\, d\zeta}{\zeta - z}$$

for points z inside γ. The number π which enters here is the same as the number π defined above. To see this let us recall here in outline the proof of the integral formula.

The first step is to prove for points z inside γ that

$$\int_\gamma \frac{f(\zeta) - f(z)}{\zeta - z}\, d\zeta = 0$$

which, since $z \notin \gamma$, is the same as

$$f(z) \int_\gamma \frac{d\zeta}{\zeta - z} = \int_\gamma \frac{f(\zeta)\, d\zeta}{\zeta - z}.$$

The problem then is to compute

$$\varphi(z) = \int_\gamma \frac{d\zeta}{\zeta - z}.$$

To do this one shows that φ is constant as a function of z (Problem 8). Then letting $z = z_0$ be the center of γ, one explicitly evaluates $\varphi(z_0)$. For the latter, γ can be parametrized by $\zeta(t) = z_0 + Re^{2\pi it}$, $0 \le t \le 1$, where R is the radius. Since $d\zeta = 2\pi i Re^{2\pi it}\, dt$ and $\zeta - z_0 = Re^{2\pi it}$, we have

$$\int_\gamma \frac{d\zeta}{\zeta - z_0} = 2\pi i$$

and the integral formula follows.

In order to define $\log z$ we shall introduce two functions, one old and one new.

For real numbers $r > 0$ define $\ln r$, the natural logarithm of r, by the integral

$$\ln r = \int_1^r \frac{dx}{x}$$

over the real interval from 1 to r. Recall from statement (B) above, $e^{\ln r} = r$ for each $r > 0$.

If $z \neq 0$, arg z, the *argument* of z, is defined to be any real number t such that $e^{it} = (z/|z|)$. The upshot of our earlier discussion is that for any real number v_0 there is a unique value of arg z in the interval $[v_0 - \pi, v_0 + \pi)$. Note that arg z = arg $(z/|z|)$.

REMARK. If v_0 is real, consider the function $z(t) = e^{it}$ on the *open* interval $(v_0 - \pi, v_0 + \pi)$. The image of this interval contains all points of the unit circle save one, $e^{i(v_0 - \pi)} = -e^{iv_0}$. It is an elementary problem in point set topology to show that the mapping $e^{it} \to t$ is continuous on the set $\{e^{it} \mid v_0 - \pi < t < v_0 + \pi\}$. The same function is *not* continuous on the full unit circle.

Lemma 1.4. Let U be an open disk which does not contain zero. If $z_0 \in U$, and if v_0 is a prescribed value of arg z_0, the function h defined by

$$h(z) = \text{arg } z, \quad v_0 - \pi \leq \text{arg } z < v_0 + \pi$$

is continuous on U.

Proof. We write arg z as the composition of arg w, $|w| = 1$, with $w(z) = (z/|z|)$. Since $w(z)$ is continuous on U, the lemma will follow from the remark preceding it if we can show that $w(U) \subseteq \{e^{it} \mid v_0 - \pi < t < v_0 + \pi\}$.

Suppose to the contrary that $w(z) = (z/|z|) = -e^{iv_0}$ for some $z \in U$. Since by definition $(z_0/|z_0|) = e^{iv_0}$, it follows that $z = -(|z|/|z_0|)z_0$ is a positive multiple of $-z_0$. U is a disk, and therefore the line segment joining z_0 to z belongs to U. But zero lies on this segment contradicting the assumption that $0 \notin U$. Thus $-e^{iv_0} \notin w(U)$. The lemma is proved.

To define log z, let U be a disk which does not contain zero. Fix $z_0 \in U$ and a value v_0 of arg z_0. Define log z as

(1.14) $\log z = \ln |z| + i \text{ arg } z, \quad v_0 - \pi \leq \text{arg } z < v_0 + \pi.$

Both $\ln |z|$ and arg z are continuous on U, the latter by Lemma 1.4. Therefore log z is also continuous. Furthermore log z is an inverse function to the exponential:

$$
\begin{aligned}
e^{\log z} &= e^{\ln|z| + i \text{ arg } z} \\
&= |z| \cdot \frac{z}{|z|} \\
&= z.
\end{aligned}
$$

We now establish the relationship between equations (1.10) and (1.14).

Theorem 1.1. *Equation* (1.14) *defines an analytic function on U. In fact if* $w_0 = \log z_0$, *the function* φ *defined by equation* (1.10) *is equal to* $\log z$.

Proof. Since $e^{\log z} = z = e^{\varphi(z)}$, there exists an integer-valued function $n(z)$ such that

$$\varphi(z) = \log z + 2\pi i n(z), \quad z \in U.$$

What is more, $n(z)$ is continuous on U because both φ and $\log z$ are. A continuous integer-valued function on a disk reduces to a constant; the constant can be evaluated by setting $z = z_0$. Here by definition $\varphi(z_0) = \log z_0$ and $n(z_0) = 0$. Thus $n(z) \equiv 0$, and the theorem is proved.

REMARK. By virtue of Theorem 1.1 we have $(d/dz) \log z = (1/z)$. For later applications we will need the Taylor series of $\log(1 - z)$ about zero. To be precise, define for $|z| < 1$

$$\log(1 - z) = \ln|1 - z| + i \arg(1 - z), \quad -\pi \leq \arg(1 - z) < \pi.$$

Being the composition of two analytic functions $\log(1 - z)$ is analytic. By the chain rule

$$\frac{d}{dz} \log(1 - z) = -\frac{1}{1 - z}.$$

Another function with the same derivative for $|z| < 1$ is the series $-\sum_{n=1}^{\infty} \frac{z^n}{n}$. Therefore $\log(1 - z) = -\sum_{n=1}^{\infty} \frac{z^n}{n} + c$ for some constant c. Setting $z = 0$, we find $c = 0$. Thus we have obtained

$$(1.15) \qquad \log(1 - z) = -\sum_{n=1}^{\infty} \frac{z^n}{n}$$

for that version of $\log(1 - z)$ with $\log 1 = 0$.

Problems

1. Let f be analytic on a disk U with $f(z) \neq 0$, $z \in U$. If $z_0 \in U$, and if w_0 is such that $e^{w_0} = f(z_0)$, there exists on U an analytic function ψ such that $\psi(z_0) = w_0$ and $e^{\psi(z)} = f(z)$. (HINT: Let $w = f(z)$, $dw = f'(z)\, dz$, and proceed in analogy with (1.10).)

2. Using the fact that $(d/dz) \log z = (1/z)$, prove that

$$\frac{\partial}{\partial x} \ln|z| = \frac{x}{x^2 + y^2}, \quad \frac{\partial}{\partial y} \ln|z| = \frac{y}{x^2 + y^2},$$

$$\frac{\partial}{\partial x} \arg z = \frac{-y}{x^2 + y^2}, \quad \frac{\partial}{\partial y} \arg z = \frac{x}{x^2 + y^2}.$$

3. If α is complex, define $(1 + z)^\alpha$, $|z| < 1$, by

(1.16) $\qquad (1 + z)^\alpha = e^{\alpha \log (1+z)}, \quad \log 1 = 0.$

(a) If k is a nonnegative integer, then prove $(d^k/dz^k)(1 + z)^\alpha = \alpha(\alpha - 1) \cdots (\alpha - k + 1)(1 + z)^{\alpha-k}$, where $(1 + z)^{\alpha-k}$ is defined by (1.16) with $\alpha = \alpha - k$.

(b) Define $\displaystyle \binom{\alpha}{k} = \frac{\alpha(\alpha - 1) \cdots (\alpha - k + 1)}{k!}$, and use Taylor's theorem to prove

$$(1 + z)^\alpha = \sum_{k=0}^{\infty} \binom{\alpha}{k} z^k.$$

(c) If $\alpha = (p/q)$ for integers p and q, show using (1.16) that $\{(1 + z)^\alpha\}^q = (1 + z)^p$, the latter being defined in the usual sense.

4. Let U be a disk of radius R centered at z_1 with $|z_1| > R$. Then $0 \notin U$ and $1/z$ is analytic on U.

(a) From the equation $(1/z) = (1/(z_1 + z - z_1))$ conclude that

$$\frac{1}{z} = \sum_{n=0}^{\infty} \frac{(-1)^n}{z_1^{n+1}} (z - z_1)^n, \quad z \in U.$$

(b) Prove that the series $f(z) = \displaystyle\sum_{n=0}^{\infty} ((-1)^n/((n + 1)z_1^{n+1}))(z - z_1)^{n+1}$

converges on U.

(c) If γ is a differentiable curve in U from z_0 to z, then

$$\int_\gamma \frac{d\varsigma}{\varsigma} = f(z) - f(z_0).$$

(d) Conclude that the function (1.10) has derivative $1/z$.

5. Let f be a function which can be expanded in a power series about a point z_0. Unless $f \equiv 0$, there exists $\delta > 0$ such that if $0 < |z - z_0| \le \delta$, then $f(z) \ne 0$.

6. Let f be analytic on a region Ω. If $z_0 \in \Omega$, there exists an $R > 0$ such that the set $\{z \mid |z - z_0| \le R\}$ belongs to Ω. Parametrize an arc γ by $z_0 + Re^{2\pi i t}$, $0 \le t \le 1$. We have already mentioned the Cauchy integral formula

$$f(z) = \frac{1}{2\pi i} \int_\gamma \frac{f(\zeta)\, d\zeta}{\zeta - z}, \quad |z - z_0| < R.$$

(a) Compute $f^{(k)}(z)$ as an integral, $k = 1, 2, \ldots$
(b) Using the ideas of Problem 4 show that

$$f(z) = \sum_{k=0}^{\infty} \frac{f^{(k)}(z_0)}{k!} (z - z_0)^k$$

is true for $|z - z_0| < R$.

7. Let f be analytic on a region Ω. Define A and B to be the sets

$$A = \{z \in \Omega \mid f^{(k)}(z) = 0, \ k = 0, 1, \ldots\},$$
$$B = \{z \in \Omega \mid f^{(k)}(z) \ne 0 \text{ for some } k\}.$$

(a) Prove that A and B are open sets, using Problem 6 for A. Since Ω is connected, conclude that either $A = \emptyset$ and $B = \Omega$ or else $A = \Omega$ and $B = \emptyset$.
(b) Use Problems 5 and 6 to show that if f vanishes on a set E with limit point $z_0 \in \Omega$, then $f \equiv 0$. This is the "uniqueness theorem" for analytic functions.

8. Prove that

$$\varphi(z_0) = \int_\gamma \frac{dz}{z - z_0}$$

is constant inside a circle γ by showing that its derivative

$$\varphi'(z_0) = \int_\gamma \frac{dz}{(z - z_0)^2}$$

vanishes.

9. In Problem 6(a) let $M = \max_{z \in \gamma} |f(z)|$. Prove Cauchy's estimate

$$\frac{|f^{(k)}(z_0)|}{k!} \le \frac{M}{R^k}.$$

10. Use Problem 9 with $k = 1$ to show that a bounded entire function reduces to a constant (Liouville's theorem). (A function is *entire* if it is defined and analytic for all z.)

2. Continuation Sequences

Our discussion relates to the uniqueness theorem for analytic functions: If f is analytic on a region Ω, and if the zeros of f comprise an infinite set with limit point in Ω, then f is identically zero. A particular consequence of this theorem is that whenever two functions f and g, analytic on Ω, agree on a nonempty open subset of Ω, they must agree on all of Ω.

Suppose U_1, U_2, and U_3 are open disks whose pairwise intersections $U_i \cap U_j$, $1 \le i, j \le 3$ are nonempty. For analytic functions f_j on U_j, $j = 1, 2, 3$, such that $f_1 \equiv f_2$ on $U_1 \cap U_2$ and $f_2 \equiv f_3$ on $U_2 \cap U_3$, we investigate the possible existence of a function on the union $U_1 \cup U_2 \cup U_3$ which reduces to f_j on U_j. Clearly, such a function will exist just when $f_1 \equiv f_3$ on $U_1 \cap U_3$. There are two cases.

Case 1. $U_1 \cap U_2 \cap U_3 \ne \emptyset$. In this case $U_1 \cap U_2 \cap U_3$ is a nonempty open subset of the region $U_1 \cap U_3$. ($U_1 \cap U_3$ is clearly connected!) Since $f_1 \equiv f_3$ on $U_1 \cap U_2 \cap U_3$, it must be that $f_1 \equiv f_3$ on $U_1 \cap U_3$ by the uniqueness theorem.

Case 2. $U_1 \cap U_2 \cap U_3 = \emptyset$. The situation is markedly different and it need not be true that $f_1 \equiv f_3$ on $U_1 \cap U_3$. For example, let U_1, U_2, and U_3 be disks, none of which contains zero, such that

$$1, \quad e^{2\pi i/3} \in U_1, \quad e^{2\pi i/3}, \quad e^{4\pi i/3} \in U_2, \quad \text{and} \quad e^{4\pi i/3}, \quad 1 \in U_3.$$

(See Fig. 1.)

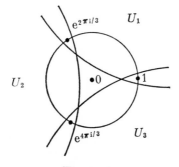

Figure 1.

We define f_1, f_2, and f_3 to be the following versions of $\log z$ (see (1.14)):

$$f_1(z) = \log z, \quad z \in U_1, \log 1 = 0,$$

$$f_2(z) = \log z, \quad z \in U_2, \log e^{2\pi i/3} = \frac{2\pi i}{3},$$

$$f_3(z) = \log z, \quad z \in U_3, \log e^{4\pi i/3} = \frac{4\pi i}{3}.$$

Here $f_1 \equiv f_2$ on $U_1 \cap U_2$ and $f_2 \equiv f_3$ on $U_2 \cap U_3$, however $f_3(1) = 2\pi i \neq f_1(1)$. This inconsistency makes it impossible to define a function on $U_1 \cup U_2 \cup U_3$ which reduces for each j to f_j on U_j.

There is an "ancestral" relationship between f_1, f_2, and f_3 in the following sense. The values of f_1 determine the values of f_3 because f_1 determines f_2, and f_2 determines f_3. We shall now introduce a device, the notion of a continuation sequence, whose purpose it is to keep account of such ancestral relationships.

For convenience of notation a pair (f, U) will be used to denote an *open* disk U upon which is defined an analytic function f. (Similarly, (g, V), (f_j, U_j), etc.)

Definition 2.1.   A finite sequence $\mathfrak{U} = \{(f_j, U_j)\}_{j=1}^n$ is a *continuation sequence* if

(i) $U_j \cap U_{j+1} \neq \emptyset, j = 1, \ldots, n - 1.$
(ii) $f_j \equiv f_{j+1}$ on $U_j \cap U_{j+1}, j = 1, \ldots, n - 1.$

The sequence $\mathfrak{U} = \{(f_j, U_j)\}_{j=1}^3$ formed from the functions and disks of the preceding example is a continuation sequence with $n = 3$. In general for $n \geq 3$ there will not exist a function on $U_1 \cup \cdots \cup U_n$ which reduces for each j to f_j on U_j.

Problems

1. Let f_1, f_2, and f_3 be the versions of $\log z$ defined in Case 2 above. For any other versions g_1, g_2, and g_3 satisfying $g_1 \equiv g_2$ on $U_2 \cap U_1$ and $g_2 \equiv g_3$ on $U_3 \cap U_2$, there exists a constant c such that $f_1 = g_1 + c$, $f_2 = g_2 + c$, $f_3 = g_3 + c$. Therefore, $g_3(1) - g_1(1) = f_3(1) - f_1(1) = 2\pi i$. Conclude that it is impossible to define $\log z$ to be analytic on a region containing $U_1 \cup U_2 \cup U_3$.

2. Show by example that the function φ in Problem 1, Section 1, need not be the composition of $\log w$, defined on the range of f, with f. That is, give an example of a disk U and a nonzero function f on U, such that $\log w$ cannot be defined on the region $f(U) = \{w \mid w = f(x), z \in U\}$. (HINT: Try $f(z) = z^8$ on $U = \{z \mid |z - 1| < 1\}$.)

3. Let $\mathfrak{U} = \{(f_j, U_j)\}_{j=1}^n$ be a continuation sequence.

   (a) If $f_1(z) = e^z$, $z \in U_1$, then $f_k(z) = e^z$, $z \in U_k$.

   (b) If F is entire, and if $f_1(z) = F(z)$, $z \in U_1$, then $f_k(z) = F(z)$, $z \in U_k$.

   (c) If $P(x_1, \ldots, x_n)$ is a polynomial in n variables, and if $P(f_1(z), f_1'(z), \ldots, f_1^{(n-1)}(z)) = 0$, $z \in U_1$, then $P(f_k(z), f_k'(z), \ldots, f_k^{(n-1)}(z)) = 0$, $z \in U_k$ (permanence of functional relations).

   (d) $\mathfrak{V} = \{(f_j', U_j)\}_{j=1}^n$ is a continuation sequence.

   (e) If f_j is constant for one j, all the functions are constant.

4. Let $U_1, \ldots, U_n$ be a sequence of disks, and suppose $0 \in U_k$ for some k. Does there exist a continuation sequence $\mathfrak{U} = \{(f_j, U_j)\}_{j=1}^n$ such that $f_1(z) = \log z$?

5. Let $U_1 = \{|z| < 1\}$, $U_2 = \{|z + 1| < 1\}$, $\ldots$, $U_n = \{|z + n| < 1\}$. Construct a continuation sequence $\mathfrak{U} = \{(f_j, U_j)\}$ with $f_1(z) = \sum_{n=0}^{\infty} z^n$, $z \in U_1$.

6. Let $\mathfrak{U} = \{(f_j, U_j)\}_{j=1}^n$ be a continuation sequence. If $U = \bigcap_{j=1}^n U_j \neq \emptyset$, there exists a function f on $U_1 \cup U_2 \cup \cdots \cup U_n$ which reduces to f_j on U_j for each j.

3. Continuation along an Arc

Continuation sequences are easier to deal with if one has some information regarding the relationship the individual disks bear to the conglomerate $U_1 \cup \cdots \cup U_n$. For this reason, among others, one usually speaks of "continuation along an arc." Before introducing this notion it will be necessary to make some general remarks concerning arcs.

Definition 3.1. Let γ be an arc with parametrization $z(t)$, $z(t)$ being a continuous function on an interval $a \leq t \leq b$. A sequence $U_1, \ldots, U_n$ is *admissible* for γ if each U_j is an open disk, and if there exist numbers

$t_1, \ldots, t_n, a \leq t_1 < t_2 < \cdots < t_n \leq b$, such that

$$z(t_j) \in U_j, j = 1, \ldots, n$$

(3.1)
$$z(t) \in \begin{cases} U_1, & a \leq t \leq t_1 \\ U_j \cup U_{j+1}, & t_j \leq t \leq t_{j+1} \\ U_n, & t_n \leq t \leq b. \end{cases}$$

REMARK. The reader should verify using (3.1) that $U_j \cap U_{j+1} \neq \emptyset$, $1 \leq j \leq n - 1$, if $U_1, \ldots, U_n$ is admissible for γ.

Roughly speaking, admissibility requires that γ be contained in the union $U_1 \cup \cdots \cup U_n$ "in order."

When one speaks of an arc γ, it is not always clear whether the set of points $\{z(t)\}_{a \leq t \leq b}$ or the function $z(t)$, $a \leq t \leq b$, is intended. We shall always mean the set *together* with the parametrization.

Definition 3.2. Parametrizations $z_1(t)$, $a \leq t \leq b$, and $z_2(\tau)$, $\alpha \leq \tau \leq \beta$, are said to be *equivalent* if there exists a continuous strictly increasing function $\tau(t)$ mapping the interval $[a, b]$ onto the interval $[\alpha, \beta]$ in such a way that $z_2(\tau) = z_1(t)$, $\tau = \tau(t)$.

If $\tau(t)$ is continuous and strictly increasing, so is the function $t(\tau)$ inverse to $\tau(t)$. Therefore Definition 3.2 is symmetric.

Taking $\tau_j = \tau(t_j)$ in (3.1) it becomes evident that a sequence $U_1, \ldots, U_n$ which is admissible for an arc γ is also admissible for an arc whose parametrization is equivalent with $z(t)$. (If $t_j < t_{j+1}$, then $\tau_j < \tau_{j+1}$.) We will assume, unless otherwise stated, that a given arc is parametrized by a function on $0 \leq t \leq 1$. If $z_1(t)$ is defined for $a \leq t \leq b$, an equivalent $z(t)$ on $0 \leq t \leq 1$ can be defined by

$$z(t) = z_1(a + (b - a)t), \quad 0 \leq t \leq 1.$$

Definition 3.3. A continuation sequence $\mathfrak{U} = \{(f_j, U_j)\}_{j=1}^n$ is an *analytic continuation along the arc* γ if the sequence $U_1, \ldots, U_n$ is admissible for γ.

We will usually speak of a "continuation along γ" dropping the word "analytic."

If $\mathfrak{U} = \{(f_j, U_j)\}_{j=1}^n$ is a continuation along γ, there is an arc η which arises in a natural way as the image of γ under $\mathfrak{U}$. If $z(t)$, $0 \leq t \leq 1$, is the parametrization of γ, and if $t_1, \ldots, t_n$ are as in (3.1), the parametrization of η is defined by

(3.2)
$$\zeta(t) = \begin{cases} f_1(z(t)), & 0 \leq t \leq t_1 \\ f_j(z(t)) \text{ or } f_{j+1}(z(t)), & t_j \leq t \leq t_{j+1} \\ f_n(z(t)), & t_n \leq t \leq 1. \end{cases}$$

Since $\mathfrak{U}$ is a continuation sequence, $f_j \equiv f_{j+1}$ on $U_j \cap U_{j+1}$. Thus, if $t_j \leq t \leq t_{j+1}$, and if $z(t) \in U_j \cap U_{j+1}$, it is irrelevant which function, f_j or f_{j+1}, is used to define $\zeta(t)$. We shall speak of an object f_j or U_j or (f_j, U_j) which is used to define $\zeta(t)$ as being *relevant* to t. For any t there are at most three pairs (f_j, U_j) relevant to t, and if $t \neq t_j$ for any j, there are at most two.

It is nearly obvious that $\zeta(t)$ is continuous. At any rate this fact will be a consequence of the discussion to follow. (Problem 1.) Our interest lies in determining the extent to which η depends upon $\mathfrak{U}$.

For fixed $t \in [0, 1]$ we claim there exists $\delta = \delta_t > 0$ such that if $s \in [0, 1]$, and if $|s - t| < \delta$, then for some j (f_j, U_j) is relevant both to s and to t. Consider first the case $t \neq t_1, \ldots, t_n$, and let U_j be relevant to t. By the continuity of $z(s)$ there exists $\delta > 0$ such that if $s \in [0, 1]$, and if $|s - t| < \delta$, then $z(s) \in U_j$. U_j will be *relevant* to such s if δ is also chosen to ensure that s and t lie in the same interval with respect to (3.1). Next, suppose $t = t_j$ for some j. If $t_j > 0$, there exists $\delta_1 > 0$ such that if $t_j - \delta_1 < s < t_j$, then U_j is relevant to s. Similarly, if $t_j < 1$, there exists $\delta_2 > 0$ such that if $t_j < s < t_j + \delta$ then U_j is relevant to s. Let $\delta = \min(\delta_1, \delta_2)$. U_j is then relevant to those numbers $s \in [0, 1]$ such that $|s - t| < \delta$.

For each t, $0 \leq t \leq 1$, let U^t be an open disk containing $z(t)$ and contained in the (obviously open) intersection of the disks which are relevant to t. The functions which are relevant to t agree on U^t, and we define f_t to be the restriction to U^t of any one of them. Let $\delta_t > 0$ be small enough so that if $0 \leq s, t \leq 1$ and if $|s - t| < \delta_t$, then

(a)
$$z(s) \in U^t,$$

and there exists a disk U_j relevant to s and t, meaning that

(b)
$$f_t \equiv f_s \text{ on } U^t \cap U^s.$$

If $\mathfrak{V} = \{(g_l, V_l)\}_{l=1}^m$ is a second continuation along γ, a similar construction is employed to associate pairs (g_t, V^t) and numbers $\epsilon_t > 0$ with each $t \in [0, 1]$. Properties (a) and (b) remain true if f and U are replaced by g and V.

Definition 3.4.   Continuations $\mathcal{U}$ and $\mathcal{V}$ along γ *have the same germ at* $z(t)$ if $f_t \equiv g_t$ on $U^t \cap V^t$.

REMARK.   The notion of a "germ" will be introduced in Section 4. The following two lemmas are practically immediate consequences of conditions (a) and (b).

Lemma 3.1.   Suppose the continuations $\mathcal{U}$ and $\mathcal{V}$ have the same germ at a point $z(t) \in \gamma$. If $s \in [0, 1]$ and $|s - t| < \min(\delta_t, \epsilon_t)$, then $\mathcal{U}$ and $\mathcal{V}$ have the same germ at $z(s)$.

Proof.   It is assumed that $f_t \equiv g_t$ on $U^t \cap V^t$. If $s \in [0, 1]$, and if $|s-t| < \min(\delta_t, \epsilon_t)$, condition (b) implies that $f_t \equiv f_s$ on $U^t \cap U^s$ and $g_t \equiv g_s$ on $V^t \cap V^s$. Therefore $f_s \equiv f_t \equiv g_t \equiv g_s$ on the open set $A = U^t \cap U^s \cap V^t \cap V^s$. A is nonempty because by (a) it contains $z(s)$, and therefore by the uniqueness theorem $f_s \equiv g_s$ on $U^s \cap V^s$. This is just the statement that $\mathcal{U}$ and $\mathcal{V}$ have the same germ at $z(s)$, and the lemma is proved.

The proof of Lemma 3.1 works "in reverse." If $s \in [0, 1]$ is such that $|s - t| < \min(\epsilon_t, \delta_t)$, and if $f_s \equiv g_s$ on $U^s \cap V^s$, then $f_t \equiv g_t$ on $U^t \cap V^t$. Therefore one can also state

Lemma 3.2.   Suppose the continuations $\mathcal{U}$ and $\mathcal{V}$ do *not* have the same germ at $z(t)$. If $s \in [0, 1]$, and if $|s - t| < \min(\delta_t, \epsilon_t)$, then $\mathcal{U}$ and $\mathcal{V}$ do not have the same germ at $z(s)$.

Lemmas 3.1 and 3.2 really say that the sets

$$E = \{t \mid \mathcal{U} \text{ and } \mathcal{V} \text{ have the same germ at } z(t)\}$$

and

$$F = \{t \mid \mathcal{U} \text{ and } \mathcal{V} \text{ do not have the same germ at } z(t)\}$$

are open as subsets of $[0, 1]$. Because they are obviously complementary sets, and because $[0, 1]$ is connected, it must be that $E = \emptyset$ or $F = \emptyset$.

Theorem 3.1.   *Continuations $\mathcal{U}$ and $\mathcal{V}$ along an arc γ will have the same germ at each point $z(t) \in \gamma$ if they have the same germ at **one** point of γ.*

Proof.   If $\mathcal{U}$ and $\mathcal{V}$ have the same germ at $z(t)$, then $E \neq \emptyset$, implying $E = [0, 1]$.

Theorem 3.2.   *Continuations $\mathcal{U}$ and $\mathcal{V}$ along an arc γ have the same germ at $z(0)$ if and only if they have the same germ at $z(1)$.*

Proof.   Immediate from Theorem 3.1.

Theorem 3.3.   *If* $\mathfrak{U}$ *and* $\mathfrak{V}$ *are continuations along an arc* γ, *the images of* γ *under* $\mathfrak{U}$ *and* $\mathfrak{V}$ *will be the same if there is one point of* γ *at which* $\mathfrak{U}$ *and* $\mathfrak{V}$ *have the same germ.*

Proof.   The images of γ under $\mathfrak{U}$ and $\mathfrak{V}$ are parametrized by $\zeta_1(t) = f_t(z(t))$ and $\zeta_2(t) = g_t(z(t))$. These functions will be the same by Theorem 3.1 if there is one point at which $\mathfrak{U}$ and $\mathfrak{V}$ have the same germ. This completes the proof.

Problems

1. Let $\zeta(t)$ be defined by (3.2). If $s \in [0, 1]$ and if $|s - t| < \delta_t$, show that $\zeta(s) = f_t(z(s))$. Therefore $\zeta(t)$ is continuous.

2. Let $f(z) = \displaystyle\sum_{n=0}^{\infty} a_n z^n$ be a power series whose radius of convergence is R, $0 < R < \infty$. Prove that f has at least one singularity on the circle $\{z \mid |z| = R\}$. That is, prove that for at least *one* θ, $0 \le \theta < 2\pi$, there is no continuation $\mathfrak{U} = \{(f_j, U_j)\}_{j=1}^{n}$ along γ_θ, $z(t) = tRe^{i\theta}$, $0 \le t \le 1$, with $f_1 \equiv f$ on $U_1 \cap \{|z| < R\}$. (HINT: Prove by contradiction. If $\mathfrak{U}$ is such a continuation along γ_θ, show that $Re^{i\theta} \in U_n$ and that $f_1 \equiv f_n$ on $U_1 \cap U_n$. Assuming there is a continuation for each θ use the Heine-Borel theorem to show that f can be defined to be analytic on a circle $|z| < R + \epsilon$, $\epsilon > 0$, meaning the power series would have radius of convergence at least $R + \epsilon$, a contradiction.)
3. If γ is a differentiable arc, then the image of γ under a continuation is also differentiable. Compute $d\zeta$ in terms of dz.

4. Germs

We have been speaking of continuations having the "same germ" at a point without actually defining "germ."

Definition 4.1.   Let f be analytic on a region Ω containing a point z. The *germ* of f at z is defined to be the set of all pairs (g, V), $z \in V$, such that $f \equiv g$ on $\Omega \cap V$. The germ of f at z is denoted by $[f]_z$.

It is important to emphasize that the germ of f at z is a collection of pairs (g, V) and not a function.

If (f, U) and (g, V) are such that $f \equiv g$ on $U \cap V$, and if $z \in U \cap V$, then we claim $[f]_z = [g]_z$. Suppose $(h, W) \in [f]_z$. Then $h \equiv f$ on $W \cap U$ by definition. Since $W \cap U \cap V \neq \emptyset$, and since $h \equiv f \equiv g$ on this set, it follows from the uniqueness theorem that $h \equiv g$ on $W \cap V$. Thus $(h, W) \in [g]_z$, and since (h, W) is arbitrary, $[f]_z \subseteq [g]_z$. By a similar argument $[g]_z \subseteq [f]_z$, and the germs are equal.

REMARK. If (f_t, U^t) and (g_t, V^t) are the pairs which were discussed in Section 3, it follows from these remarks that $\mathfrak{U}$ and $\mathfrak{V}$ have the same germ at $z(t)$ (in the sense of Definition 3.4) if and only if $[f_t]_{z(t)} = [g_t]_{z(t)}$.

Definition 4.2.   An element $(g, V) \in [f]_z$ is called a *representative* of the germ $[f]_z$.

Naturally (g, V) is a representative of $[f]_z$ just when $[g]_z = [f]_z$.

Definition 4.3.   Let $\mathfrak{U}$ be a continuation along an arc γ. If (f_t, U^t) is defined as in Section 3, the germ $[f_t]_{z(t)}$ will be referred to as the *germ of* $\mathfrak{U}$ *at* $z(t)$. The germs at $z(0)$ and $z(1)$ will be called respectively the *initial* and *terminal* germs; the continuation itself will be called a continuation of $[f_0]_{z(0)}$ along γ.

REMARK.   The germ $[f_t]_{z(t)}$ is independent of the choice of (f_t, U^t). If $\tilde{U}^t$ is another disk containing $z(t)$ and contained in each of the disks relevant to t, then obviously $\tilde{f}_t \equiv f_t$ on $U^t \cap \tilde{U}^t$. Thus $[\tilde{f}_t]_{z(t)} = [f_t]_{z(t)}$.

Problems

1. Let f be analytic on a neighborhood of 0, and consider $[f]_0$, the germ of f at 0. Define Ω to be the set of z which are contained in some disk V for which there is a representative $(g, V) \in [f]_0$.

   (a) Show that Ω is open. In fact show that Ω is a "star shaped" region. That is, Ω is open and for each $z \in \Omega$ and t, $0 \leq t \leq 1$, it is true that $tz \in \Omega$.

   (b) Define an analytic function φ on Ω such that $[\varphi]_0 = [f]_0$. Be careful to prove that φ is well defined.

   (c) Let $f(z) = \log(1 - z)$, $\log 1 = 0$, for $|z| < 1$. What is Ω? Same question for $f(z) = (1 - z)^{1/2}(1 + z)^{1/2}$, $|z| < 1$, defined with the help of Problem 3, Section 1. Same question for $f(z) = \prod_{j=0}^{n=1} (1 - \alpha_j z)^{1/2}$, $\alpha_j = e^{2\pi i j/n}$.

(d) Let $f(z) = \sum\limits_{n=0}^{\infty} z^{n!}$. By considering $f(re^{i\theta})$, $\theta = (2\pi p/q)$, show that $\Omega = \Delta$.

2. Let $[f]_z$, $[g]_z$, and $[h]_z$ be germs of functions at z. Define $[f]_z + [g]_z = [f + g]_z$. (How do you interpret $f + g$?)

   (a) Show that $([f]_z + [g]_z) + [h]_z = [f]_z + ([g]_z + [h]_z)$.
   (b) Show that $[f]_z + [0]_z = [f]_z$.
   (c) Show that $[f]_z - [f]_z = [0]_z$.

   Define $[f]_z \cdot [g]_z = [f \cdot g]_z$ (How do you interpret $f \cdot g$?)

   (a') Show that $([f]_z \cdot [g]_z)[h]_z = [f]_z([g]_z \cdot [h]_z)$.
   (b') Show that $[f]_z \cdot [1]_z = [f]_z$.
   (c') Show that $[f]_z([g]_z + [h]_z) = [f]_z[g]_z + [f]_z[h]_z$.
   (d') If $f(z) \neq 0$, show that $[f]_z \cdot [1/f]_z = [1]_z$.

   Define $\lambda[f]_z = [\lambda f]_z$ for complex numbers λ.

   (a'') Show that $\lambda([f]_z + [g]_z) = \lambda[f]_z + \lambda[g]_z$.
   (b'') Show that $(\lambda_1 + \lambda_2)[f]_z = \lambda_1[f]_z + \lambda_2[f]_z$.
   (c'') Show that $1[f]_z = [f]_z$.
   (d'') Show that $(\lambda[f]_z)[g]_z = \lambda([f]_z[g]_z) = [f]_z(\lambda[g]_z)$.
   (e'') Show that $\lambda\mu[f]_z = \lambda[\mu f]_z$.

   Finally note that $[f]_z + [g]_z = [g]_z + [f]_z$ and $[f]_z \cdot [g]_z = [g]_z \cdot [f]_z$.

   These facts imply that the collection $\{[f]_z\}$ of germs of analytic functions at z is in a natural way a *commutative algebra over the complex numbers*.

3. Let f_1 and f_2 be analytic on a region Ω. If $[f_1]_{z_0} = [f_2]_{z_0}$ for some $z_0 \in \Omega$, then $f_1 \equiv f_2$.

5. Existence of Continuations

It is usually a difficult problem to decide for a given germ whether there is a continuation of it along a given arc. Delving deeply into this matter of existence is beyond the scope of the present chapter; however, some elementary observations will be made.

It may be that the given germ is related analytically to another germ, a continuation of which is known along the given arc. The latter continuation often gives rise to a continuation of the first germ. For example, if $[g]_\alpha$ is the germ of a representative (g, U) at α, and if γ is an arc from α

along which there is a continuation of $[g]_\alpha$, then for any of the following pairs (f, U) there is a continuation along γ of the germ $[f]_\alpha$.

(5.1) $f(z) = g^{(k)}(z), \quad k > 0.$

(5.2) $f(z) = F(g(z)), \quad F$ entire.

(5.3) $f(z) = c + \int_{\gamma_z} g(\zeta)\, d\zeta.$

(5.4) $f(z) = P(f(z), f^{(1)}(z), \ldots, f^{(k)}(z)),$

   where P is a polynomial in $k + 1$ variables.

The arc γ_z in equation (5.3) is assumed to be a differentiable curve in U joining a fixed point z_0 to a variable point z. Cauchy's theorem for a disk tells us that the integral depends only upon z (and z_0).

Verification that the germs $[f]_a$ defined by equations (5.1)–(5.4) are continuable along γ is left to the reader in Problem 1.

The following lemma concerning the existence of admissible sequences is purely topological. It will be used in the proof of Theorem 5.1.

Lemma 5.1.   Let γ be an arc parametrized by $z(t)$, $0 \le t \le 1$, and suppose $\{U^t\}_{0 \le t \le 1}$ is a collection of open disks such that $z(t) \in U^t$ for each t. There exist numbers $t_1, \ldots, t_n$ such that, setting $U^{t_i} = U_j$ for each j, $U_1, \ldots, U_n$ is admissible for γ.

Proof.   For each t select, using the continuity of z, a number $\delta_t > 0$ such that if $0 \le s \le 1$, and if $|s - t| < \delta_t$, then $z(s) \in U^t$. The corresponding collection of intervals $I_t = \{s \mid |s - t| < \delta_t\}$ comprises an open covering of the interval $[0, 1]$. By the Heine-Borel theorem there exists a finite subcovering $I_{t_1}, \ldots, I_{t_n}$. We may assume $t_1 \le t_2 \le \cdots \le t_n$, and what is decisive, *we may also assume the integer n is as small as possible.* In other words there is no subcovering with fewer than n elements. Henceforth, to simplify notation we set $U^{t_i} = U_j$ and wherever t_j appears as a subscript, we replace it by j. Notice that by the minimality of n, $t_1 < t_2 < \cdots < t_n$.

The sequence $U_1, \ldots, U_n$ turns out to be admissible for γ. To see this we will prove that the numbers $t_1, \ldots, t_n$ satisfy (3.1).

If $t_j \le t \le t_{j+1}$, (3.1) requires that $z(t)$ belong to $U_j \cup U_{j+1}$. This will certainly be so if $t \in I_j \cup I_{j+1}$, since by the definition of $\delta_j(\delta_{j+1})$, if $t \in I_j(I_{j+1})$, it must be that $z(t) \in U_j(U_{j+1})$. Surely, $t \in I_k$ for *some* k because $I_1, \ldots, I_n$ is a covering. Let k be as small as possible. There are two cases:

Case 1. $k \leq j$. By definition of I_k $|t - t_k| < \delta_k$. We claim it follows that $|t - t_j| < \delta_j$. Indeed, if $|t - t_j| \geq \delta_j$, it is a consequence of the inequality $t_k < t_j \leq t$ that $I_j \subseteq I_k$, which contradicts the minimality of n. Thus $t \in I_j$ if $k \leq j$.

Case 2. $k \geq j + 1$. Here one proves by the method of Case 1 that $t \in I_{j+1}$ (meaning $k = j + 1$).

Whichever case is true, we have established that $t \in I_j \cup I_{j+1}$, and therefore $z(t) \in U_j \cup U_{j+1}$. It is left to be proved that $z(t) \in U_1$, for $0 \leq t \leq t_1$ and that $z(t) \in U_n$ for $t_n \leq t \leq 1$. Since these arguments also follow the lines of Case 1, they will be left to the reader. Pending them, the sequence $U_1, \ldots, U_n$ is admissible for γ, and the lemma is proved.

Theorem 5.1. *Let γ be an arc parametrized by $z(t)$, $0 \leq t \leq 1$. We suppose given pairs (h_t, U^t) and numbers $\delta_t > 0$ such that if $0 \leq s, t \leq 1$, and if $|s - t| < \delta_t$, then*

(a) $$z(s) \in U^t$$

and

(b) $$h_t \equiv h_s \text{ on } U^s \cap U^t.$$

Under these conditions there exists a continuation $\mathfrak{U} = \{(h_j, U_j)\}_{j=1}^{n}$ along γ whose germ at $z(t)$ is $[h_t]_{z(t)}$, $0 \leq t \leq 1$.

Proof. Select $I_1, \ldots, I_n$ and $U_1, \ldots, U_n$ as in the proof of Lemma 5.1. The sequence $U_1, \ldots, U_n$ is admissible for γ, and for each $j < n$ the interval $[t_j, t_{j+1}]$ is contained in the union $I_j \cup I_{j+1}$. The former is connected, and since $t_j \in I_j$ and $t_{j+1} \in I_{j+1}$, it is true that $I_j \cap I_{j+1} \neq \emptyset$. Set $h_{t_j} = h_j$ for each j. The sequence $\mathfrak{U} = \{(h_j, U_j)\}_{j=1}^{n}$ is, we claim, a continuation sequence and therefore a continuation along γ. To see that $\mathfrak{U}$ is a continuation sequence fix $j < n$ and select $t \in I_j \cap I_{j+1}$. From the definitions of δ_j and δ_{j+1} follow the identities $h_t \equiv h_j$ on $U_j \cap U^t$ and $h_t \equiv h_{j+1}$ on $U_{j+1} \cap U^t$. Since $U_j \cap U^t \cap U_{j+1} \neq \emptyset$ (it contains $z(t)$) the uniqueness theorem implies $h_j \equiv h_{j+1}$ on $U_j \cap U_{j+1}$. Therefore $\mathfrak{U}$ is a continuation sequence and *a fortiori* a continuation along γ. The theorem is proved.

Theorem 5.1 is a converse of sorts to the construction of Section 3. In that section pairs (f_t, U^t) and numbers $\delta_t > 0$ satisfying (a) and (b) were constructed from a given continuation. In Theorem 5.1 of course the continuation is constructed from the given pairs and numbers.

We conclude with a second (and somewhat trivial) application of

Lemma 5.1. Suppose h is analytic on a region Ω, and let $[h]_\alpha$ denote the germ of h at a fixed point $\alpha \in \Omega$. We will see that $[h]_\alpha$ can be continued along any arc γ in Ω from α. (What else could one expect?) For each t let U^t be an open disk in Ω containing $z(t)$. (We assume as usual that γ is parametrized by $z(t)$, $0 \leq t \leq 1$.) By Lemma 5.1 there exists a subcollection $U_1, \ldots, U_n$ which is admissible for γ. On U_j define $h_j(z) = h(z)$. Clearly, $\mathfrak{U} = \{(h_j, U_j)\}_{j=1}^n$ is a continuation along γ.

The observation of the preceding paragraph can be combined with (5.3) to yield a continuation of $\log z$. We take for Ω the region consisting of the nonzero complex numbers and for h the function $h(z) = 1/z$.

Theorem 5.2.   *Let z_0 and w_0 be such that $e^{w_0} = z_0$. If γ is an arc from z_0 which does not go through 0, there exists a continuation $\mathcal{V} = \{(f_j, U_j)\}_{j=1}^n$ along γ such that $f_1(z_0) = w_0$, and $e^{f_j(z)} = z$, $z \in U_j$.*

Proof.   Let $\mathfrak{U} = \{(h_j, U_j)\}_{j=1}^n$ be a continuation of $1/z$ along γ. $\mathfrak{U}$ exists by the remarks preceding this theorem. In (5.3) take $g = h_1$, $U = U_1$, $c = w_0$, and $\gamma_z = $ a curve from z_0 to z in U_1. Let $f_1 = f$ be the function defined by (5.3), and use Problem 2 to obtain a continuation $\mathcal{V} = \{(f_j, U_j)\}_{j=1}^n$ along γ. To see that $e^{f_j(z)} = z$, $z \in U_j$, one can either use the construction of Problem 2, or one can argue as follows. First, $e^{f_1(z)} = z$, $z \in U_1$, by construction. Then $n - 1$ applications of the uniqueness theorem imply successively that $e^{f_2(z)} = z$, $e^{f_3(z)} = z$, $\ldots$, $e^{f_n(z)} = z$, and the theorem is proved.

The continuation $\mathcal{V}$ of Theorem 5.2 is called a *continuation of* $\log z$ along γ.

The method of Theorem 5.2 can be used to effect other continuations of the logarithm. For example suppose φ is analytic on a region Ω with $\varphi(z) \neq 0$, $z \in \Omega$. Then $h = \varphi'/\varphi$ is analytic on Ω and hence continuable along any arc in Ω. An application of (5.3) gives rise this time to continuations of $\log \varphi$ (Problem 3).

Problems

1. Prove that there exist continuations along γ of the germs $[f]_\alpha$, representatives of which are defined by equations (5.1)–(5.4).
2. Let $U_1, \ldots, U_n$ be a sequence of disks none of which contains zero, and suppose $U_j \cap U_{j+1} \neq \emptyset$, $j = 1, \ldots, n - 1$. If $e^{w_0} = z_0$, and if $z_0 \in U_1$, define f_1 on U_1 using (1.10). Construct a continuation sequence $\mathfrak{U} = \{(f_j, U_j)\}_{j=1}^n$.

3. Let φ be analytic on a region Ω, and suppose $\varphi(z) \neq 0$, $z \in \Omega$. Prove that $\log \varphi$ can be continued along an arbitrary arc in Ω. (Refer to Problem 1, Section 1.)

4. Let Ω be a region, and suppose $0 \notin \Omega$. It is possible to continue $z^{1/2}$ along an arbitrary arc in Ω.

6. The Winding Number

This section concerns closed curves. It will be devoted to the definition and discussion of an integer called the "winding number" of a curve about a point. Roughly speaking the winding number $n(\gamma, w)$ of a closed curve γ about a point $w \notin \gamma$ is the number of times γ encircles w in the counterclockwise direction.

Theorem 6.1. *If w is a point which is not on a closed curve γ, and if $\mathfrak{U}$ is a continuation of $\log(z - w)$ along γ, denote by $\zeta(t)$, $0 \leq t \leq 1$, the parametrization of the image (Section 3) of γ under $\mathfrak{U}$. The number*

$$(6.1) \qquad n(\gamma, w) = \frac{\zeta(1) - \zeta(0)}{2\pi i}$$

is an integer which is independent of $\mathfrak{U}$.

Proof. Since $e^{\zeta(t)} = z(t) - w$, where γ is parametrized as usual by $z(t)$, and since $z(1) = z(0)$ for the closed curve γ, it is true that $e^{\zeta(1)} = e^{\zeta(0)}$. Therefore by Lemma 1.3 $(\zeta(1) - \zeta(0))/2\pi i$ is an integer.

Suppose $\mathfrak{U}_1$ is a second continuation of $\log(z - w)$ along γ, and let the image of γ under $\mathfrak{U}_1$ be parametrized by $\zeta_1(t)$. Of course, $e^{\zeta(t)} = e^{\zeta_1(t)}$ for each t, and therefore there exists an integer-valued function $k = k(t)$ such that $\zeta_1(t) = \zeta(t) + 2\pi i k$. Both $\zeta_1(t)$ and $\zeta(t)$ are continuous, and so $k(t)$ is a continuous integer-valued function on $[0, 1]$. Such a function must reduce to a constant because $[0, 1]$ is connected, and it follows that $\zeta_1(1) - \zeta_1(0) = \zeta(1) - \zeta(0)$. Thus $n(\gamma, w)$ is independent of $\mathfrak{U}$. and the theorem is proved.

Definition 6.1. The integer $n(\gamma, w)$ defined in (6.1) is called the *winding number* of γ about w.

For example, let γ be the unit circle parametrized by $z(t) = e^{2\pi i t}$, $0 \leq t \leq 1$, and let $w = 0$. Taking $\zeta(t) = 2\pi i t$, we have $n(\gamma, 0) = 1$.

It is sometimes convenient when a point w does not lie on the curve γ

to define a second curve $\gamma_0 = \gamma - w$ which does not contain 0. The parametrization of γ_0 is $z(t) - w$, and of course

$$
\begin{aligned}
n(\gamma_0, 0) &= n(\gamma - w, 0) \\
&= n(\gamma, w).
\end{aligned}
$$

If U is an open disk, and if $w \notin U$, then $\log(z - w)$ can be defined either by (1.10) or (1.14) to be analytic on U. If γ is a closed curve in U, the pair $(\log(z - w),\ U)$ is trivially a continuation along γ (with $n = 1$), and therefore $n(\gamma, w) = 0$ for any $w \notin U$. We have proved

Lemma 6.1.   If γ is a closed curve contained in an open disk U, and if w is a point not in U, then $n(\gamma, w) = 0$.

Lemma 6.2.   Let γ_1 and γ_2 be closed curves parametrized by $z_1(t)$ and $z_2(t)$, respectively. ($0 \leq t \leq 1$.) Define γ to be the arc whose parametrization is $z(t) = z_1(t)z_2(t)$. If neither γ_1 nor γ_2 contains 0, then

(6.2) $$n(\gamma, 0) = n(\gamma_1, 0) + n(\gamma_2, 0).$$

Proof.   Denote by $\mathfrak{U}$, $\mathfrak{U}_1$, and $\mathfrak{U}_2$ fixed continuations of $\log z$ along γ, γ_1, and γ_2, respectively. Also denote parametrizations of the images of these curves under their respective continuations by $\zeta(t)$, $\zeta_1(t)$, and $\zeta_2(t)$, $0 \leq t \leq 1$. We have for each t

$$
\begin{aligned}
e^{\zeta(t)} &= z(t) \\
&= z_1(t)z_2(t) \\
&= e^{\zeta_1(t)}e^{\zeta_2(t)} \\
&= e^{\zeta_1(t)+\zeta_2(t)}.
\end{aligned}
$$

By an argument we have seen before (in Theorem 6.1) the difference $\zeta(t) - \zeta_1(t) - \zeta_2(t)$ is independent of t. Therefore $\zeta(1) - \zeta(0) = (\zeta_1(1) - \zeta_1(0)) + (\zeta_2(1) - \zeta_2(0))$, and (6.2) follows.

An important consequence of Lemmas 6.1 and 6.2 is the geometrically obvious fact that if γ winds n times around a point w it must wind n times around all points sufficiently close to w. More precisely $n(\gamma, w)$ is "locally constant."

Theorem 6.2.   Let w be a point not on a closed curve γ. If $z(t), 0 \leq t \leq 1$, is the parametrization of γ, define

$$
\delta = \min_{0 \leq t \leq 1} |z(t) - w|.
$$

Then for any w_1 such that $|w_1 - w| < \delta$ we have $n(\gamma, w_1) = n(\gamma, w)$.

Proof. We remark first that δ, the infimum of a continuous, nonzero function on a compact set, is positive. Suppose now w_1 is such that $|w_1 - w| = \delta_1 < \delta$. Setting up the function $\zeta(t) = ((w - w_1)/(z(t) - w))$, we have $\max_{0 \le t \le 1} |\zeta(t)| \le \delta_1/\delta < 1$. Therefore if γ_1 is the arc parametrized by $z_1(t) = 1 + \zeta(t)$, $0 \le t \le 1$, γ_1 is a subset of the open disk of radius 1 about 1. By Lemma 6.1 $n(\gamma_1, 0) = 0$. Let γ_2 be parametrized by $z_2(t) = z(t) - w$. As remarked earlier $n(\gamma_2, 0) = n(\gamma, w)$. Now $z(t) - w_1 = z_1(t)z_2(t)$ and by Lemma 6.2

$$\begin{aligned} n(\gamma, w_1) &= n(\gamma - w_1, 0) \\ &= n(\gamma_1, 0) + n(\gamma_2, 0) \\ &= 0 + n(\gamma, w) \\ &= n(\gamma, w). \end{aligned}$$

Thus $n(\gamma, w_1) = n(\gamma, w)$, and the theorem is proved.

An almost immediate consequence of Theorem 6.2 is that $n(\gamma, w)$ is constant on connected sets.

Theorem 6.3. *Let U be a region which contains no points of a closed curve γ. Then the function $n(\gamma, w)$ is constant on U.*

Proof. For each integer n the set $A_n = \{w \mid n(\gamma, w) = n\}$ is open by Theorem 6.2. Define open subsets U_n of U by $U_n = A_n \cap U$. We claim $U_{n_0} = U$ for some n_0. To see this let n_0 be such that $U_{n_0} \ne \emptyset$. The set $V = \bigcup_{n \ne n_0} U_n$ is open and disjoint from U_{n_0}. Because U is connected, and because $U = U_{n_0} \cup V$, it must be that $U_{n_0} = \emptyset$ or $V = \emptyset$. The former is assumed not to be true, and therefore $V = \emptyset$. Thus $n(\gamma, w) = n_0$ on U, and the theorem is proved.

We have seen that $n(\gamma, 0) = 1$ when γ is the unit circle with its natural parametrization. It follows from Theorem 6.3 that $n(\gamma, z) = 1$, $|z| < 1$.

When γ is a differentiable curve, there is a familiar integral formula for $n(\gamma, w)$.

Theorem 6.4. *If γ is a closed differentiable curve, and if $w \notin \gamma$, then*

$$(6.3) \qquad n(\gamma, w) = \frac{1}{2\pi i} \int_\gamma \frac{dz}{z - w}.$$

Proof. Let $\mathfrak{U} = \{(f_j, U_j)\}_{j=1}^n$ be a continuation of $\log(z - w)$ along γ, and define φ_j for $j < n$ to be the function on $U_j \cup U_{j+1}$ which reduces to f_j on U_j and f_{j+1} on U_{j+1}. Select numbers $t_1, \ldots, t_n$ satisfying (3.1).

Since $z'(t)$ is continuous, we have for $j < n$

(6.4)
$$\frac{1}{2\pi i} \int_{t_j}^{t_{j+1}} \frac{z'(t)}{z(t) - w} \, dt = \frac{1}{2\pi i} [\varphi_j(z(t_{j+1})) - \varphi_j(z(t_j))]$$
$$= \frac{1}{2\pi i} [f_{j+1}(z(t_{j+1})) - f_j(z(t_j))].$$

We establish (6.3) by using (6.4) as follows:

$$\frac{1}{2\pi i} \int_\gamma \frac{dz}{z - w} = \frac{1}{2\pi i} \int_0^1 \frac{z'(t)}{z(t) - w} \, dt$$

$$= \frac{1}{2\pi i} \int_0^{t_1} \frac{z'(t)}{z(t) - w} \, dt + \sum_{j=1}^{n-1} \frac{1}{2\pi i} \int_{t_j}^{t_{j+1}} \frac{z'(t)}{z(t) - w} \, dt$$

$$+ \frac{1}{2\pi i} \int_{t_n}^1 \frac{z'(t)}{z(t) - w} \, dt$$

$$= \frac{f_1(z(t_1)) - f_1(z(0))}{2\pi i} + \sum_{j=1}^{n-1} \frac{f_{j+1}(z(t_{j+1})) - f_j(z(t_j))}{2\pi i}$$

$$+ \frac{f_n(z(1)) - f_n(z(t_n))}{2\pi i}$$

$$= \frac{f_n(z(1)) - f_1(z(0))}{2\pi i}$$

$$= n(\gamma, w).$$

Equation (6.3) is true, and the theorem is proved.

Theorem 6.4 extends to the case of a closed piecewise differentiable curve. (A curve which is the union of finitely many differentiable curves joined end to end.) The extension is left to the reader in Problem 1.

If f is analytic on a region Ω, and if γ is an arc in Ω, we shall denote by $f(\gamma)$ the image of γ under f. If γ is parametrized by $z(t)$, $0 \le t \le 1$, then $f(\gamma)$ is parametrized by $f(z(t))$, $0 \le t \le 1$. If γ is closed and piecewise differentiable, and if $f(z) \ne w$ for $z \in \gamma$, the formula

(6.5)
$$n(f(\gamma), w) = \frac{1}{2\pi i} \int_\gamma \frac{f'(z)}{f(z) - w} \, dz$$

is a consequence of Theorem 6.4.

Problems

1. If γ is a piecewise differentiable closed curve parametrized by $z(t)$, $0 \le t \le 1$, and if $w \notin \gamma$, then

$$n(\gamma, w) = \frac{1}{2\pi i} \int_\gamma \frac{dz}{z - w}.$$

(For γ to be *piecewise differentiable* there must exist numbers $s_1, \ldots,$ s_m, where $0 < s_1 < s_2 < \cdots < s_m < 1$, such that $z(t)$ is continuously differentiable on each of the intervals $[0, s_1]$, $[s_1, s_2]$, $\ldots,$ $[s_n, 1]$. Evidently, an arc equivalent with γ in the sense of Definition 3.2 need not be piecewise differentiable.)
2. Let Ω be a region upon which is defined a single-valued determination of $\log z$. If γ is a closed curve in Ω, then $n(\gamma, 0) = 0$.
3. If γ is a closed curve, show that $\lim_{z \to \infty} n(\gamma, z) = 0$.

7. The Argument Principle

In certain situations the number of zeros of an analytic function can be expressed in terms of a winding number. This is the "argument principle" which will be stated in Theorem 7.1.

We suppose fixed for the discussion a region Ω, a subregion $U \subset \Omega$, and a closed curve γ with the property that

(7.1) $$n(\gamma, z) = \begin{cases} 1, z \in U \\ 0, z \notin U \cup \gamma. \end{cases}$$

We think of γ as a boundary of U and will see presently that γ does contain the topological boundary[1] of U. In most applications γ and U are relatively uncomplicated, and (7.1) can be verified directly.

Suppose $z = \lim_{n \to \infty} z_n$ is a limit of points in U. If $z \notin U$, we claim $z \in \gamma$. To see this we combine (7.1) with Theorem 6.1. Should z not belong to γ, then $n(\gamma, z) = 0$ by (7.1). However by Theorem 6.1 $n(\gamma, z) = \lim_{n \to \infty} n(\gamma, z_n)$, and the right-hand side is 1, again by (7.1). From this contradiction we conclude that $z \in \gamma$ as claimed. The reader should show by example that γ need not consist entirely of limit points of U.

The set $U \cup \gamma$ is closed because by the last paragraph it contains all its

---

[1] The *topological boundary* of a region consists of those limit points of the region which do not themselves belong to the region.

limit points. If V is a disk containing γ, then $U \subseteq V$ because $n(\gamma, z) = 0$ if $z \notin V$. Therefore $U \cup \gamma$ is bounded and hence compact.

It is necessary to have one final assumption, an assumption which is really a special case of the argument principle itself. If h is analytic on Ω, and if $h(z) \neq 0$ for $z \in U \cup \gamma$, then we assume

$$(7.2) \qquad\qquad n(h(\gamma), 0) = 0.$$

One usually disguises the assumption (7.2) by invoking the Cauchy integral theorem. It is assumed that γ is differentiable and that for every function φ analytic on a region containing $U \cup \gamma$,

$$(7.3) \qquad\qquad \int_\gamma \varphi(\zeta)\, d\zeta = 0.$$

Taking $\varphi = h'/h$, where h is as in the preceding paragraph, it follows from (7.3) that

$$n(h(\gamma), 0) = \int_\gamma \frac{h'}{h}(\zeta)\, d\zeta$$
$$= 0.$$

(Of course, h'/h will not in general be analytic on Ω, however it will be analytic whenever $h(z) \neq 0$, and the latter is a region containing $U \cup \gamma$.)

It is often the case that the Cauchy integral theorem is unnecessary for (7.2). For example, let γ be for certain z_0 and $R > 0$ the circle of radius R about z_0 parametrized in the natural way by $z(t) = z_0 + Re^{2\pi i t}$, $0 \le t \le 1$. U will be the inside of γ, and for each r ($0 \le r \le R$) we let γ_r be the circle given by $z_r(t) = z_0 + re^{2\pi i t}$, $0 \le t \le 1$. Note that $\gamma_R = \gamma$. Now suppose h is analytic on a region containing $U \cup \gamma$, and suppose $h(z) \neq 0$ for $z \in U \cup \gamma$. It follows for each r, $0 \le r \le R$, that the number $\Psi(r) = n(h(\gamma_r), 0)$ is well defined. Of course, Ψ is integer-valued, and Ψ is easily proved to be continuous (Problem 4). Therefore Ψ is constant, and because $\Psi(0) = 0$, it must be that $\Psi(R) = n(h(\gamma), 0) = 0$. Thus (7.2) obtains.

What follows is the argument principle.

Theorem 7.1. Ω, U, *and* γ *are assumed to be as above. If* f *is analytic on* Ω, *and if* $f(z) \neq 0$ *for* $z \in \gamma$, *then* $n(f(\gamma), 0)$ *represents the number of zeros*[2] *of* f *in* U.

Proof.   If f is nonzero on U, there is nothing to prove because we can take $h = f$ in assumption (7.2). If f does vanish on U, we claim it can do

---

[2] Counting multiplicities. A zero of order n is counted as n zeros.

so at only finitely many points. Indeed an infinite subset of U has a limit point in $U \cup \gamma$ which is contained in the region (Ω) of analyticity. If f vanished on such a set, f would vanish identically by the uniqueness theorem, but we have assumed $f \not\equiv 0$. Let $z_1, \ldots, z_k$ be the zeros of f in U with multiplicities $n_1, \ldots, n_k$. There exists an analytic function h on Ω such that

$$(7.4) \qquad f(z) = (z - z_1)^{n_1}(z - z_2)^{n_2} \cdots (z - z_k)^{n_k}h(z),$$

and furthermore $h(z) \neq 0$ for $z \in U \cup \gamma$. By Lemma 6.2 (for the product of $n_1 + \cdots + n_k + 1$ parametrizations instead of only two) $n(f(\gamma), 0) = n_1 n(\gamma - z_1, 0) + \cdots + n_k n(\gamma - z_k, 0) + n(h(\gamma), 0)$. This equality together with equations (7.1) and (7.2) tells us

$$(7.5) \qquad n(f(\gamma), 0) = n_1 + \cdots + n_k.$$

The right-hand side of (7.4) is the number of zeros of f in U, counting multiplicities, and therefore the theorem is proved.

REMARK. If γ is piecewise differentiable, in which case $n(f(\gamma), 0)$ is expressed by the integral (6.5), it is useful to compute f'/f by means of (7.4). Doing so, one obtains

$$(7.6) \qquad \frac{f'(z)}{f(z)} = \frac{n_1}{(z - z_1)} + \cdots + \frac{n_k}{(z - z_k)} + \frac{h'(z)}{h(z)},$$

from which the integral (6.5) can be computed:

$$
\begin{aligned}
n(f(\gamma), 0) &= \frac{1}{2\pi i} \int_\gamma \frac{f'(z)}{f(z)}\, dz \\
&= \sum_{j=1}^{k} \frac{n_j}{2\pi i} \int_\gamma \frac{dz}{z - z_j} + \frac{1}{2\pi i} \int_\gamma \frac{h'(z)}{h(z)}\, dz \\
&= n_1 + \cdots + n_k.
\end{aligned}
$$

Theorem 7.1 applies immediately to the function $f(z) - w$ to yield

Theorem 7.1'.   *Let notations be fixed as in Theorem 7.1. If $f(z) \neq w$ for $z \in \gamma$, then $n(f(\gamma), w)$ represents the number of times f assumes the value w in U.*

REMARK. If U is a disk with boundary γ (natural parametrization), the assumptions of Theorems 7.1 and 7.1' hold for any region containing $U \cup \gamma$. Thus Theorems 7.1, 7.1', and their consequences are true for disks.

The "open mapping theorem" is practically a direct consequence of Theorem 7.1′.

Theorem 7.2.   (Open Mapping Theorem)   *The image of a region* Ω *under a nonconstant analytic function f is an open set.*

Proof.   Denote by $f(\Omega)$ the image of Ω under f. $f(\Omega) = \{f(z) \mid z \in \Omega\}$. Given $w_0 \in f(\Omega)$ let $z_0 \in \Omega$ be such that $f(z_0) = w_0$. Because f is nonconstant, there exists a circle γ which together with its inside is contained in Ω, and such that γ is centered at z_0 and $f(z) \neq w_0, z \in \gamma$. By Theorem 7.1′ $n(f(\gamma), w_0) \neq 0$. There exists according to Theorem 6.1 a number $\delta > 0$ such that if $|w - w_0| < \delta$, then $n(f(\gamma), w) = n(f(\gamma), w_0)$. Again by Theorem 7.1′ $w \in f(\Omega)$. Since w_0 is arbitrary, $f(\Omega)$ is open, and the theorem is proved.

For a final application (aside from the problems) of the argument principle we prove Rouché's theorem, known sometimes as the "dog walking" theorem.[3]

Theorem 7.3.   (Rouché)   *Let* Ω, *U, and* γ *be as in Theorem* 7.1.   *If f and g are analytic on* Ω, *and if* $|g(z)| < |f(z)|$ *for each* $z \in \gamma$, *then f + g has the same number of zeros in U as does f.*

Proof.   On γ define $h(z) = 1 + g(z)/f(z)$. Since $|g(z)| < |f(z)|$ for $z \in \gamma$, the image $h(\gamma)$ of γ under h lies in the open disk of radius 1 about 1. By Lemma 6.1 $n(h(\gamma), 0) = 0$, and since $f + g = f \cdot h$ on γ, Lemma 6.2 tells us

$$\begin{aligned}
n((f + g)(\gamma), 0) &= n((f \cdot h)(\gamma), 0) \\
&= n(f(\gamma), 0) + n(h(\gamma), 0) \\
&= n(f(\gamma), 0).
\end{aligned}$$

It now follows from Theorem 7.1 that $f + g$ and f have the same number of zeros in U.

REMARK.   Sometimes Rouché's theorem is given an equivalent formulation. Instead of assuming $|g(z)| < |f(z)|$ on γ it is assumed that $|g(z) - f(z)| < |f(z)|$ on γ. The conclusion corresponding to this assumption is that $(g - f) + f = g$ and f have the same number of zeros in U.

---

[3] A man, $f(z(t))$, walks a dog, $f(z(t)) + g(z(t))$ holding him on a leash of variable length $|g(z(t))|$. As the man walks around a tree, 0, the dog will follow so long as $|g(z(t))| < |f(z(t))|$.

Problems

1. Let f be analytic in a neighborhood of z_0, and suppose $f'(z_0) \neq 0$.

   (a) If $w_0 = f(z_0)$, there exists $\epsilon > 0$ such that $f(z) \neq w_0$ for $0 < |z - z_0| \leq \epsilon$.

   (b) Set $\delta = \min\limits_{|z-z_0|=\epsilon} |f(z) - w_0|$. If $|w - w_0| < \delta$, there exists a *unique* value of z with $|z - z_0| < \epsilon$, such that $f(z) = w$. Define $h(w) = z$.

   (c) Prove h is analytic for $|w - w_0| < \delta$. Do this by first showing $f'(z) \neq 0$ if $|f(z) - w_0| < \delta$. Then prove

   $$\lim_{w' \to w} \frac{h(w') - h(w)}{w' - w} = \lim_{z' \to z} \frac{z' - z}{f(z') - f(z)}.$$

   (d) By definition of h, $f(h(w)) = w$ for $|w - w_0| < \delta$. Show that in some neighborhood of z_0, $h(f(z)) = z$.

   Usually h will be referred to as "the version of f^{-1} with $f^{-1}(w_0) = z_0$."

2. Let f, z_0, ϵ, and δ be as in Problem 1. Prove that

   $$f^{-1}(w) = \frac{1}{2\pi i} \int_\gamma \frac{\zeta f'(\zeta)}{f(\zeta) - w} \, d\zeta,$$

   where γ is the circle $\{\zeta \mid |\zeta - z_0| = \epsilon\}$ with the natural parametrization. (HINT: $f(\zeta) - w = (\zeta - w)g_w(\zeta)$, where g_w is analytic and nonvanishing inside and on γ.)

3. The following is also called the "argument principle." Let Ω, U, and γ satisfy the hypotheses of Theorem 7.1. If f is *meromorphic* on Ω with neither poles nor zeros on γ, then $n(f(\gamma), 0) = n - m$, where n and m are, respectively, the number of zeros and the number of poles of f in U. (HINT: Write

   $$f(z) = \frac{\prod\limits_{j=1}^{k} (z - a_j)^{n_i}}{\prod\limits_{i=1}^{l} (z - b_i)^{m_i}} \, h(z),$$

   where h has neither poles nor zeros in U. Argue as in Theorem 7.1.)

4. Let f be *continuous* and nonvanishing on the annulus $A(r_1, r_2) = \{z \mid r_1 < |z| < r_2\}$. If γ_r is the circle of radius r centered at 0 with the natural parametrization, define

   $$N(r) = n(f(\gamma_r), 0), \quad r_1 < r < r_2.$$

(a) For fixed r, $r_1 < r < r_2$, let $\delta = \min\limits_{|z|=r} |f(z)|$. Prove there exists $\epsilon > 0$ such that if $|r - s| < \epsilon$, then $\max\limits_{0 \le \theta \le 2\pi} |f(re^{i\theta}) - f(se^{i\theta})| < \delta/2$. For such s prove $N(s) = N(r)$.

(b) Using (a) and a connectedness argument conclude that $N(r)$ is constant.

(c) If f is a continuous function defined on the plane, and if $N(r) \ne 0$ for some r, then f has a zero. (HINT: If $f(0) \ne 0$, $N(0) = 0$.)

5. Prove there is no continuous retraction of the unit disk onto its boundary. That is, prove there exists no continuous function f on $\{z \mid |z| \le 1\}$ such that

(a) $|f(z)| = 1$, $|z| \le 1$

and

(b) $f(z) = z$, $|z| = 1$.

6. Prove the "Brouwer fixed point theorem." If f is a continuous mapping of $\{z \mid |z| \le 1\}$ into itself, there exists a fixed point, a point z_0 such that $f(z_0) = z_0$. (HINT: If $f(z) - z$ is not zero for any z such that $|z| = 1$, let $h(z) = f(z) - z$ and prove $N(1) = 1$ for h.)

7. Let $P(z) = a_n z^n + a_{n-1} z^{n-1} + \cdots + a_0$. If $a_n \ne 0$ prove that P has n zeros. (Fundamental theorem of algebra.)

8. The polynomial $P(z) = 3z^{15} + 4z^8 + 6z^5 + 19z^4 + 3z + 1$ has

(a) 4 zeros for $|z| < 1$,

(b) 11 zeros for $1 < |z| < 2$.

9. Prove the "maximum principle": If f is analytic on a region Ω, and if $z_0 \in \Omega$ is a point such that $|f(z_0)| \ge |f(z)|$ for each $z \in \Omega$, then f reduces to a constant.

10. If $P(z) = a_0 + a_1 z + \cdots + a_n z^n$ with $0 < a_0 < a_1 < \cdots < a_n$, then P has n zeros inside the unit circle. (Consider $(1 - z)P(z)$ as $f + g$, where $f(z) = -a_n z^{n+1}$.)

11. Assume Ω, U, and γ to be related as in Theorem 7.1, and furthermore assume γ is piecewise differentiable. If f and g are analytic on Ω, and if $f(z) \ne 0$ on γ, then

$$\frac{1}{2\pi i} \int_\gamma g(\zeta) \frac{f'(\zeta)}{f(\zeta)} d\zeta = \sum_{\substack{f(z)=0 \\ z \in U}} g(z).$$

(If f has an n-fold zero at $z \in U$, then $g(z)$ occurs n times in the sum.)

12. Let Ω be a region containing closed curves $\gamma_1, \ldots, \gamma_n$, and suppose U is a subregion of Ω such that

$$\sum_{j=1}^{n} n(\gamma_j, z) = \begin{cases} 1, & z \in U \\ 0, & z \notin U \cup \gamma_1 \cup \cdots \cup \gamma_n. \end{cases}$$

Formulate an argument principle in this situation.

8. The Monodromy Theorem

Returning to the topic of analytic continuation *per se*, recall Theorem 3.2 which says that the terminal germ of a continuation along an arc is uniquely determined by the initial germ of that continuation. If we think of an arc as simply a path between fixed end points, it is natural to ask whether the terminal germ is "independent of path." In other words, if γ_0 and γ_1 are separate arcs between points α and β, and if $[f]_\alpha$ is a germ such that there are continuations $\mathfrak{U}_0$ and $\mathfrak{U}_1$ of $[f]_\alpha$ along γ_0 and γ_1, must $\mathfrak{U}_0$ and $\mathfrak{U}_1$ have the same germ at β? In general the answer is "no." For example take $\alpha = 1 = \beta$ to be the same, and define parametrizations of γ_0 and γ_1 by $z_0(t) = e^{2\pi i t}$ and $z_1(t) = 1, 0 \leq t \leq 1$. Let $\mathfrak{U}_0 = \{(f_j, U_j)\}_{j=1}^{3}$ be the continuation of $\log z$ constructed in Section 2, and let $\mathfrak{U}_1 = \{(f_1, U_1)\}$. So defined, $\mathfrak{U}_0$ and $\mathfrak{U}_1$ have the same initial germ $[f_1]_1$ but different terminal germs $[f_3]_1$ and $[f_1]_1$.

The situation of the preceding example is explained very well by the monodromy theorem, Theorem 8.1. Before this remark can be amplified, and before the monodromy theorem can be stated, it is necessary to engage in some purely topological preliminaries. We shall introduce the generalization of equality, called *homotopy*, between curves. The monodromy theorem will then say that under appropriate assumptions continuations of a germ $[f]_\alpha$ along arcs γ_0 and γ_1 from α to β will have the same germ at β if the arcs are "equal" in the sense of homotopy.

In all that follows γ_0 and γ_1 will be assumed to be arcs from α to β parametrized by $z_0(t)$ and $z_1(t)$, $0 \leq t \leq 1$. Naturally, $z_0(0) = \alpha = z_1(0)$ and $z_0(1) = \beta = z_1(1)$.

Definition 8.1. A continuous function $z(s, t)$, $0 \leq s, t \leq 1$, is called a *homotopy* between γ_0 and γ_1 if

(8.1) $\qquad z(0, t) = z_0(t) \quad \text{and} \quad z(1, t) = z_1(t), \quad 0 \leq t \leq 1$

and

(8.2) $\qquad z(s, 0) = \alpha \quad \text{and} \quad z(s, 1) = \beta, \quad 0 \leq s \leq 1.$

Note that for each s the function $z_s(t) = z(s, t)$, $0 \le t \le 1$, provides a parametrization of an arc γ_s from α to β. The arcs γ_s provide a continuous transition from γ_0 to γ_1 or vice-versa. (Indeed $w(s, t) = z(1 - s, t)$ is a homotopy which reverses the roles of γ_0 and γ_1.)

There always exists a homotopy between γ_0 and γ_1. For example define

$$(8.3) \qquad z(s, t) = sz_1(t) + (1 - s)z_0(t).$$

Definition 8.2.   If the arcs γ_0 and γ_1 lie in a region Ω, we say they are *homotopic with respect to* Ω and write $\gamma_0 \underset{\Omega}{\sim} \gamma_1$, if there exists a homotopy $z(s, t)$ between γ_0 and γ_1 such that $z(s, t) \in \Omega$ for $0 \le s, t \le 1$. Where Ω is understood, we write $\gamma_0 \sim \gamma_1$.

In preparation of the monodromy theorem we fix a region Ω, a point $\alpha \in \Omega$, and a germ $[f]_\alpha$ at α. The following assumption is crucial: *If γ is an arc in Ω from α, there shall exist a continuation of $[f]_\alpha$ along γ.*

Theorem 8.1.   (Monodromy Theorem)   *If $\gamma_0 \sim \gamma_1$, then continuations of $[f]_\alpha$ along γ_0 and γ_1 have the same terminal germ.*

Proof.   Because $\gamma_0 \sim \gamma_1$, there is a homotopy $z(s, t)$ between γ_0 and γ_1 such that $z(s, t) \in \Omega$ for all s, t. If $0 \le s \le 1$ denote by γ_s the arc $z_s(t) = z(s, t)$, and let $\mathfrak{U}_s$ be a continuation of $[f]_\alpha$ along γ_s. (We assume $\mathfrak{U}_0$ and $\mathfrak{U}_1$ are the given continuations.) Suppose $\mathfrak{U}_s = \{(f_j^s, U_j^s)\}_{j=1}^{n_s}$.

Fix s and $n = n_s$. The sequence $U_1^s, \ldots, U_n^s$ is admissible for γ_s. Using the uniform continuity of $z(s, t)$ in s and t, there exists $\delta_s > 0$ such that if $0 \le s' \le 1$ and $|s - s'| < \delta_s$, then $U_1^s, \ldots, U_n^s$ is admissible for $\gamma_{s'}$ (Problem 3.) Thus if $s' \in [0, 1]$, and if $|s' - s| < \delta_s$, $\mathfrak{U}_s$ is a continuation along $\gamma_{s'}$. By Theorem 3.2 both $\mathfrak{U}_s$ and $\mathfrak{U}_{s'}$ have the same terminal germ.

It is a consequence of the preceding paragraph that each of the sets

$$A = \{s' \mid \mathfrak{U}_{s'} \text{ has the same terminal germ as } \mathfrak{U}_0\}$$

and

$$B = \{s' \mid \mathfrak{U}_{s'} \text{ does not have the same terminal germ as } \mathfrak{U}_0\}$$

is open as a subset of $[0, 1]$. By the connectedness of $[0, 1]$ either $A = \emptyset$ or $B = \emptyset$; since $0 \in A$, it must be that $B = \emptyset$. Therefore, $A = [0, 1]$, and in particular $1 \in A$. Thus $\mathfrak{U}_0$ and $\mathfrak{U}_1$ have the same terminal germ. The theorem is proved.

Let Ω be the set of nonzero complex numbers. If γ_0 and γ_1 are the arcs described in the first paragraph, it cannot be that $\gamma_0 \underset{\Omega}{\sim} \gamma_1$ because there are continuations of log z along γ_0 and γ_1 with identical initial germs and different terminal germs.

Definition 8.3. A region Ω is *simply connected* if whenever γ_0 and γ_1 are arcs in Ω with mutual end points, γ_0 and γ_1 are homotopic with respect to Ω.

If Ω is a (convex) region such that whenever z_0 and z_1 belong to Ω, the line segment joining them belongs to Ω, then Ω is simply connected. (The line segment between z_0 and z_1 is the set of points z expressible as $z = sz_1 + (1 - s)z_0$, $0 \le s \le 1$.) Indeed, (8.3) defines a homotopy with respect to Ω between curves in Ω.

Theorem 8.2. *Suppose Ω, α, and $[f]_\alpha$ are as in Theorem 8.1. If Ω is simply connected, there exists a function φ, analytic on Ω, such that the germ $[\varphi]_\alpha$ of φ at α is $[f]_\alpha$.*

Proof. Fix $z \in \Omega$ and an arc γ_z in Ω from α to z. There exists a continuation $\mathfrak{U}_z$ of $[f]_\alpha$ along γ_z, and because Ω is simply connected, the monodromy theorem implies that the germ $[f_z]_z$ of $\mathfrak{U}_z$ at z is independent of γ_z. Let (f_z, U_z) be a representative of $[f_z]_z$, and define

$$\varphi(z) = f_z(z).$$

Repeating this for each $z \in \Omega$, φ is defined on all of Ω.

To see that φ is analytic at z, let (f_z, U_z) and γ_z be as above. If $\zeta \in U_z$, let γ_ζ be the arc consisting of γ_z with the line segment from z to ζ attached. Clearly, $\mathfrak{U}_z$ is a continuation of $[f]_\alpha$ along γ_ζ, and therefore $\varphi(\zeta) = f_z(\zeta)$. It follows that φ is analytic on U_z and in particular at z. Since z is arbitrary, φ is analytic on Ω, and obviously $[\varphi]_\alpha = [f]_\alpha$.

Immediate corollaries to Theorem 8.2 and Theorem 5.3 are Theorems 8.3 and 8.4.

Theorem 8.3. *Let Ω be a simply connected region which does not contain 0. If α and β are such that $\alpha = e^\beta$, there exists a single valued determination of $\log z$ on Ω with $\log \alpha = \beta$.*

Proof. For $[f]_\alpha$ we take that germ of $\log z$ at α for which $\log \alpha = \beta$. By Theorem 5.3 this germ can be continued along any arc in Ω, and by Theorem 8.2 there exists an analytic function φ on Ω such that $[\varphi]_\alpha = [f]_\alpha$. Since $e^{\varphi(z)} = z$ in a neighborhood of α, the uniqueness theorem implies that $e^{\varphi(z)} = z$, $z \in \Omega$. Therefore, φ is the desired determination of $\log z$ on Ω.

The proof of Theorem 8.4 is similar and will be left to the reader.

Theorem 8.4. *Let Ω be a simply connected region. If f is analytic on Ω, and if $f(z) \neq 0$ for $z \in \Omega$, then there exists a single-valued determination φ of $\log f$ on Ω. If z_0 and w_0 are such that $e^{w_0} = f(z_0)$, the function φ can be chosen so that $\varphi(z_0) = w_0$.*

Problems

1. Let f be an entire function without zeros. Then $f(z) = e^{g(z)}$ for some entire function g.
2. Let f and g be entire functions. If f and g have the same zeros counting multiplicities, then $f(z) = e^{h(z)}g(z)$ for some entire function h.
3. Let $z(s, t)$ be a homotopy, and define γ_s to be the arc parametrized by $z_s(t) = z(s, t)$. If $U_1, \ldots, U_n$ is admissible for γ_s, there exists $\delta > 0$ such that if $s' \in [0, 1]$ and $|s' - s| < \delta$, then $U_1, \ldots, U_n$ is admissible for $\gamma_{s'}$. (HINT: Let $t_1, \ldots, t_n$ be as in (3.1). Find $\delta > 0$ such that the same $t_1, \ldots, t_n$ work for $|s' - s| < \delta$.)
4. Let Ω_1 and Ω_2 be regions between which there exists a continuous one-to-one correspondence. Prove: If Ω_1 is simply connected, then Ω_2 is simply connected.

9. Composition of Germs

While a germ is a set and not a function, we have seen in Section 4, Problem 2, that it is possible to define addition and multiplication between germs, provided the germs "live" at the same point. What is more, these operations of addition and multiplication obey laws similar to those obeyed by the familiar operations of addition and multiplication for functions. One can carry the analogy between germs and functions further; for example, it is possible to "compose" germs, and this we shall do now.

Let $[f]_z$ and $[g]_w$ be germs related by assumption as follows: if $(\varphi, U) \in [f]_z$, then $\varphi(z) = w$. We shall define a germ $[h]_z$ at z called the "composition" of $[g]_w$ and $[f]_z$. To do this fix $(\varphi, U) \in [f]_z$ and $(\psi, V) \in [g]_w$. Because φ is continuous on U with $\varphi(z) = w$, there exists a disk W in U, containing z, such that $\varphi(W) \subseteq V$. Of course, $(\varphi, W) \in [f]_z$. On W define

(9.1) $$h(\zeta) = \psi(\varphi(\zeta))$$

and let $[h]_z$ denote the germ of h at z. Observe (Problem 1) that $[h]_z$ depends only upon $[g]_w$ and $[f]_z$ and not upon the particular representatives chosen.

Definition 9.1. The germ $[h]_z$ defined by (9.1) is called the *composition* of $[g]_w$ and $[f]_z$. One writes

(9.2) $$[h]_z = [g]_w \circ [f]_z.$$

The operation of composition obeys an *associative* law. If $[f_1]_{z_1}$, $[f_2]_{z_2}$, and $[f_3]_{z_3}$ are germs such that both $[f_2]_{z_2} \circ [f_1]_{z_1}$ and $[f_3]_{z_3} \circ [f_2]_{z_2}$ are defined, then

(9.3) $$[f_3]_{z_3} \circ ([f_2]_{z_2} \circ [f_1]_{z_1}) = ([f_3]_{z_3} \circ [f_2]_{z_2}) \circ [f_1]_{z_1}.$$

The proof is easy. Select $(f_i, U_i) \in [f_i]_{z_i}$, $i = 1, 2, 3$, such that $f_1(U_1) \subseteq U_2$ and $f_2(U_2) \subseteq U_3$. Then (h, U_1), where

$$h(z) = f_3(f_2(f_1(z))),$$

is a representative of both germs (9.3); the germs are therefore equal, and (9.3) is true.

In one situation it is always possible to define the *inverse* to a germ. Suppose $[f]_{z_0}$ is a germ such that if $(\varphi, U) \in [f]_{z_0}$, then $\varphi'(z_0) \neq 0$. Fix $(\varphi, U) \in [f]_{z_0}$ and set $w_0 = \varphi(z_0)$. According to Problems 1 and 2 of Section 7, it is possible to define on a neighborhood of w_0 an analytic function ψ having the properties

    (a) $\psi(w_0) = z_0$;
    (b) $\psi(\varphi(z)) = z$ in a neighborhood of z_0;
    (c) $\varphi(\psi(w)) = w$ in a neighborhood of w_0.

Denote by $\lfloor z \rfloor_{z_0}$ and $[w]_{w_0}$ the germs of the identity functions at z_0 and w_0, respectively. Properties (a)–(c) imply

$$[\psi]_{w_0} \circ [f]_{z_0} = [z]_{z_0}$$

and

$$[f]_{z_0} \circ [\psi]_{w_0} = [w]_{w_0}.$$

Definition 9.2. The germ $[\psi]_{w_0}$ defined above will be called the *inverse* of the germ $[f]_{z_0}$. The former will usually be denoted by $[f^{-1}]_{w_0}$.

REMARK. Hereinafter when we are working with a germ $[f]_{z_0}$, the symbol $[f^{-1}]_{w_0}$ will be taken to mean that $f(z_0) = w_0$ and f^{-1}, if multiple valued, is chosen so that $f^{-1}(w_0) = z_0$. For example, if $f(z) = e^z$, the inverse to $[f]_0$ is the germ at $1 = e^0$ of $\log z$, $\log 1 = 0$.

The inverse germ is *unique*. To see this suppose $[g]_{w_0}$ shares with $[f^{-1}]_{w_0}$ the property $[g]_{w_0} \circ [f]_{z_0} = [z]_{z_0}$. We will show that $[g]_{w_0} = [f^{-1}]_{w_0}$. After noticing that $[z]_{z_0} \circ [f^{-1}]_{w_0} = [f^{-1}]_{w_0}$ and $[g]_{w_0} \circ [w]_{w_0} = [g]_{w_0}$, we find from the associative law that

$$
\begin{aligned}
[f^{-1}]_{w_0} &= [z]_{z_0} \circ [f^{-1}]_{w_0} \\
&= ([g]_{w_0} \circ [f]_{z_0}) \circ [f^{-1}]_{w_0} \\
&= [g]_{w_0} \circ ([f]_{z_0} \circ [f^{-1}]_{w_0}) \\
&= [g]_{w_0} \circ [w]_{w_0} \\
&= [g]_{w_0}
\end{aligned}
$$

as claimed.

Occasionally, a statement like "f^{-1} can be continued along an arc γ in Ω from w_0 with values in Ω_1 and initial value z_0" will be made. Precisely the statement means $f(z_0) = w_0$, $[f^{-1}]_{w_0}$ exists, and there exists a continuation of the latter along γ. Furthermore the image of γ under the continuation lies in Ω_1.

Problems

1. Prove that Definition 9.1 is meaningful.
2. Prove that $[f]_{z_0} \circ [z]_{z_0} = [f]_{z_0}$; also $[w]_{w_0} \circ [f]_{z_0} = [f]_{z_0}$.
3. If $[f]_{z_0}$ and $[g]_{w_0}$ are germs such that $[g]_{w_0} \circ [f]_{z_0} = [z]_{z_0}$, show that

   (a) $[f]_{z_0} \circ [g]_{w_0} = [w]_{w_0}$;
   (b) if $(\varphi, U) \in [f]_{z_0}$, then $\varphi'(z_0) \neq 0$.

4. If $[f]_{z_0} = [f_1]_{z_1} \circ [f_0]_{z_0}$, then when $[f^{-1}]_{w_0}$ exists, it is equal to $[f_0^{-1}]_{z_1} \circ [f_1^{-1}]_{w_0}$; in particular $[f_0^{-1}]_{z_1}$ and $[f_1^{-1}]_{w_0}$ must exist individually.

10. Composition of Continuations

It is useful, particularly in the study of "covering surfaces," to have at one's disposal a means for "composing" continuations. If $\mathfrak{U}$ and $\mathfrak{V}$ are continuations along arcs γ and η, and if an appropriate condition is satisfied, we will define a continuation $\mathfrak{W}$ along γ, called the composition of $\mathfrak{U}$ and $\mathfrak{V}$. The condition to be satisfied is that η should be the image of γ under $\mathfrak{U}$.

Fix γ, η, $\mathfrak{U}$, and $\mathfrak{V}$ as above, and assume as mentioned that η is the image of γ under $\mathfrak{U}$. If $z(t)$, $0 \leq t \leq 1$, is the parametrization of γ, a parametrization $\zeta(t)$ of η is defined by (3.2). Denote the germs of $\mathfrak{U}$ by $[f_t]_{z(t)}$. If $(\varphi_t, U^t) \in [f_t]_{z(t)}$, the definition of $\zeta(t)$ is such that $\zeta(t) = \varphi_t(z(t))$. Therefore if $[g_t]_{\zeta(t)}$ is the germ of $\mathfrak{V}$ at $\zeta(t)$, the composition

(10.1) $$[h_t]_{z(t)} = [g_t]_{\zeta(t)} \circ [f_t]_{z(t)}$$

is defined for each t.

Theorem 10.1. *There exists a continuation $\mathfrak{W}$ along γ whose germ at $z(t)$ is given by (10.1) for each t.*

Proof. By Theorem 5.1 it is sufficient to find representatives (h_t, U^t) $\in [h_t]_{z(t)}$ and numbers $\mu_t > 0$ such that if $s \in [0, 1]$, and if $|s - t| < \mu_t$, then $z(s) \in U^t$ and

(10.2) $$h_t \equiv h_s \quad \text{on } U^t \cap U^s.$$

We use the construction of Section 3. Select $(f_t, U^t) \in [f_t]_{z(t)}$ and $\delta_t > 0$ such that if $s \in [0, 1]$ and $|s - t| < \delta_t$, then $z(s) \in U^t$ and

(10.3) $$f_t \equiv f_s \quad \text{on } U^t \cap U^s.$$

Similarly, choose $(g_t, V^t) \in [g_t]_{\zeta(t)}$ and $\epsilon_t > 0$ such that if $s \in [0, 1]$ and $|s - t| < \epsilon_t$, then $\zeta(s) \in V^t$ and

(10.4) $$g_t \equiv g_s \quad \text{on } V^t \cap V^s.$$

Finally, it can be assumed, by making U^t and δ_t smaller if necessary, that

(10.5) $$f_t(U^t) \subseteq V^t, \quad 0 \leq t \leq 1.$$

Define $\mu_t = \min(\delta_t, \epsilon_t)$. If $s \in [0, 1]$ and $|s - t| < \mu_t$, both (10.3) and (10.4) must hold (in addition to the fact $z(s) \in U^t$). By 10.5

$$f_t(U^t \cap U^s) = f_s(U^t \cap U^s)$$
$$\subseteq V^t \cap V^s.$$

Thus if $z \in U^t \cap U^s$,

$$h_t(z) = g_t(f_t(z))$$
$$= g_s(f_s(z))$$
$$= h_s(z).$$

Of course, $(h_t, U^t) \in [h_t]_{z(t)}$. Equation (10.2) is verified, and the theorem is proved.

The initial germ of $\mathfrak{W}$ is $[g_0]_{\zeta(0)} \circ [f_0]_{z(0)}$. Using this we prove

Theorem 10.2.   *Suppose there is a continuation of the germ $[f]_{z_0}$ along an arc γ, and let η denote the image of γ under the continuation. If there exists a continuation of $[f^{-1}]_{f(z_0)}$ along η, the image of η under the latter is γ.*

Proof.   Denote by $\mathfrak{U}$ and $\mathfrak{V}$ the continuations of $[f]_{z_0}$ and $[f^{-1}]_{f(z_0)}$, and let $\mathfrak{W}$ be their composition. The image of η under $\mathfrak{V}$ is the same as the image of γ under $\mathfrak{W}$. However, the initial germ of $\mathfrak{W}$ is $[f^{-1}]_{f(z_0)} \circ [f]_{z_0} = [z]_{z_0}$, and therefore by Theorem 3.1, the image of γ under $\mathfrak{W}$ is γ. The theorem is proved.

Problem

1. Formulate an associative law for the composition of continuations.

11. Covering Surfaces

The following brief discussion describes certain of the elementary properties of an "analytic covering." The language of coverings is useful, particularly in Chapters 3 and 4.

Definition 11.1.   A triple $\Omega_1 \xrightarrow{f} \Omega$ is a *covering* (or *analytic covering*) if f is analytic on Ω_1, and if f satisfies the properties

(a) $f(z) \in \Omega$ for each $z \in \Omega_1$;

(b) if $z_0 \in \Omega_1$ and $w_0 \in \Omega$ are related by $f(z_0) = w_0$, and if γ is an arc from w_0 in Ω, it is possible to continue f^{-1} along γ with values in Ω_1 and initial value z_0.

Ω_1 is a *covering surface* (or *analytic covering surface*) of Ω; f is a *covering map*.

The following are simple examples of coverings. (See Problem 2.)

(1) $\Omega \xrightarrow{f} \Omega$, where Ω is an arbitrary region and $f(z) = z$.

(2) $\Omega_1 \xrightarrow{f} \Omega$, where Ω_1 is the plane, Ω is the plane minus the origin, and $f(z) = e^z$.

(3) $\Omega \xrightarrow{f} \Omega$, where Ω is as in (2) and $f(z) = z^n$, $n > 0$. Notice that $\Omega_1 \xrightarrow{f} \Omega_1$ *cannot* be a covering because f^{-1} cannot be defined in a neighborhood of 0.

(4) $\Omega_2 \xrightarrow{f} \Omega_1$, where f is a one-to-one analytic mapping of Ω_2 onto Ω_1.

The examples above are given at the risk of oversimplification. As we will see in Chapter 3, a covering $\Omega_1 \xrightarrow{f} \Omega$ is generally a complicated object, much more so than examples (1)–(4).

Two important consequences of Definition 11.1 are

Theorem 11.1. *If $\Omega_1 \xrightarrow{f} \Omega$ is a covering, then*

(c) $f'(z) \neq 0$ *for each $z \in \Omega_1$*

and

(d) $f(\Omega_1) = \Omega$; f *maps Ω_1 onto Ω.*

Proof. If $z \in \Omega$ and $w = f(z)$, the germ $[f^{-1}]_w$ can only be defined if $f'(z) \neq 0$. Thus condition (b) of Definition 11.1 guarantees $f'(z) \neq 0$.

To prove (d) fix $z_0 \in \Omega_1$ and $w_0 = f(z_0) \in \Omega$. If w is an arbitrary point of Ω, there exists an arc γ in Ω joining w_0 to w. By condition (b) there exists a continuation of f^{-1} along γ with values in Ω_1 and initial value z_0. If η denotes the image of γ under this continuation, then η is an arc joining z_0 to a point z. By Theorem 10.2 the image of η under a continuation of $[f]_{z_0}$, in this case $f(\eta)$, is γ. Thus $f(z) = w$ meaning w belongs to the range of f. Since w is arbitrary, the theorem is proved.

Condition (b) of Definition 11.1 actually assumes more than it is necessary to assume. We shall replace it by an apparently weaker, but in reality equivalent, condition after first observing

Lemma 11.1. Let γ and γ_1 be arcs whose parametrizations $w(t)$ and $w_1(t)$, $0 \leq t \leq 1$, are related by

$$w_1(t) = w\left(\frac{1}{2} + \frac{t}{2}\right), \quad 0 \leq t \leq 1.$$

If $\mathfrak{u}$ is a continuation along γ, and if $[f_t]_{w(t)}$ denotes the germ of $\mathfrak{u}$ at $z(t)$, define

(11.1) $$[h_t]_{w_1(t)} = [f_{1/2+t/2}]_{w(1/2+t/2)}.$$

There exists a continuation $\mathfrak{v}$ along γ_1 whose germs are given by (11.1) for each t.

Proof. Using the construction of Section 3 select for each t a representative $(f_t, U^t) \in [f_t]_{w(t)}$ and a number $\delta_t > 0$ such that if $s \in [0, 1]$, and if $|s - t| < \delta_t$, then $w(s) \in U^t$ and $f_t \equiv f_s$ on $U^t \cap U^s$. Define

$$(h_t, V^t) = (f_{1/2+t/2}, U^{1/2+t/2})$$

for $0 \leq t \leq 1$, and let $\epsilon_t = 2\delta_t$. If $s \in [0, 1]$ and if $|s - t| < \epsilon_t$, then

$$\left| \frac{1}{2} + \frac{s}{2} - \left(\frac{1}{2} + \frac{t}{2} \right) \right| = \tfrac{1}{2}|s - t| < \delta_t.$$

Therefore $w_1(s) \in V^t$ and $h_t \equiv h_s$ on $V^t \cap V^s$. By Theorem 5.1 there exists a continuation $\mathcal{V}$ along γ_1 with the desired germs.

Theorem 11.2. *Suppose f is analytic on a region Ω_1 with range in a region Ω. $\Omega_1 \xrightarrow{f} \Omega$ is a covering if there exist points $z_0 \in \Omega_1$ and $w_0 \in \Omega$ with $f(z_0) = w_0$ such that*
  (b′) *if γ is an arc from w_0 in Ω, there exists a continuation of f^{-1} along γ with values in Ω_1 and initial value z_0.*

Proof.   Condition (b) of Definition 11.1, which is assumed here for one point, must be verified for all points. To do this we suppose $z_1 \in \Omega_1$ and $w_1 \in \Omega$ are points such that $f(z_1) = w_1$. Let γ_1 be an arc from w_1 in Ω.

Since Ω_1 is connected, there exists an arc γ_0' in Ω_1 joining z_0 to z_1. Denote by γ_0 the curve $f(\gamma_0')$ which joins w_0 to w_1 in Ω. Let the arcs γ_0 and γ_1 be parametrized by $w_0(t)$ and $w_1(t)$, $0 \leq t \leq 1$. Joining these arcs end-to-end we define γ to be the arc parametrized by

$$(11.2) \qquad w(t) = \begin{cases} w_0(2t), & 0 \leq t \leq \tfrac{1}{2} \\ w_1(2(t - \tfrac{1}{2})), & \tfrac{1}{2} < t < 1. \end{cases}$$

The function (11.2) is continuous at $t = \tfrac{1}{2}$ because $w_0(1) = w_1 = w_1(0)$; notice also that $w_1(t) = w(1/2 + t/2)$.

According to (b′) there exists a continuation $\mathcal{U}$ of $[f^{-1}]_{w_0}$ along γ. By Theorem 10.2 the image of γ_0 (i.e., that part of γ parametrized by $w(t)$, $0 \leq t \leq \tfrac{1}{2}$) is γ_0'. Therefore the germ of $\mathcal{U}$ at $t = \tfrac{1}{2}$ is $[f^{-1}]_{w_1}$. Applying Lemma 11.1, there exists a continuation $\mathcal{V}$ along γ_1 with germs (11.1). By what we have just seen, the initial germ of this continuation is $[f^{-1}]_{w_1}$. Thus (b) holds for w_1; since w_1 is arbitrary, the theorem is proved.

The results of Section 10 make it possible to compose coverings.

Theorem 11.3.   *Let $\Omega_2 \xrightarrow{f_2} \Omega_1$ and $\Omega_1 \xrightarrow{f_1} \Omega$ be coverings. Then $\Omega_2 \xrightarrow{f} \Omega$ is a covering where f is the composition*

$$f(z) = f_1(f_2(z)), \quad z \in \Omega_2.$$

Proof.   Obviously $f(z) \in \Omega$ for each $z \in \Omega_2$. If $z_0 \in \Omega_2$ and $w_0 \in \Omega$ are such that $f(z_0) = w_0$, then by definition $w_0 = f_1(\zeta_0)$, where $\zeta_0 = f_2(z_0)$.

Problem 3, Section 9, tells us that

(11.3) $$[f^{-1}]_{w_0} = [f_2^{-1}]_{\zeta_0} \circ [f_1^{-1}]_{w_0}.$$

Let γ be an arbitrary arc in Ω from w_0. $\Omega_1 \xrightarrow{f_1} \Omega$ is a covering; therefore there exists a continuation $\mathfrak{U}$ of $[f_1^{-1}]_{w_0}$ along γ with the image of γ being an arc η in Ω_1 from ζ_0. Similarly, there exists a continuation $\mathfrak{V}$ of $[f_2^{-1}]_{\zeta_0}$ along η, the image of η belonging to Ω_2. The composition $\mathfrak{W}$ of these continuations is a continuation of the germ (11.3) along γ, and of course the image of γ under $\mathfrak{W}$ is contained in Ω_2. Since z_0, w_0 were arbitrary, $\Omega_2 \xrightarrow{f} \Omega$ is a covering, and the theorem is proved.

The remainder of the section deals with simply connected covering surfaces. We first prove

Lemma 11.2. Let $\Omega_1 \xrightarrow{f} \Omega$ be a covering where Ω is simply connected. Then f is a one-to-one mapping of Ω_1 onto Ω.

Proof. It is sufficient to check that f is one-to-one because f is known to be onto. (Theorem 11.1.) Suppose $z_1, z_2 \in \Omega_1$ are such that $f(z_1) = f(z_2)$. We will show that $z_1 = z_2$.

Let γ' be an arc in Ω_1 joining z_1 to z_2. Then $\gamma = f(\gamma')$ is a closed arc in Ω with end point $f(z_1) = f(z_2)$, By Theorem 10.2 the image of γ under a continuation of $[f^{-1}]_{f(z_1)}{}^1$ is γ'; the terminal germ is therefore $[f^{-1}]_{f(z_2)}$. Because Ω is assumed to be simply connected, γ is homotopic with respect to Ω to the "arc" consisting of the point $f(z_1)$. A continuation of $[f^{-1}]_{f(z_1)}$ along the latter trivially has terminal germ $[f^{-1}]_{f(z_1)}$. By the monodromy theorem we have $[f^{-1}]_{f(z_1)} = [f^{-1}]_{f(z_2)}$. Therefore $z_1 = z_2$, and f is one-to-one.

Definition 11.2. A region Ω_1 is a *universal covering surface* of a region Ω if Ω_1 is simply connected, and if there exists a covering $\Omega_1 \xrightarrow{f} \Omega$.

Example 2 above exhibits the plane as a universal covering surface of the plane minus a point. It is important to note that there is no *a priori* reason why a region should have a universal covering surface. Chapters 3 and 4 treat this existence problem in full.

A universal covering surface derives its name from the following "universal" property.

Theorem 11.4. *Let $\Omega_1 \xrightarrow{f_1} \Omega$ be a covering, and suppose Ω_1 is simply connected. If $\Omega_2 \xrightarrow{f_2} \Omega$ is a covering, there exists a covering $\Omega_1 \xrightarrow{f} \Omega_2$ such that $f_1 = f_2(f)$.*

---

[1] $[f^{-1}]_{f(z_1)}$ is the germ of f^{-1} at $f(z_1)$, where $f^{-1}(f(z_1)) = z_1$. Similarly for $[f^{-1}]_{f(z_2)}$.

Proof. Fix points $z_1 \in \Omega_1$, $z \in \Omega$, and $z_2 \in \Omega_2$ such that $f_1(z_1) = z = f_2(z_2)$. Define $[f]_{z_1} = [f_2^{-1}]_z \circ [f_1]_{z_1}$. If γ is an arc from z_1 in Ω_1, $f_1(\gamma)$ is an arc from z in Ω. It is possible because $\Omega_2 \xrightarrow{f_2} \Omega$ is a covering to continue $[f_2^{-1}]_z$ along $f_1(\gamma)$ with values in Ω_2. Composition of this continuation with f_1 yields a continuation of the germ $[f]_{z_1}$ along γ. Since γ is an arbitrary arc from z_1 in Ω_1, there exists by Theorem 8.2 a function f analytic on Ω_1 whose germ at z_1 is $[f]_{z_1}$. By construction, $f(w) \in \Omega_2$ for each $w \in \Omega_1$.

We will establish condition (b') of Theorem 11.2 from which it will follow that $\Omega_1 \xrightarrow{f} \Omega_2$ is a covering. Notice that $[f^{-1}]_{z_2} = [f_1^{-1}]_z \circ [f_2]_{z_2}$ (Problem 3, Section 9), and therefore $f_1 = f_2(f)$ by the uniqueness theorem.

Let γ be an arc in Ω_2 from z_2. $\Omega_1 \xrightarrow{f_1} \Omega$ is a covering, so therefore there is a continuation of $[f_1^{-1}]_z$ along $f_2(\gamma)$. Composing this continuation with f_2 yields a continuation of $[f^{-1}]_{z_2} = [f_1^{-1}]_z \circ [f_2]_{z_2}$ along γ. The image of γ lies in Ω_1; therefore by Theorem 11.2, $\Omega_1 \xrightarrow{f} \Omega$ is a covering.

A corollary to Theorem 11.4 and Lemma 11.2 is

Theorem 11.5. *If Ω_1 and Ω_2 are universal covering surfaces of a region Ω, there exists a one-to-one analytic mapping between Ω_1 and Ω_2.*

Proof. There exist by assumption coverings $\Omega_1 \xrightarrow{f_1} \Omega$ and $\Omega_2 \xrightarrow{f_2} \Omega$. Applying Theorem 11.4 to the fact that Ω_1 is simply connected, there is a covering $\Omega_1 \xrightarrow{f} \Omega_2$. Then applying Lemma 11.2 to the fact that Ω_2 is simply connected, the covering map f is one-to-one. The theorem is proved.

Theorem 11.6. *The plane and the disk cannot be universal covering surfaces of the same region.*

Proof. By Liouville's theorem there can be no one-to-one analytic mapping of the plane onto the disk (Problem 1). The result now follows from Theorem 11.5.

Problems

1. There does not exist a one-to-one analytic mapping from the plane to the disk.
2. Verify that the mappings (1)–(4) at the beginning of the section are coverings.

chapter 2

Geometric Considerations

1. Complex Projective Space

Our discussion begins with a concrete setting for the complex plane with a "point at infinity" adjoined. It has generally been found necessary for this purpose to work in a higher-dimensional space and "project."

The reader is probably familiar with the operation of stereographic projection which represents each complex number as a point on the surface of a sphere (the "Riemann sphere") in three dimensions. One point, usually the north pole, of the sphere is unused by the representation, and this exceptional point is taken for a point at infinity. Despite its geometric simplicity stereographic projection is unsatisfactory from both the analytic and algebraic points of view. A principal defect of the method is the lack of a "natural" interpretation in terms of it for the "fractional linear transformations." These will be of some import in the study of complex mappings.

What follows is the notion of a complex projective space which, though more complicated, avoids the above-stated difficulty.

We will use, without formal definition, certain algebraic notions (vector space, matrix, *et al.*) which may be unfamiliar to the reader. If so, he should be able to glean definitions from the context, while the correlative facts used will admit proofs which are not difficult.

In this and succeeding chapters the bold-faced letters **R** and **C** will be used to denote respectively the real and complex numbers.

Let V be the set of ordered pairs of complex numbers,

$$V = \{(z, w) \mid z, w \in \mathbf{C}\}.$$

If $\zeta_1 = (z_1, w_1)$, $\zeta_2 = (z_2, w_2)$, and a complex number λ (called a "scalar") are given, the equation

$$\zeta_1 - \lambda\zeta_2 = (z_1 - \lambda z_2, \, w_1 - \lambda w_2)$$

defines for V the algebraic operations of a vector space. Where no confusion will arise we shall write 0 for $(0, 0)$, the zero vector.

Of principal interest to us are subsets V_0, V_1, and V_2 of V, where V_0 consists of the nonzero vectors, and V_1, V_2 are defined by

$$V_1 = \{(z, w) \mid z \neq 0\},$$

$$V_2 = \{(z, w) \mid w \neq 0\}.$$

By definition $V_0 = V_1 \cup V_2$. In fact, the only vectors of V_0 not belonging to, say, V_1 are those of the form $(0, w)$, $w \neq 0$. The intersection $V_1 \cap V_2$ consists of those vectors $\zeta = (z, w)$ neither of whose coordinates is zero.

If $\zeta \in V_0$, let $[\zeta]$ be the set of nonzero scalar multiples of ζ. The set $[\zeta]$ is a subset of V_0, and

$$[\zeta] = \{\lambda\zeta \mid \lambda \in \mathbf{C}, \, \lambda \neq 0\}.$$

If for certain vectors ζ_1, $\zeta_2 \in V_0$ it is true that $[\zeta_1] = [\zeta_2]$, we shall write $\zeta_1 \sim \zeta_2$ and speak of ζ_1 and ζ_2 as being *equivalent*. The reader should have no trouble verifying that $\zeta_1 \sim \zeta_2$, i.e., $[\zeta_1] = [\zeta_2]$ if, and only if, $[\zeta_1] \cap [\zeta_2] \neq \emptyset$. An equivalent, and for us more useful, condition is the existence of a scalar λ such that

(1.1) $\zeta_1 - \lambda\zeta_2 = 0.$

The reader should also verify this condition.

Definition 1.1.   The *one-complex-dimensional projective space* $\mathbf{P}$ is the space whose "points" are the distinct sets $[\zeta]$ which occur for $\zeta \in V_0$.

The space $\mathbf{P}$ bears as yet no relationship to the complex plane. Letting $\{\infty\}$ denote the set whose sole element is the symbol ∞ we will describe a one-to-one correspondence between the points of $\mathbf{P}$ and the points of $\mathbf{C} \cup \{\infty\}$. The "point" ∞ will, of course, be our "point at infinity."

If $\zeta_1 = (\tau_1, 1)$ and $\zeta_2 = (\tau_2, 1)$, (1.1) implies that ζ_1 and ζ_2 correspond to the same point of $\mathbf{P}$ only if $\tau_1 = \tau_2$ and consequently $\zeta_1 = \zeta_2$. Therefore, for any $\zeta \in V_0$ there is *at most* one vector of the form $(\tau, 1) \in [\zeta]$.

If there is to be a vector $(\tau, 1)$ in a given class $[\zeta]$, then because $(\tau, 1) \in V_2$, it must be that $[\zeta] \subset V_2$. We claim conversely that for any class $[\zeta] \subset V_2$ there is a vector of the form $(\tau, 1)$ in $[\zeta]$. If $\zeta = (z, w)$, then since $w \neq 0$, we can write $\zeta = w(z/w, 1)$ which implies that $(z/w, 1) \in [\zeta]$.

In view of the preceding paragraphs it makes sense to define for $[\zeta] \subset V_2$ the function

(1.2)
$$\varphi([\zeta]) = \tau,$$

where $(\tau, 1)$ is the unique vector of its kind in the class $[\zeta]$. If $\mathbf{P}_2$ is the subset of $\mathbf{P}$ corresponding to the classes $[\zeta]$ of V_2, (1.2) provides a one-to-one mapping from $\mathbf{P}_2$ into the τ plane. Furthermore, φ is onto. This is because for any complex τ the vector $(\tau, 1)$ belongs to V_2 and by definition $\varphi([(\tau, 1)]) = \tau$. The sole point of $\mathbf{P}$ which is not in $\mathbf{P}_2$ is the class $[(1, 0)]$, and we define

$$\varphi([1, 0)]) = \infty.$$

In other words, the ratio $\lambda/0$, $\lambda \neq 0$, is being defined to be ∞.

If in the discussion above the roles of V_1 and V_2 be interchanged, there arises another one-to-one mapping ψ of $\mathbf{P}$ onto $\mathbf{C} \cup \{\infty\}$. If $\zeta = (z, w) \in V_1$, the equation corresponding to (1.2) is

(1.3)
$$\psi([\zeta]) = \frac{w}{z},$$

while for $\zeta = (0, 1) \notin V_1$

$$\psi([\zeta]) = \infty.$$

The statement $z \to \infty$ will be taken to mean $(1/z) \to 0$.

Problems

1. A complex-valued function f on $\mathbf{P}$ is *analytic* if each of the functions

$$f_1(\tau) = f(\varphi^{-1}\tau), \quad \tau \in \mathbf{C}$$

and

$$f_2(\tau) = f(\psi^{-1}\tau), \quad \tau \in \mathbf{C}$$

is entire. Prove: If f is analytic on $\mathbf{P}$, then f is constant.

2. A function f on $\mathbf{P}$ with values in $\mathbf{C} \cup \{\infty\}$ is *meromorphic* if each of the functions

$$f_1(\tau) = f(\varphi^{-1}\tau), \quad \tau \in \mathbf{C}$$

and

$$f_2(\tau) = f(\psi^{-1}\tau), \quad \tau \in \mathbf{C}$$

is analytic except for isolated singularities which are poles. (A pole will occur where $f = \infty$.)

(a) If f is meromorphic on **P**, then unless f is constant, f assumes any given value at most finitely many times.

(b) If f is nonconstant and meromorphic on **P**, then f assumes each value in $\mathbf{C} \cup \{\infty\}$ at least once. (HINT: Consider $1/(f - \lambda)$.)

(c) Suppose f is nonconstant and meromorphic on **P**. Let f_1 have zeros $a_1, \ldots, a_k$ with multiplicities $m_1, \ldots, m_k$ and poles $b_1, \ldots, b_l$ with multiplicities $n_1, \ldots, n_l$. There exists a constant α such that

$$f_1(z) = \frac{\alpha \prod_{p=1}^{k} (z - a_p)^{m_p}}{\prod_{q=1}^{l} (z - b_q)^{n_q}}.$$

(d) A nonconstant meromorphic function f on **P** assumes each value in $\mathbf{C} \cup \{\infty\}$ the same, finite number of times. (Counting multiplicities. Apply the argument principle to f_1.)

2. Linear Transformations

A transformation

$$A\zeta = \zeta'$$

of V into V is *linear* if for each pair $\zeta_1, \zeta_2 \in V$ and $\lambda \in \mathbf{C}$ the equation

$$A(\zeta_1 - \lambda\zeta_2) = A\zeta_1 - \lambda A\zeta_2$$

is true. A linear transformation A can be realized through an appropriate 2×2 matrix which it is customary to denote also by A,

$$A = \begin{pmatrix} a & b \\ c & d \end{pmatrix}.$$

In column notation the matrix A sends the vector $\zeta = \begin{pmatrix} z \\ w \end{pmatrix}$ into the vector ζ',

$$\zeta' = A\zeta$$

$$= \begin{pmatrix} a & b \\ c & d \end{pmatrix} \begin{pmatrix} z \\ w \end{pmatrix}$$

$$= \begin{pmatrix} az + bw \\ cz + dw \end{pmatrix}.$$

It will be convenient now to deviate from this standard notation and write instead

$$A\zeta = \begin{pmatrix} a & b \\ c & d \end{pmatrix} (z, w)$$

$$= (az + bw, cz + dw).$$

If A and B are linear transformations, then the transformation $C = AB$, defined on ζ by $C\zeta = (AB)\zeta = A(B\zeta)$, is linear. If $A = \begin{pmatrix} a & b \\ c & d \end{pmatrix}$ and $B = \begin{pmatrix} \alpha & \beta \\ \gamma & \delta \end{pmatrix}$, the transformation AB has matrix the product of A and B,

$$AB = \begin{pmatrix} a\alpha + b\gamma & a\beta + b\delta \\ c\alpha + d\gamma & c\beta + d\delta \end{pmatrix}.$$

A linear transformation A is *nonsingular* if the equation $A\zeta = 0$ has only the solution $\zeta = 0$. If A has matrix $A = \begin{pmatrix} a & b \\ c & d \end{pmatrix}$, then A is nonsingular if, and only if, the determinant $\det A = ad - bc$ is nonzero. If A is nonsingular, there is a unique linear transformation A^{-1}, *the inverse of* A, whose matrix is

$$A^{-1} = \frac{1}{ad - bc} \begin{pmatrix} d & -b \\ -c & a \end{pmatrix},$$

such that for each $\zeta \in V$

$$A^{-1}A\zeta = \zeta = AA^{-1}\zeta.$$

If $I = \begin{pmatrix} 1 & 0 \\ 0 & 1 \end{pmatrix}$, the equation $A^{-1}A = I = AA^{-1}$ holds.

The condition that A be nonsingular is (trivially) equivalent to the condition, important for us, that a vector $\zeta \in V_0$ map into a vector $A\zeta \in V_0$. In fact, if A is nonsingular, both A and A^{-1} map V_0 onto V_0. From this point on we shall be assuming all transformations nonsingular.

Suppose now A is as above and $\zeta_1 \sim \zeta_2$. By (1.1) there exists λ such that $\zeta_1 - \lambda\zeta_2 = 0$, and since A is linear

$$A\zeta_1 - \lambda A\zeta_2 = A(\zeta_1 - \lambda\zeta_2)$$

$$= A0$$

$$= 0.$$

Therefore, $A\zeta_1 \sim A\zeta_2$. Conversely, if $A\zeta_1 \sim A\zeta_2$ application of A^{-1} yields $A^{-1}A\zeta_1 \sim A^{-1}A\zeta_2$ or $\zeta_1 \sim \zeta_2$. Thus, we conclude that a *nonsingular linear transformation A induces a one-to-one mapping between the classes*

$[\zeta]$ *of points* $\zeta \in V_0$. *The image of the class* $[\zeta]$ *is the class* $[A\zeta]$. *Furthermore, the inverse of the induced transformation is the transformation induced by* A^{-1}. In other words, nonsingular linear transformations of V induce in a natural way one-to-one mappings of **P** onto itself.

If $\lambda \neq 0$, the transformation λA with matrix

$$\lambda A = \begin{pmatrix} \lambda a & \lambda b \\ \lambda c & \lambda d \end{pmatrix}$$

induces the same mapping of **P** as does A. We claim conversely that if A and B induce the same mapping of **P**, then $A = \lambda B$ for some $\lambda(\neq 0)$. Indeed, to say that A and B induce the same mapping of **P** is to say that

$$A\zeta \sim B\zeta$$

or

(2.1) $$B^{-1}A\zeta \sim \zeta$$

for each $\zeta \in V_0$. Let $\begin{pmatrix} a & b \\ c & d \end{pmatrix}$ be the matrix of $B^{-1}A$. Successively letting $\zeta = (1, 0)$, $\zeta = (0, 1)$, and $\zeta = (1, 1)$, we obtain from (2.1)

$$\begin{pmatrix} a & b \\ c & d \end{pmatrix} (1, 0) = (a, c) \sim (1, 0),$$

(2.2) $$\begin{pmatrix} a & b \\ c & d \end{pmatrix} (0, 1) = (b, d) \sim (0, 1),$$

$$\begin{pmatrix} a & b \\ c & d \end{pmatrix} (1, 1) = (a + b, c + d) \sim (1, 1).$$

The first two equations of (2.2) imply $b = c = 0$, while these in conjunction with the third imply $a = d$. Therefore, $B^{-1}A = \lambda I$ for some constant $\lambda(= a)$ with $I = \begin{pmatrix} 1 & 0 \\ 0 & 1 \end{pmatrix}$. It now follows that $A = \lambda B$.

The result of the last paragraph is that the set of transformations which induce the same transformation of **P** as a given transformation A is the set $\{\lambda A, \lambda \neq 0\}$. Among these transformations there are just two, B_1 and B_2, which satisfy

$$\det B_1 = \det B_2 = 1.$$

If $B_1 = \lambda_1 A$, $B_2 = \lambda_2 A$, then $\det B_j = \lambda_j^2 \det A = 1$, and so $\lambda_1 = -\lambda_2$, $B_1 = -B_2$.

Definition 2.1. The set of matrices $A = \begin{pmatrix} a & b \\ c & d \end{pmatrix}$ with complex entries such that $\det A = 1$ is called $SL(2, \mathbf{C})$.

If[1] A, B are two matrices with determinant 1, then since $\det(AB^{-1} = \det A \cdot 1/\det B = 1$, $AB^{-1} \in SL(2, \mathbf{C})$. Therefore, $SL(2, \mathbf{C})$ is itself a group.

Let H be the subgroup of $SL(2, \mathbf{C})$ consisting of two elements I and $-I$. H is obviously normal, so the quotient group $\mathcal{G}$ can be defined by

$$\mathcal{G} = SL(2, \mathbf{C})/H.$$

$\mathcal{G}$ arises from $SL(2, \mathbf{C})$ by identifying matrices B_1, B_2 if $B_1 = -B_2$.

We have seen that for every transformation of $\mathbf{P}$ induced by a linear transformation A of V there are two elements B_1, $B_2 \in SL(2, \mathbf{C})$ with $B_1 = -B_2$ which induce the same transformation of $\mathbf{P}$ as A. Because B_1, B_2 are identified as one in $\mathcal{G}$, *there is a one-to-one correspondence between the transformations of* $\mathbf{P}$ *induced by nonsingular linear transformations of* V *and the elements of* $\mathcal{G}$. This correspondence is homomorphic, for if A, B go into a, $b \in \mathcal{G}$, then $A \cdot B$ goes into the product $ab \in \mathcal{G}$.

Problem

1. A mapping $f(p)$ of $\mathbf{P}$ into $\mathbf{P}$ is *analytic* if the function $f(p) = \varphi(F(p))$ is meromorphic on $\mathbf{P}$. (See Problems, Section 1, Chapter 2.)

   (a) If $F(p)$ is one-to-one and analytic, then $F(p)$ is linear (and conversely).

   (b) If $f(z)$ is a one-to-one analytic function on $\mathbf{C}$, the mapping $\varphi^{-1}f(\varphi(p))$ defined for $p \in \mathbf{P}_2$ can be extended to all of $\mathbf{P}$ to be a one-to-one analytic mapping.

3. Fractional Linear Transformations

Given a linear transformation A of V which induces a transformation A_0 of $\mathbf{P}$ onto $\mathbf{P}$, consider the diagram:

(3.1)

$$
\begin{array}{ccc}
\mathbf{P} & \xrightarrow{\ A_0\ } & \mathbf{P} \\
\varphi \downarrow & & \downarrow \varphi \\
\mathbf{C} \cup \{\infty\} & \xdashrightarrow{\ T\ } & \mathbf{C} \cup \{\infty\}
\end{array}
$$

The dashed arrow in (3.1) indicates that T has yet to be defined. Because

[1] The remaining remarks of the present section are unimportant for what follows and may be ignored by the reader unfamiliar with group theory.

$\varphi(p)$ is a one-to-one mapping of **P** *onto* $\mathbf{C} \cup \{\infty\}$ it is possible to define $T\tau$ for each $\tau \in \mathbf{C} \cup \{\infty\}$ by

$$T\tau = \varphi(A_0(\varphi^{-1}\tau)).$$

It is immediate that T provides a one-to-one mapping between $\mathbf{C} \cup \{\infty\}$ and $\mathbf{C} \cup \{\infty\}$.

Suppose the matrix of A is $A = \begin{pmatrix} a & b \\ c & d \end{pmatrix}$. The class of $\varphi^{-1}\tau$ for $\tau \in \mathbf{C}$ is $[(\tau, 1)]$, and the class $A_0[(\tau, 1)]$ is by definition the class $[A(\tau, 1)]$ or $[(a\tau + b, c\tau + d)]$. If $c\tau + d \neq 0$, the latter class is the same as $[(a\tau + b)/(c\tau + d), 1)]$, and this tells us

(3.2)
$$T\tau = \frac{a\tau + b}{c\tau + d}.$$

If $c\tau + d = 0$, then

$$T\tau = \infty.$$

To compute $T\infty$ proceed as above with the class $\varphi^{-1}\infty = [(1, 0)]$ to obtain

$$T\infty = \frac{a}{c}, \quad c \neq 0$$

or

$$T\infty = \infty, \quad c = 0.$$

The function (3.2) needs no reference to **P** for its definition. Simply adopt the convention that $T\tau = \infty$ if $c\tau + d = 0$ and $T\infty = a/c$ or ∞ as $c \neq 0$ or $c = 0$. The mapping T is called a *fractional linear transformation*. If $\tau \in \mathbf{C}$ and $c\tau + d \neq 0$, then T is analytic at τ with derivative

$$T'\tau = \frac{ad - bc}{(c\tau + d)^2}.$$

From this equation we see the condition det $A \neq 0$ as being equivalent with the condition that T be nonconstant.

If S and T are fractional linear transformations, the composition H defined by $H\tau = S(T\tau)$ is at least a one-to-one mapping of $\mathbf{C} \cup \{\infty\}$ onto itself. We shall observe that in fact H is again fractional linear.

Let A and B be linear transformations of V inducing the mappings A_0 and B_0 of **P** which give rise via (3.1) to S and T, respectively. The product transformation AB induces a mapping $(AB)_0$ of **P** which is easily seen to be the same as $A_0 B_0$, i.e., $(AB)_0 p = A_0(B_0 p)$ for each $p \in \mathbf{P}$. Noting for each $\tau \in \mathbf{C} \cup \{\infty\}$ that $B_0\varphi^{-1}(\tau) = \varphi^{-1}(T\tau)$ we compute $H\tau$ by (3.1).

We have

$$H\tau = S(T\tau)$$
$$= \varphi(A_0\varphi^{-1}(T\tau))$$
$$= \varphi(A_0B_0\varphi^{-1}(\tau))$$
$$= \varphi((AB)_0\varphi^{-1}(\tau))$$

which implies that H is the fractional linear transformation arising from AB. The equation for $H\tau = S(T\tau)$ is therefore

$$(3.3) \qquad H\tau = \frac{(a\alpha + b\gamma)\tau + a\beta + b\delta}{(c\alpha + d\gamma)\tau + c\beta + d\delta},$$

where $A = \begin{pmatrix} a & b \\ c & d \end{pmatrix}$ and $B = \begin{pmatrix} \alpha & \beta \\ \gamma & \delta \end{pmatrix}$.

If the matrix B of T is inverse to the matrix A of S, we shall have from (3.3) that

$$ST\tau = \tau$$

for all τ. That is, $T = S^{-1}$ is the fractional linear transformation inverse to S. (While S, a one-to-one mapping of $\mathbf{C} \cup \{\infty\}$ onto itself, is guaranteed of an inverse mapping, there is no *a priori* guarantee that said mapping be fractional linear.) To compute S^{-1}, it is not necessary to take

$$B = A^{-1} = \frac{1}{ad - bc}\begin{pmatrix} d & -b \\ -c & a \end{pmatrix}$$

since the factor $1/(ad - bc)$ is irrelevant to a mapping of $\mathbf{P}$. Thus

$$(3.4) \qquad S^{-1}\tau = \frac{d\tau - b}{-c\tau + a}$$

is the equation for S^{-1}.

In succeeding sections there will be no cause to refer to $\mathbf{P}$ or V. "Fractional linear transformations" or, when no confusion can arise, "linear transformations" will be taken to mean transformations of $\mathbf{C} \cup \{\infty\}$ of the form (3.2). (With $ad - bc \neq 0$, of course.) The rules for composition and inverses are given by (3.3) and (3.4), respectively.

4. Properties of Fractional Linear Transformations

The set $\mathbf{C} \cup \{\infty\}$ will be referred to as the *extended complex plane*. By "extended complex number" or "complex number" we will mean an element of $\mathbf{C} \cup \{\infty\}$.[1] Similarly an "extended line" or "line" will be a straight line in $\mathbf{C}$ with the point ∞ added.

Lemma 4.1. If S and T are fractional linear transformations such that for distinct complex numbers z_1, z_2, and z_3 the equality $Sz_j = Tz_j$, $j = 1, 2, 3$, holds, then $Sz \equiv Tz$.

Proof. Let

$$Sz = \frac{az + b}{cz + d} \quad \text{and} \quad Tz = \frac{\alpha z + \beta}{\gamma z + \delta}.$$

Case 1. None of z_1, z_2, z_3, Sz_1, Sz_2, Sz_3 is infinite. In this case $Sz = Tz$ if, and only if,

$$Q(z) = (az + b)(\gamma z + \delta) - (cz + d)(\alpha z + \beta) = 0.$$

By assumption $Q(z_1) = Q(z_2) = Q(z_3) = 0$ which is impossible for a quadratic polynomial unless it vanishes identically. Therefore, $Sz \equiv Tz$ as claimed.

Case 2. One or more of z_1, z_2, z_3, Sz_1, Sz_2, Sz_3 is ∞. Let $Uz = 1/(z - a)$, where a is none of the above 6 numbers. Then $USU^{-1} = A_1$ and $UTU^{-1} = A_2$ satisfy

$$A_1 w_j = A_2 w_j,$$

where $w_j = Uz_j$, $j = 1, 2, 3$ is finite for each j and $A_1 w_j$ is finite for $j = 1, 2, 3$. Case 1 applies to give $A_1 z \equiv A_2 z$ and therefore

$$Tz = U^{-1}A_2Uz \equiv U^{-1}A_1Uz = Sz.$$

Lemma 4.2. Given distinct points z_1, z_2, z_3 there is a transformation T sending z_1 into 0, z_2 into 1, and z_3 into ∞.

Proof. Suppose first z_1, z_2, z_3 are finite. To arrive at T let $T_1 z = (z - z_1)$ which sends z_1 into 0. $T_2 z = (z - z_1)/(z - z_3)$ sends z_1 into 0, z_3 into ∞. By normalizing T_2, T is defined as

(4.1) $$Tz = \frac{z - z_1}{z - z_3} \frac{z_2 - z_3}{z_2 - z_1}.$$

If $z_1 = \infty$, let $z_1 \to \infty$ in (4.1). The limiting value for fixed z, z_2, z_3 is

$$Tz = \frac{z_2 - z_3}{z - z_3}$$

---

[1] In the present chapter only.

which sends ∞ into 0, z_2 into 1, and z_3 into ∞. Similarly, the cases $z_2 = \infty$, $z_3 = \infty$ produce

$$Tz = \frac{z - z_1}{z - z_3} \quad \text{and} \quad Tz = \frac{z - z_1}{z_2 - z_1}, \quad \text{respectively.}$$

Theorem 4.1. *For any two prescribed triples of distinct points z_1, z_2, z_3 and w_1, w_2, w_3 there is a linear transformation T such that $Tz_j = w_j$, $j = 1, 2, 3$.*

Proof. By Lemma 4.2 there are transformations T_1, T_2 such that

$$T_1 z_1 = 0 = T_2 w_1$$
$$T_1 z_2 = 1 = T_2 w_2$$
$$T_1 z_3 = \infty = T_2 w_3.$$

The transformation $T = T_2^{-1} T_1$ is as required.

The construction leading to Theorem 4.1 proves that if z_1, z_2, z_3, w_1, w_2, w_3 are real (or ∞) then T can be chosen to have real coefficients. The same is true for T^{-1}, meaning T maps the extended real line onto itself. If S is a linear transformation sending z_1, z_2, z_3 into w_1, w_2, w_3, respectively, then by Lemma 4.1 $Sz \equiv Tz$, and S maps the extended real line onto itself. This proves

Corollary 4.1. *If T is a fractional linear transformation such that for distinct real numbers z_1, z_2, z_3 the (extended) numbers Tz_1, Tz_2, Tz_3 are real, then T maps the extended real line onto itself.*

Lemma 4.3. *If γ is a circle of radius R centered at a point a, if w_1, w_2, w_3 are distinct points of γ, and if z_1, z_2, z_3 are distinct real numbers, there is a transformation T sending the extended real numbers onto γ such that $Tz_j = w_j$, $j = 1, 2, 3$.*

Proof. The transformation $Sz = (z - i)/(z + i)$ maps the real line onto $|w| = 1$. Multiplying S by R and translating by a gives

$$T_1 z = R \cdot Sz + a,$$

a mapping of the real line onto γ. If $\zeta_1 = T_1^{-1} w_1, \zeta_2 = T_1^{-1} w_2, \zeta_3 = T_1^{-1} w_3$, let U be a transformation sending z_j into ζ_j, $j = 1, 2, 3$. Then $Tz = T_1 U$ maps the extended reals onto γ with $Tz_j = w_j$, $j = 1, 2, 3$ as required.

The reader can check that Lemma 4.3 remains true if we take for γ a straight line (including ∞).

Lemma 4.4.   Given distinct points z_1, z_2, z_3 there exists a unique circle or straight line γ passing through z_1, z_2, z_3.

Proof.   In case one of the z's, say z_1, is ∞ the lemma is trivial for in that case γ can be taken to be the (unique) straight line through z_2 and z_3. Assume therefore that z_1, z_2, and z_3 are finite. If there is to be such a circle γ, it must have a center, a, and radius, R, and therefore we seek a solution to the equations

$$(4.2) \qquad |z_j - a|^2 = R^2 = |z_j|^2 + |a|^2 - 2Re(\bar{z}_j a); \quad j = 1, 2, 3.$$

If the second equation of (4.2) is subtracted from the first and the third, two simultaneous equations arise,

$$(4.3) \qquad \begin{aligned} |z_1|^2 - |z_2|^2 + 2Re((\bar{z}_2 - \bar{z}_1)a) &= 0, \\ |z_3|^2 - |z_2|^2 + 2Re((\bar{z}_2 - \bar{z}_3)a) &= 0. \end{aligned}$$

Let $\bar{z}_2 - \bar{z}_1 = \alpha + i\beta$, $\bar{z}_2 - \bar{z}_3 = \delta + i\epsilon$, $a = x + iy$. Then z_1, z_2, z_3 lie on a straight line if, and only if, $\beta/\alpha = \epsilon/\delta$, and in this case the line is (of course) unique. Assume therefore that $\beta/\alpha \neq \epsilon/\delta$, or $\beta\delta - \epsilon\alpha \neq 0$. Equations (4.3) become

$$(4.4) \qquad \begin{aligned} |z_1|^2 - |z_2|^2 + 2(\alpha x - \beta y) &= 0, \\ |z_3|^2 - |z_2|^2 + 2(\delta x - \epsilon y) &= 0. \end{aligned}$$

In order for there to exist a unique solution to equations (4.4), it is necessary that the determinant $-4(\alpha\epsilon - \beta\delta) \neq 0$ which is what we have assumed. Therefore a exists and is unique, and R can be computed from (4.2).

Theorem 4.2.   *A linear transformation T takes the extended real line onto a circle or an extended line.*

Proof.   Let $w_1 = T0$, $w_2 = T1$, $w_3 = T\infty$. By Lemma 4.4 there is a unique circle or straight line γ passing through w_j, $j = 1, 2, 3$. By Lemma 4.3 there is a transformation S sending the extended real line onto γ with $S0 = w_1$, $S1 = w_2$, $S\infty = w_3$. By Lemma 4.1, $Sz \equiv Tz$, and so Tz must map the extended real numbers onto γ.

As a corollary to Theorem 4.2 we have

Theorem 4.3. *The image of a circle or an (extended) line γ under a linear transformation T is a circle or an (extended) line.*

Proof. Let S map the extended real line onto γ. By Theorem 4.2 the image, η, of the real line under $U = TS$ is a circle or an extended line. But η is also the image of γ under T which proves the theorem.

Problems

1. If a, b, c, and d are real numbers with $ad - bc \neq 0$, the transformation $Tz = \dfrac{az + b}{cz + d}$ will map the real axis onto itself. Give a useful criterion for determining whether T maps the upper half-plane onto the upper or the lower half-plane.

2. A fractional linear transformation which is not the identity has at most two fixed points. Which transformations have

   (a) no finite fixed points?
   (b) one finite fixed point?
   (c) two finite fixed points?

3. Find a linear transformation which

   (a) maps $\{|z| < 1\}$ onto $\operatorname{Im} z > 0$;
   (b) sends $\frac{1}{2}$, 1, and 2 onto 0, i, and ∞, respectively;
   (c) maps $|z - i| < 1$ onto $|w - 3| < 2$.

4. If z_1, z_2, z_3, z_4 are finite and distinct, define

   $$(*) \qquad (z_1, z_2, z_3, z_4) = \frac{z_1 - z_2}{z_1 - z_4} \frac{z_3 - z_4}{z_3 - z_2}$$

   the *cross ratio* of the four points.

   (a) Observe that $(z_1, z_2, z_3, z_4) = Tz_1$, where T maps z_2, z_3, z_4 onto 0, 1, ∞, respectively.
   (b) Extend the definition $(*)$ to the case where one of the points is infinite.
   (c) If S is linear, show that

   $$(z_1, z_2, z_3, z_4) = (Sz_1, Sz_2, Sz_3, Sz_4).$$

(d) Show that the linear transformation $w = Tz$ which sends z_2, z_3, z_4 onto w_2, w_3, w_4, respectively, satisfies

$$(z, z_2, z_3, z_4) = (w, w_2, w_3, w_4).$$

(e) What is the locus of points z such that (z, z_2, z_3, z_4) is real?

5. If S and T leave the same points fixed, then $ST = TS$.

6. If z_1, z_2, z_3 are not collinear, the perpendicular bisectors of the lines $z_1 z_2$ and $z_2 z_3$ meet in a point which is the center of the unique circle containing z_1, z_2, and z_3.

7. Verify that Lemma 4.3 is true for a straight line γ.

5. Symmetry

A complex number z and its conjugate $\bar{z}$ are said to be *symmetric* with respect to the real axis. If T is a linear transformation which maps the extended real numbers onto themselves, T may be chosen to have real coefficients by Section 4. Therefore, $T\bar{z} = \overline{Tz}$, and the symmetric points z, $\bar{z}$ are sent into symmetric points Tz and $\overline{Tz}$. We have proved

Lemma 5.1. If T is a linear transformation which preserves the extended real numbers, then T maps points symmetric with respect to **R** (= real numbers) into points symmetric with respect to **R**.

Definition 5.1. Points z and z^* are said to be *symmetric* with respect to a given circle or straight line γ if there is a linear transformation T which takes γ onto **R** such that

$$Tz = \overline{Tz^*}.$$

It is not clear from the definition that if S is another linear transformation taking γ onto **R**, then $Sz = \overline{Sz^*}$. To see that this is so we observe that the transformation ST^{-1} maps **R** onto **R**. Therefore, by Lemma 5.1

$$Sz = ST^{-1}Tz = ST^{-1}\overline{Tz^*}$$

$$= \overline{ST^{-1}Tz^*}$$

$$= \overline{Sz^*}.$$

Thus given a circle γ, there is for each point z a *unique* point z^* symmetric to z with respect to γ. The mapping which sends z into z^* is called *reflec-*

tion in γ. Reflection is *not* an analytic mapping. To see this let $\varphi(z) = z^*$ be reflection, and let T be a linear transformation of γ onto **R**. Then $T\varphi(z) = \overline{Tz}$ or

$$\varphi(z) = T^{-1}(\overline{Tz})$$

which is not an analytic function.

Theorem 5.1. *If z, z^* are symmetric with respect to γ, then for any linear transformation S, Sz and Sz^* are symmetric with respect to $S\gamma$.*

Proof. $S\gamma$ is a circle by Theorem 4.3. Let T be a mapping of $S\gamma$ onto **R**. Then TS maps γ onto **R**, and since z, z^* are assumed to be symmetric with respect to γ, $TSz = \overline{TSz^*}$. In terms of $S\gamma$ this last equation is simply the condition that Sz and Sz^* be symmetric points. The theorem is proved.

Using Theorem 5.1 it is easy to compute for a given circle γ the mapping $\varphi(z) = z^*$.

Lemma 5.2. *If γ is the circle $|w| = 1$, reflection in γ is given by $w^* = 1/\bar{w}$.*

Proof. The mapping $Tz = (z - i)/(z + i)$ sends the extended real line onto $|w| = 1$ and clearly satisfies $T(-z) = 1/Tz$. The inverse of T is $T^{-1}w = (iw + i)/(-w + 1) = -i(w + 1)/(w - 1)$, and

$$\overline{T^{-1}w} = i\,\frac{\bar{w} + 1}{\bar{w} - 1}$$

$$= -T^{-1}\bar{w}.$$

It follows that

$$w^* = T\overline{T^{-1}w}$$

$$= T(-T^{-1}\bar{w})$$

$$= \frac{1}{T(T^{-1}\bar{w})}$$

$$= \frac{1}{\bar{w}}$$

as claimed.

Theorem 5.2. *If γ is the circle of radius R about a point a, then*

(5.1) $$z^* = \frac{R^2}{\bar{z} - \bar{a}} + a.$$

Proof. Let $Tz = (z - a)/R$ map γ onto $|w| = 1$. By Theorem 5.1 $(Tz)^* = Tz^*$, the first reflection with respect to $|w| = 1$, the second with respect to γ. From Lemma 5.2 we have, therefore,

$$Tz^* = \frac{R}{\bar{z} - \bar{a}}$$

and applying T^{-1} to both sides

$$z^* = \frac{R^2}{\bar{z} - \bar{a}} + a.$$

REMARK. It is clear from (5.1) that, as we have shown before, $z \rightarrow z^*$ is not an analytic mapping.

Problems

1. If γ is the unit circle, find the image under reflection in γ of

   (a) the line $\operatorname{Re} z = 1$;
   (b) the circle $|z - \frac{1}{2}i| = \frac{1}{2}$;
   (c) the circle $|z - 2| = 1$.

2. Show that reflection preserves the magnitude, but not the sense, of angles.

3. If γ_1, γ_2 are circles, define
   $$f(z) = (z^{*1})^{*2}$$
   where *1, *2 denote reflection in γ_1, γ_2, respectively. Show that $f(z)$ is meromorphic (analytic with at most one pole), and formulate a general result for $(\ldots (z^{*1})^{*2} \ldots)^{*n}$, where *1, $\ldots$, *n are reflections in circles $\gamma_1, \ldots , \gamma_n$, respectively.

4. Let there be given

   (a) circles γ_1 and γ_2;
   (b) points z, z^* symmetric with respect to γ_1 together with points w, w^* symmetric with respect to γ_2;
   (c) a linear transformation T such that $Tz = w$, $Tz^* = w^*$, and $T\zeta = \eta$ for a certain pair ζ, η with $\zeta \in \gamma_1$ and $\eta \in \gamma_2$.

   Show that T maps γ_1 onto γ_2.

5. Let γ be a circle centered at z_0. If ζ lies inside γ, $\zeta \neq z_0$, denote by L the line perpendicular to the radial segment $z_0\zeta$ at ζ. L intersects γ in points A, B. Let L_1, L_2 be the tangents to γ at A, B, respectively. Prove: $\zeta^* = L_1 \cap L_2$.

6. Schwarz's Lemma

The following lemma due to H. A. Schwarz, though an easy consequence of the maximum principle for analytic functions, is one of the most important tools for the study of complex mappings. It will play a major role in many theorems to follow, particularly in Chapters 3 and 4.

Lemma 6.1. (H. A. Schwarz) Let f be analytic and bounded by 1 for $|z| < 1$. If $f(0) = 0$, then either

(6.1)
$$|f(z)| < |z|, \quad z \neq 0,$$
$$|f'(0)| < 1$$

or else $f(z) = cz$ for some constant c of absolute value 1.

Proof. Define h by

$$h(z) = \begin{cases} \dfrac{f(z)}{z}, & z \neq 0 \\ f'(0), & z = 0. \end{cases}$$

If $|z| < r < 1$, the maximum principle applies to the analytic function h to give

$$|h(z)| \leq \max_{|w|=r} |h(w)|.$$

The assumption on f guarantees that $\max_{|w|=r} |h(w)| \leq 1/r$. Letting $r \to 1$ gives $|h(z)| \leq 1$, $z \in \Delta$. If $|h(z)| = 1$ for some $z \in \Delta$, then by the maximum principle h is constant. In this case $h(z) \equiv c$, where $|c| = 1$, and *a fortiori* $f(z) = cz$. On the other hand, if $|h(z)| < 1$ for each z, (6.1) is true. The lemma is proved.

As a first application of Schwarz's lemma we prove

Lemma 6.2. Let f be a one-to-one analytic mapping of the unit disk Δ, $\Delta = \{z \mid |z| < 1\}$, onto itself. If $f(0) = 0$, then $f(z) = cz$ for a certain constant c of modulus 1.

Proof. Both f and f^{-1} satisfy the hypotheses of Lemma 6.1. Therefore, since $z = f^{-1}(f(z))$, we have

$$|z| = |f^{-1}f(z)| \leq |f(z)|.$$

Applying Schwarz's lemma $f(z) = cz$ as claimed.

Lemma 6.3. If $|z| < 1$ and $|a| < 1$, then

$$(6.2) \qquad \left| \frac{z - a}{1 - \bar{a}z} \right| \leq \frac{|z| + |a|}{1 + |a|\,|z|} < 1.$$

Proof. Define r_1 and r_2 by

$$r_1 = 1 - \left| \frac{z - a}{1 - \bar{a}z} \right|^2 = \frac{(1 - |a|^2)(1 - |z|^2)}{|1 - \bar{a}z|^2},$$

$$r_2 = 1 - \frac{(|a| + |z|)^2}{(1 + |a|\,|z|)^2} = \frac{(1 - |a|^2)(1 - |z|^2)}{(1 + |a|\,|z|)^2}.$$

By the triangle inequality $|1 - \bar{a}z| \leq 1 + |a|\,|z|$, and so $r_1 \geq r_2$. Therefore, $1 - r_1 \leq 1 - r_2$ or

$$\left| \frac{z - a}{1 - \bar{a}z} \right|^2 \leq \frac{(|a| + |z|)^2}{(1 + |a|\,|z|)^2}$$

which is the square of the first inequality of (6.2).

Fixing $|a|$, the function

$$\psi(r) = \frac{r + |a|}{1 + |a|r}$$

has derivative

$$\psi'(r) = \frac{1 - |a|^2}{(1 + |a|r)^2} > 0.$$

Thus, $\psi(r)$ increases with r. Since $\psi(1) = 1$, the second half of (6.2) follows.

Lemma 6.4. The linear fractional transformation

$$(6.3) \qquad Tz = e^{i\theta}\frac{z - a}{1 - \bar{a}z}, \quad |a| < 1,\ \theta \text{ real}$$

maps $|z| \leq 1$ onto itself.

Proof. If $|z| = 1$, then $z\bar{z} = 1$ and

$$|Tz| = \left| \frac{z - a}{1 - \bar{a}z}\frac{\bar{z}}{\bar{z}} \right| = \left| \frac{z - a}{\bar{z} - \bar{a}}\bar{z} \right|$$

$$= 1.$$

Thus, T sends $|z| = 1$ onto itself. If $|z| < 1$, Lemma 6.3 shows that $|Tz| < 1$. Considerations of symmetry (Theorem 5.1) imply that $|Tz| > 1$ if $|z| > 1$, and the lemma is proved.

It is now possible to prove that (6.3) gives the most general one-to-one analytic mapping of Δ onto itself.

Theorem 6.1. *Let f be a one-to-one analytic mapping of Δ onto itself. Then for some θ real and $|a| < 1$*

$$f(z) = e^{i\theta} \frac{z - a}{1 - \bar{a}z}.$$

Proof.   Suppose $\alpha = f(0)$. Define T by

$$Tz = \frac{z - \alpha}{1 - \bar{\alpha}z}.$$

Then $Tf(z)$ also gives a one-to-one mapping of Δ onto itself with $Tf(0) = T\alpha = 0$. By Lemma 6.2 $Tf(z) = cz$ for some constant c of modulus 1. We apply T^{-1},

$$T^{-1}w = \frac{w + \alpha}{\bar{\alpha}w + 1},$$

to obtain

$$f(z) = \frac{cz + \alpha}{\bar{\alpha}cz + 1}.$$

Then letting $e^{i\theta} = c$, $a = -e^{-i\theta}\alpha$, we find

$$f(z) = e^{i\theta} \frac{z - a}{1 - \bar{a}z}$$

which is (6.3).

Theorem 6.1 enables us to determine the most general mapping of one disk $\Delta_1 = \{z \mid |z - a| \leq R_1\}$ onto another disk $\Delta_2 = \{z \mid |z - b| \leq R_2\}$. Let U, V be linear transformations which map $|z| < 1$ onto Δ_1, Δ_2, respectively. If T is a one-to-one analytic transformation of Δ_1 onto Δ_2, then

$$Sz = V^{-1}TUz$$

is a one-to-one analytic transformation of Δ onto Δ. Therefore, Sz is given by (6.3). T can be computed as the composition of three linear transformations

$$Tw = VSU^{-1}w.$$

In particular T itself is linear.

In case Δ_1, Δ_2 are both the disk of radius R centered at 0, U and V can be taken to be

$$Uz = Vz = R \cdot z.$$

If $Sz = e^{i\theta}(z - a)/(1 - \bar{a}z)$ is as in (6.3), then

$$Tw = VSU^{-1}w$$

(6.4)
$$= Re^{i\theta} \frac{(w/R) - a}{1 - \bar{a}(w/R)}$$

$$= Re^{i\theta} \frac{w - aR}{R - \bar{a}w}.$$

Thus, letting $b = aR$

(6.5)
$$Tw = R^2 e^{i\theta} \frac{w - b}{R^2 - \bar{b}w}.$$

If $\Delta_1 = \{w \mid |w| \leq R\}$ and $\Delta_2 = \{w \mid |w| \leq S\}$, similar calculations give

(6.6)
$$Tw = Se^{i\theta} \frac{w - aR}{R - \bar{a}w},$$

or letting $b = aR$

(6.7)
$$Tw = RSe^{i\theta} \frac{w - b}{R^2 - \bar{b}w},$$

as the most general one-to-one analytic mapping between Δ_1 and Δ_2.

We shall conclude this section with the generalization due to Pick of Schwarz's lemma.

Let f be analytic on $\Delta_1 = \{z \mid |z| < R\}$, and suppose $|f(z)| < S$ if $z \in \Delta_1$. That is, f takes its values in the disk $\Delta_2 = \{z \mid |z| < S\}$. Fixing $z_0 \in \Delta_1$ with $f(z_0) = w_0 \in \Delta_2$, let T_1, T_2 be transformations taking Δ_1, Δ_2 onto Δ with z_0, w_0 going into 0. By (6.7) with first $R = R, S = 1, b = z_0$, $\theta = 0$ and then $R = S, S = 1, b = w_0, \theta = 0$, we have

$$T_1z = R \frac{z - z_0}{R^2 - \bar{z}_0 z},$$

(6.8)

$$T_2w = S \frac{w - w_0}{S^2 - \bar{w}_0 w}.$$

Define an analytic function φ on Δ by

$$\varphi(z) = T_2 f(T_1^{-1}z).$$

Then $\varphi(0) = 0$ and $|\varphi(z)| \leq 1$ if $|z| \leq 1$. By Schwarz's lemma either

$$|\varphi(z)| < |z|, \quad z \neq 0$$

or else

$$\varphi(z) = cz$$

for some constant c of modulus 1. In the latter case let $z = T_1\zeta$, $\zeta \in \Delta_1$. We have

$$f(\zeta) = T_2^{-1}\varphi(T_1\zeta)$$
$$= T_2^{-1}cT_1\zeta,$$

and f is a linear transformation of Δ_1 onto Δ_2. In the former case we find

$$|T_2f(\zeta)| < |T_1\zeta|$$

for all $\zeta \in \Delta_1$, $\zeta \neq z_0$. Therefore, by (6.8)

$$(6.9) \qquad \left| S\frac{f(\zeta) - f(z_0)}{S^2 - \overline{f(z_0)}f(\zeta)} \right| < \left| R\frac{\zeta - z_0}{R^2 - \bar{z}_0\zeta} \right|.$$

Theorem 6.2. (Pick) *If f is analytic on Δ_1 with values in Δ_2, then either f is linear, or else for each $z_0 \in \Delta_1$ the inequalities*

$$(6.10) \qquad \left| S\frac{f(z) - f(z_0)}{S^2 - \bar{f}(z_0)f(z)} \right| < \left| R\frac{z - z_0}{R^2 - \bar{z}_0z} \right|, \quad z \neq z_0$$

and

$$(6.11) \qquad |f'(z_0)| < \frac{R}{S}\frac{S^2 - |f(z_0)|^2}{R^2 - |z_0|^2}$$

will hold.

Proof. We have proved that unless f is linear (6.10) holds. We have left to prove that if f is not linear, (6.11) holds. For fixed z_0 define g by

$$g(z) = \begin{cases} S\dfrac{f(z) - f(z_0)}{S^2 - \bar{f}(z_0)f(z)} \cdot \dfrac{1}{R}\dfrac{R^2 - \bar{z}_0z}{z - z_0}, & z \neq z_0 \\[2ex] \dfrac{S}{R}f'(z_0) \cdot \dfrac{R^2 - |z_0|^2}{S^2 - |f(z_0)|^2}, & z = z_0. \end{cases}$$

The function g is analytic, and by (6.10) $|g(z)| < 1$ for $z \neq z_0$. From the maximum principle we conclude that $|g(z_0)| < 1$, which is equivalent with (6.11).

For future reference we record the situation in case $R = S = 1$ when (6.10) and (6.11) yield

(6.12)
$$\left| \frac{f(z) - f(z_0)}{1 - \bar{f}(z_0)f(z)} \right| \leq \left| \frac{z - z_0}{1 - \bar{z}_0 z} \right|$$

and the inequality, cruder than (6.11), obtained from (6.11) by replacing $1 - |f(z_0)|^2$ by 1

(6.13)
$$|f'(z_0)| \leq \frac{1}{1 - |z_0|^2}.$$

Problems

1. Given $|\alpha| < 1$ and a real number θ define $Tz = e^{i\theta}(z - \alpha)/(1 - \bar{\alpha}z)$. Following steps (a) and (b) below prove that T maps Δ one-to-one onto itself.

   (a) $|Tz| = 1$ for $|z| = 1$. By the maximum principle $|Tz| < 1$ for $|z| < 1$.

   (b) T^{-1} is analytic on Δ, and $|T^{-1}w| = 1$ for $|w| = 1$.

2. Give a direct proof of (6.11) by computing $\varphi'(0)$, where

$$\varphi(z) = T_2 f(T_1^{-1}z).$$

3. Let f be analytic on Δ with $f(0) = i$. If Im $f(z) > 0$ for each z, then

$$|f(z)| \leq \frac{1 + |z|}{1 - |z|}.$$

4. If α is positive and real, denote by Δ_α the set $\{z \mid |z| < \alpha\}$. Let f be analytic and bounded by M on Δ_R with $f(0) = 0$. Suppose f^{-1} can be defined on Δ_r with values in Δ_R and $f^{-1}(0) = 0$. Prove

   (i) $|f^{-1}(z)| \leq (|z|/r)R$, $z \in \Delta_r$;

   (ii) $|f(z)| < r$ if $|z| < (rR/M)$. (NOTE: $r < M$);

   (iii) $f^{-1}(f(z)) = z$, $z \in \Delta_{rR/M}$. f is one-to-one on $\Delta_{rR/M}$.

   (iv) $\min_{|z| = rR/M} |f(z)| \geq (r^2/M)$. (HINT: $|f^{-1}(w)| < (rR/M)$ for $|w| < (r^2/M)$.)

5. If $a_1, \ldots, a_n$ are (not necessarily distinct) points of Δ, set up a function $B(z)$

$$B(z) = \prod_{i=1}^{n} \frac{z - a_i}{1 - \bar{a}_i z}.$$

(a) B is analytic on Δ, and $|B(z)| = 1$ for $|z| = 1$.

(b) If $|\alpha| < 1$, then B assumes the value α n times inside Δ. (Apply Rouché's theorem with $f = B$, $g = \alpha$.) B is an n-to-one mapping of Δ onto Δ.

6. Let f be analytic and bounded by M on Δ. If $a_1, \ldots, a_n$ are among the zeros of f, then

$$|f(z)| \leq M|B(z)|,$$

where B is defined in Problem 5. Under which circumstances does equality hold?

7. Let f be as in Problem 6 but with the additional assumption $f \not\equiv 0$. Suppose f has a zero of order k, $k \geq 0$, at $z = 0$. (If $f(0) \neq 0$, $k = 0$.) Define $\alpha = |f^{(k)}(0)|$. Of course, $\alpha \neq 0$.

(i) Define $f_1(z) = \dfrac{f(z)}{z^k}$, $z \neq 0$, $\dfrac{f^{(k)}(0)}{k!}$, $z = 0$.

Show that f_1 is bounded by M on Δ.

(ii) Denote by $a_1, a_2, \ldots$ the sequence of zeros of f distinct from $z = 0$. If f has a zero of order l at z, then z should appear l times on the list. Prove $\beta = \lim_{n \to \infty} \prod_{k=1}^{n} |a_k|$ exists.

(iii) Using Problem 6 for f_1 (at $z = 0$), prove $\beta \geq (\alpha/k!M)$. Thus, $\beta \neq 0$.

(iv) $\displaystyle\sum_{k=1}^{\infty} \ln|a_k| > -\infty$. Thus $\displaystyle\sum_{k=1}^{\infty} \ln|a_k|$ converges.

8. Let f be analytic on Δ and continuous on $\{z \mid |z| \leq 1\}$. If $f(z) \neq 0$ for $|z| = 1$, then f has only finitely many zeros.

9. If f is as in Problem 8, and if $|f(z)| = 1$ for $|z| = 1$, prove

(a) If f has no zeros, then $f(z) \equiv e^{i\theta}$ for some θ. (Use Rouché's theorem, or else apply the maximum principle to f and $1/f$.)

(b) If f has n zeros, then $f(z) = e^{i\theta}B(z)$ for some θ and B.

10. Again let f be as in Problem 8. Then for some B (formed from the zeros of f) and F, $f(z) = B(z)F(z)$, where F has no zeros in Δ. Furthermore, $|F(z)| = |f(z)|$ if $|z| = 1$.

11. Continuing with Problem 10, assume $f(0) \neq 0$. Because F has no zeros, it is possible to define an analytic version of $\log F$. Prove

    (a)
    $$\log F(0) = \frac{1}{2\pi i} \int_{|z|=1} \log F(e^{i\theta}) \frac{dz}{z}$$

    $$= \frac{1}{2\pi} \int_{-\pi}^{\pi} \log F(e^{i\theta}) \, d\theta.$$

    In particular, equating real parts,

    $$\ln |F(0)| = \frac{1}{2\pi} \int_{-\pi}^{\pi} \ln|F(e^{i\theta})| \, d\theta.$$

    (b) Use (a) to show

    $$\frac{1}{2\pi} \int_{-\pi}^{\pi} \ln|f(e^{i\theta})| \, d\theta = \ln|f(0)| - \sum_{k=1}^{n} \ln|a_k|,$$

    where $a_1, \ldots, a_n$ denote the zeros of f. This is *Jensen's formula*.

12. Suppose f and f_1 are functions analytic on a region Ω and taking values in Δ. If f maps Ω one-to-one onto Δ, then for $z, w \in \Omega$, $z \neq w$,

    $$D(f_1(z), f_1(w)) \leq D(f(z), f(w)),$$

    where $D(\zeta, \eta) = |(\zeta - \eta)/(1 - \bar{\eta}\zeta)|$. Furthermore, the inequality is strict unless f_1 also maps Ω one-to-one onto Δ.

13. Let f be a one-to-one analytic mapping of Δ onto a region Ω with $f(0) = w_0$. Define Ω_r, $0 \leq r < 1$, by

    $$\Omega_r = f(\Delta_r)$$

    $$= \{f(z) \mid z \in \Delta_r\}.$$

    (a) If φ is analytic on Δ with values in Ω, and if $\varphi(0) = w_0$, then $\varphi(z) \in \Omega_r$ for $z \in \Delta_r$.

    (b) There exist constants $A_r < \infty$, $0 \leq r < 1$, such that if φ is analytic on Δ with $\varphi(0) = 0$, and if $-1 < \operatorname{Re} \varphi < 1$, then $|\operatorname{Im} \varphi(z)| < A_r$ for $z \in \Delta_r$.

    (c) If φ is analytic on Δ with $\varphi(0) = 0$, and if $\operatorname{Re} \varphi \leq x$ for some $x > 0$, then

    $$|\varphi(z)| \leq \frac{2xr}{1 - r}.$$

7. Non-Euclidean Geometry

A one-to-one analytic transformation of Δ onto itself has the form (6.3) according to Theorem 6.1. The composition of two transformations of Δ is a transformation of Δ as is the inverse of a transformation of Δ. These transformations therefore form a group, G. The purpose of the present section is to discuss the "geometry" of the action of G on Δ. "Geometry" in this context is loosely defined as a study of those objects or properties which are left invariant under transformations of G. The reader will find it interesting to give such a loose definition of plane geometry, taking for G the "rigid motions" of the plane.

Of paramount importance, not only for the geometry itself, but for the applications of the geometry to function theory, is a distance $d(z, w)$ between points of Δ. Properties the distance must enjoy are

(1) $d(z, z) = 0$, for all $z \in \Delta$;
(2) $d(z, w) = d(w, z)$, for all $z, w \in \Delta$;
(3) $d(z, w) > 0$, if $z \neq w$;
(4) $d(z, w) < d(z, \zeta) + d(\zeta, w)$, $z, \zeta, w \in \Delta$ (triangle inequality);
(5) $d(Tz, Tw) = d(z, w)$.

We will "discover" $d(z, w)$ by discussing the implications of its existence. Therefore, assume $d(z, w)$ exists.

If we take $z = 0$, w arbitrary, and $T\zeta = e^{i\theta}\zeta$, then by (5)

$$d(0, w) = d(0, e^{i\theta}w).$$

Thus, $d(0, w)$ depends only upon $|w|$.

If $z, w \in \Delta$ are arbitrary, then

$$T\zeta = \frac{\zeta - z}{1 - \bar{z}\zeta}$$

takes z into 0, w into $(w - z)/(1 - \bar{z}w)$. Using (5) together with the preceding observation,

$$d(z, w) = d(0, D(z, w)),$$

where

$$D(z, w) = \left| \frac{w - z}{1 - \bar{z}w} \right|.$$

For each r, $0 \leq r < 1$ let $\psi(r)$ be defined by

$$\psi(r) = d(0, r) = d(0, re^{i\theta}).$$

We will attempt to express $\psi(r)$ as the integral of a "density" $\varphi(s)$,

$$\psi(r) = \int_0^r \varphi(s)\,ds.$$

Letting $D = D(z, w)$ it will then hold that

$$d(z, w) = d(0, D) = \int_0^D \varphi(s)\,ds.$$

Dividing both sides by $|z - w|$ and letting $z \to w$ gives

$$\lim_{z \to w} \frac{d(z, w)}{|z - w|} = \lim_{z \to w} \frac{1}{|z - w|} \int_0^D \varphi(s)\,ds$$

(7.1)
$$= \frac{1}{1 - |w|^2} \varphi(0).$$

Normalize φ by setting $\varphi(0) = 1$.

If $z = r$ and $w = r + \Delta r$, we conclude from the triangle inequality $(d(0, r + \Delta r) \leq d(0, r) + d(r, r + \Delta r))$ that

$$\int_r^{r + \Delta r} \varphi(s)\,ds \leq d(r, r + \Delta r).$$

Dividing by $\Delta r > 0$ and taking account of (7.1) as $\Delta r \to 0$ yields $\varphi(r) \leq 1/(1 - r^2)$. Let us try $\varphi(r) = 1/(1 - r^2)$. Integration gives as candidate for $\psi(r)$

$$\psi(r) = \frac{1}{2} \log \frac{1 + r}{1 - r},$$

and $d(z, w)$

$$d(z, w) = \frac{1}{2} \log \frac{1 + D}{1 - D}, \quad D = D(z, w).$$

Properties (1)–(3) above are now immediate for $d(z, w)$ while property (5) is almost obvious. $D(z, w)$ is by definition $|Tw|$, where T is a transformation of Δ sending z into 0. By (6.3) if T_1 and T_2 are two such, $|T_1 w| = |T_2 w|$. Let S be an arbitrary element of G. If U is a transformation of Δ sending Sz into 0, then US sends z into 0, and

$$D(Sz, Sw) = |USw| = D(z, w)$$

which is (5). Property (4), which is more difficult to establish, will be proved shortly.

Lemma 7.1. If γ is a piecewise differentiable arc joining 0 to z, then

(7.2)
$$d(0, z) \leq \int_\gamma \frac{|d\zeta|}{1 - |\zeta|^2}$$

with equality holding just when γ is the radial segment from 0 to z. (If $z = re^{i\theta}$, *the* radial segment from 0 to z must be an arc parametrized by $z(t) = r(t)e^{i\theta}$, $r'(t) \geq 0$.)

Proof. Let γ be parametrized by

$$\zeta(t) = r(t)e^{i\theta(t)}, \quad 0 \leq t \leq 1,$$

where $\theta(t)$, while not single-valued, has single-valued derivative

$$\frac{d\theta}{dt} = \frac{\partial\theta}{\partial x} x'(t) + \frac{\partial\theta}{\partial y} y'(t)$$

$$= \frac{x(t)y'(t) - y(t)x'(t)}{x^2(t) + y^2(t)}.$$

The differential $d\zeta$ is given by

$$d\zeta = [r'(t)e^{i\theta(t)} + ir(t)e^{i\theta(t)}\theta'(t)]\, dt$$

valid for all but at most finitely many t as is

$$|d\zeta| = |r'(t) + ir(t)\theta'(t)|\, dt.$$

Standard properties of the integral give rise to

$$d(0, z) = \int_0^{|z|} \frac{dr}{1 - r^2} = \int_0^1 \frac{r'(t)}{1 - r^2}\, dt$$

$$\leq \int_0^1 \frac{|r'(t)|}{1 - r^2}\, dt$$

(7.3)
$$\leq \int_0^1 \frac{|r'(t) + ir(t)\theta'(t)|}{1 - r^2}\, dt$$

$$= \int_\gamma \frac{|d\zeta|}{1 - |\zeta|^2}.$$

The first inequality of (7.3) will be strict unless $r'(t) \geq 0$ as will the second unless $r(t)\theta'(t) \equiv 0$. These last two conditions are equivalent with γ being the radial segment jointing 0 to z.

The right side of (7.2) is an "invariant." If γ is a piecewise differentiable arc, and if $T \in G$ is arbitrary, then setting $\eta = T\gamma$,

(7.4)
$$\int_\gamma \frac{|dz|}{1 - |z|^2} = \int_\eta \frac{|dw|}{1 - |w|^2}$$

holds. Since $|dw| = |dT/dz|\, |dz|$, (7.4) will follow from the equality

(7.5)
$$\frac{|dT/dz|}{1 - |Tz|^2} = \frac{1}{1 - |z|^2}.$$

Suppose $Tz = e^{i\theta}(z - a)/(1 - \bar{a}z)$ for some θ, a. The quantities $|dT/dz|$ and $1 - |Tz|^2$ are given by

$$\left| \frac{dT}{dz} \right| = \frac{1 - |a|^2}{|1 - \bar{a}z|^2},$$

$$(1 - |Tz|^2) = 1 - \frac{|z - a|^2}{|1 - \bar{a}z|^2}$$

$$= \frac{(1 - |z|^2)(1 - |a|^2)}{|1 - \bar{a}z|^2}.$$

Dividing the first by the second gives (7.5).

Theorem 7.1. *If z, w are points of Δ, and if γ is a piecewise differentiable curve in Δ joining z to w, then*

$$(7.6) \qquad d(z, w) \leq \int_\gamma \frac{|d\zeta|}{1 - |\zeta|^2}.$$

Furthermore, equality holds in (7.6) if, and only if, γ is the arc of a circle which intersects the unit circle at right angles.

Proof. Let $T\zeta = (\zeta - z)/(1 - \bar{z}\zeta)$. The image $\eta = T\gamma$ of γ under T is an arc joining 0 to $(w - z)/(1 - \bar{z}w)$. Applying the invariance of (7.2) and Lemma 7.1 successively gives

$$\int_\gamma \frac{|d\zeta|}{1 - |\zeta|^2} = \int_\eta \frac{|dw|}{1 - |w|^2}$$

$$(7.7) \qquad\qquad\qquad \geq d\left(0, \frac{w - z}{1 - w\bar{z}}\right)$$

$$= d(z, w).$$

Equality holds in (7.7) if, and only if, η is the radial segment joining 0 to $(w - z)/(1 - \bar{z}w)$. In this case η extends in both directions to become a diameter of Δ. Under T^{-1} this diameter must go into the arc of a circle which intersects the unit circle in two points. Because T^{-1} preserves angles, the angle of this intersection must be the same as the angle of intersection of a circle with one of its diameters, i.e., a right angle. If there were two such circles, the reader can show that there would be distinct diameters of Δ going through 0 and $(w - z)/(1 - \bar{z}w)$, an absurdity.

The fourth requirement of $d(z, w)$ is now easily verified. If z, ζ, $w \in \Delta$ are given, let γ_1, γ_2 be the arcs joining z to ζ and ζ to w such that (7.6) is an equality, first with $z = z$, $w = \zeta$, then with $z = \zeta$, $w = w$. Define γ to be γ_1 followed by γ_2. By Theorem 7.1

$$(7.8) \qquad d(z, w) \leq \int_\gamma \frac{|d\zeta|}{1 - |\zeta|^2} = \int_{\gamma_1} \frac{|d\zeta|}{1 - |\zeta|^2} + \int_{\gamma_2} \frac{|d\zeta|}{1 - |\zeta|^2}$$

$$= d(z, \zeta) + d(\zeta, w).$$

Equality can hold in (7.8) just when γ itself is the arc of a circle intersecting $|z| = 1$ at right angles, and ζ lies between z and w on this arc.

REMARK. Going back to the version of Pick's theorem given in (6.12), that theorem says that if $f(z)$ is of bound one in Δ, then

$$D(f(z), f(z_0)) \leq D(z, z_0)$$

with equality holding for no pair $z \neq z_0$ unless f is a linear map of Δ onto Δ. In terms of our distance the statement is

$$(7.9) \qquad d(f(z), f(z_0)) \leq d(z, z_0).$$

A function F on Δ with values in Δ is an *isometry* if for each pair z, $w \in \Delta$

$$(7.10) \qquad d(F(z), F(w)) = d(z, w)$$

holds. If, for example, F is linear, then (7.10) holds by property (5) of $d(z, w)$. A nonanalytic example of an isometry is the mapping

$$F(z) = \bar{z}$$

which, since $D(z, w) = D(\bar{z}, \bar{w})$, satisfies (7.10).

If F and G are isometries, then the composition $H(z) = FG(z)$ is again an isometry since

$$d(H(z), H(w)) = d(FG(z), FG(w))$$

$$= d(G(z), G(w))$$

$$= d(z, w)$$

after two applications of (7.10). Our purpose is now to express an arbitrary isometry as the composition of "elementary" isometries.

Suppose F is an isometry such that $F(0) = 0$ and $F(\frac{1}{2}) = \frac{1}{2}$. Then we claim $F(x) = x$ for $-1 < x < 1$. To see this note that $F(x)$ by (7.10) must lie at a distance $d(0, x)$ from 0 and $d(x, \frac{1}{2})$ from $\frac{1}{2}$. Since if, say, $x < 0$

$$d(x, \tfrac{1}{2}) = d(x, 0) + d(0, \tfrac{1}{2}),$$

we have

$$d(F(x), \tfrac{1}{2}) = d(F(x), 0) + d(0, \tfrac{1}{2})$$

which from the triangle inequality implies that $F(x)$, 0, and $\frac{1}{2}$ lie on the same straight line with 0 between $F(x)$ and $\frac{1}{2}$. Since also $d(F(x), 0) = d(x, 0)$, we have

$$F(x) = x$$

for $x < 0$. Similar argument gives $F(x) = x$, $-1 < x < 1$.

If $F(x) = x$ for real x, then the point $F(iy)$ must lie equidistant from x and $-x$ for each x. Since also $d(0, iy) = d(0, F(iy))$, it follows that $F(iy) = iy$ or $-iy$. If $F(\frac{1}{2}i)$, say, is $\frac{1}{2}i$, then $F(iy) = iy$ for $-1 < y < 1$. If $F(\frac{1}{2}i) = -\frac{1}{2}i$, then $F(iy) = -iy$ for real y.

Suppose now $F(x) = x$ and $F(iy) = iy$ for real x, y. Then it is left to the reader to show that $F(z) = z$ for all z. Similarly, if $F(x) = x$ and $F(iy) = -iy$, then $F(z) = \bar{z}$ for all z. We now can state

Theorem 7.2.   *If F is an isometry of Δ, then F has one of two forms: Either F is analytic, given by a linear transformation $F(z) = Sz$, or else F is conjugate analytic, given by a conjugate linear transformation $S\bar{z}$.*

Proof.   If $F(0) = \alpha$, $F(\frac{1}{2}) = \beta$, let T be a linear transformation such that $T\alpha = 0$, $T\beta = \frac{1}{2}$. T exists because $d(\alpha, \beta) = d(0, \frac{1}{2})$. By the discussion preceding the theorem either $TF(z) = z$ or $TF(z) = \bar{z}$. Thus, F is linear, $T^{-1}z$, or else conjugate linear, $T^{-1}\bar{z}$, as was to be proved.

Sets A and B in Δ are *congruent* if there exists an isometry of Δ which takes A onto B.

The geometry we have been discussing is one form of "non-Euclidean" geometry. The model is due to Poincare, and it corresponds to Lobatchewskian geometry.

Problems

1. A non-Euclidean triangle ABC is the figure obtained by joining points A and B, B and C, C and A by non-Euclidean straight lines. The "angles" of this triangle are the (Euclidean) angles of intersection at the vertices A, B, and C. Prove: The sum of the angles of a nondegenerate, non-Euclidean triangle is less than π. (A triangle is *degenerate* if its vertices lie on a non-Euclidean straight line.)
2. Define

$$\frac{i}{2} \frac{dz \wedge d\bar{z}}{(1 - |z|^2)^2} = \frac{dx\, dy}{(1 - (x^2 + y^2))^2}.$$

Prove that this object is an invariant area element; find the area of a non-Euclidean disk of non-Euclidean radius r.

3. Let Λ be the differential operator $(1/(1 - x^2 - y^2)^2)(\partial^2/\partial x^2 + \partial^2/\partial y^2)$. If f has continuous partial derivatives of first and second order, define $f_T(z) = f(Tz)$, $T \in G$, $\varphi(z) = \Lambda f(z)$, $\varphi_T(z) = \varphi(Tz)$, $T \in G$. Prove that $\Lambda f_T(z) = \varphi_T(z)$. Λ is the invariant Laplacian for our geometry; it is called the Laplace-Betrami operator.

4. Prove:

(a) If $z, w \in \Delta$, and if $z \neq w$, then

$$(7.11) \qquad\qquad |z - w| < d(z, w).$$

(b) If $r < 1$, and if $z, w \in \Delta_r$, $z \neq w$, then

$$(7.12) \qquad\qquad d(z, w) \leq \frac{|z - w|}{1 - r^2}.$$

5. Let L be a non-Euclidean straight line. If $\zeta \notin L$, there exist exactly two non-Euclidean straight lines, L_1 and L_2, containing ζ such that L_i and L have a common point of intersection with $\{z \mid |z| = 1\}$. (We say L_i and L "meet at ∞.") Thus the parallel postulate fails for non-Euclidean geometry. (The adjective "non-Euclidean" derives from this fact.)

6. Fill in the details of the proof of Theorem 7.2.

7. If two sides and the included angle of two non-Euclidean triangles are equal, the triangles are congruent.

8. The Schwarz Reflection Principle

Given a region Ω and a circle γ, denote by Ω^* the set of points symmetric to points of Ω with respect to γ.

$$\Omega^* = \{z \mid z^* \in \Omega\}.$$

Taking γ for the moment to be the real line, we associate with an analytic function f on Ω, a function f^* on Ω^*, where f^* is defined by

$$f^*(z) = \bar{f}(\bar{z}), \quad z \in \Omega^*.$$

If $z_0 \in \Omega^*$, then about the point $\bar{z}_0 \in \Omega$, f has a Taylor expansion

$$f(\bar{z}) = \sum_{n=0}^{\infty} a_n(\bar{z} - \bar{z}_0)^n$$

and

$$f^*(z) = \bar{f}(\bar{z}) = \sum_{n=0}^{\infty} \bar{a}_n(\bar{\bar{z}} - \bar{\bar{z}}_0)^n = \sum_{n=0}^{\infty} \bar{a}_n(z - z_0)^n$$

provides us with an expansion of f^* about z_0. Therefore, f^* is analytic on Ω^*. The Schwarz reflection principle is not much deeper than this fact.

Lemma 8.1. Let f be analytic inside a rectangle γ and continuous on γ. Then

(8.1) $$\int_\gamma f(z)\, dz = 0.$$

REMARK. If f is analytic in a region containing γ and its inside, then (8.1) is the Cauchy integral theorem, and in fact (8.1) will be deduced from this theorem.

Proof. Let z_0 be the center of γ with $z(t) = z_0 + \zeta(t)$ a parametrization of γ. If $0 < \alpha < 1$, $z_\alpha(t) = z_0 + \alpha\zeta(t)$ is a parametrization of a closed curve γ_α contained inside γ. By the Cauchy integral theorem

$$\int_{\gamma_\alpha} f(\zeta)\, d\zeta = 0.$$

Let $L = \int |\zeta'(t)|\, dt$ be the length of γ, and set $M = \max\limits_{z \in \gamma} |f(z)|$. Because f is continuous on γ, $M < \infty$, and if z lies inside γ, $|f(z)| \le M$ by the maximum principle. Given $\epsilon > 0$, let $\delta > 0$ be chosen so that $\delta < \epsilon/(L + ML)$. If α is sufficiently close to 1, $|f(z_0 + \zeta(t)) - f(z_0 + \alpha\zeta(t))| < \delta$ because f is uniformly continuous inside and on γ. It follows that

$$\left| \int_\gamma f(z)\, dz \right| = \left| \int_\gamma f(z)\, dz - \int_{\gamma_\alpha} f(z)\, dz \right|$$

$$= \left| \int f(z_0 + \zeta(t))\zeta'(t)\, dt - \int f(z_0 + \alpha\zeta(t))\alpha\zeta'(t)\, dt \right|$$

$$= \left| \int [f(z_0 + \zeta(t)) - f(z_0 + \alpha\zeta(t))]\zeta'(t)\, dt \right.$$
$$\left. + \int [f(z_0 + \alpha\zeta(t)) \cdot (1 - \alpha)\zeta'(t)]\, dt \right|$$

$$\le \int |f(z_0 + \zeta(t)) - f(z_0 + \alpha\zeta(t))|\, |\zeta'(t)|\, dt$$
$$+ \int |f(z_0 + \alpha\zeta(t))|(1 - \alpha)|\zeta'(t)|\, dt$$

$$\le \delta L + ML(1 - \alpha)$$

if α is sufficiently large. Arranging matters so that also $1 - \alpha < \delta$, it follows by our choice of δ that

$$\left| \int_\gamma f(z) \, dz \right| < \epsilon.$$

Letting $\epsilon \to 0$ the lemma obtains.

Recall from the elementary theory the following version of *Morera's theorem.*

Theorem. (Morera) *If f is continuous on a disk U, and if $\int_\gamma f(z) \, dz = 0$ for each closed piecewise differentiable arc γ in U, then f is analytic.*

Morera's theorem is proved by fixing a point $z_0 \in U$ and setting up the integral $F(z) = \int_{\gamma_z} f(\zeta) \, d\zeta$, where for each z γ_z is a piecewise differentiable arc in U from z_0 to z. Making use of different paths from z_0 to z, one proves $F'(z) = f(z)$. Thus, F is analytic, and f, the derivative of an analytic function, is also analytic.

Because f is assumed to be continuous, it is only necessary, in order to prove F is analytic, to demonstrate that $(\partial F / \partial x) = f$ and $(\partial F / \partial iy) = f$. To compute $\partial F / \partial x$ and $\partial F / \partial iy$ at a point z, one can take for γ_z a rectangular arc from z_0 to z. If $\partial F / \partial x$ is our interest, the last segment of the arc should be horizontal; for $\partial F / \partial iy$, the last segment should be vertical. Thus Morera's theorem needs only to assume $\int_\gamma f(\zeta) \, d\zeta = 0$ for rectangles having z_0 for one vertex and having sides parallel to the axes. With this in mind we prove

Lemma 8.2. Let f be continuous on a disk U which intersects the real axis in an arc γ. If f is analytic for those $z \in U$ such that $\text{Im } z > 0$ or $\text{Im } z < 0$, then f is analytic on U.

Proof. Fix $z_0 \in \gamma$. If η is a rectangle in U with vertex z_0 and sides parallel to the axes, it is a consequence of Lemma 8.1 that $\int_\eta f(\zeta) \, d\zeta = 0$. Thus by Morera's theorem and the remark preceding this lemma, f is analytic.

In the first version of the Schwarz reflection principle Ω is assumed to be a region in the upper (or lower) half-plane which is bounded in part by an arc γ of the real axis. Let $\tilde{\Omega}$ be the interior of the set $\Omega \cup \gamma \cup \Omega^*$.

(Certain points of γ may not be interior to $\Omega \cup \gamma \cup \Omega^*$. In fact, $\tilde{\Omega}$ may not be connected.)

Theorem 8.1.   *If f is analytic on Ω, continuous on $\Omega \cup \gamma$, and real on γ, then the function $\tilde{f}(z)$ defined on $\tilde{\Omega}$ by*

$$\tilde{f}(z) = \begin{cases} f(z), & z \in \Omega \cup \gamma \\ f^*(z), & z \in \Omega^* \end{cases}$$

is analytic on $\tilde{\Omega}$. ($f^*(z) = \overline{f(\bar{z})}$ is defined at the beginning of the present section.)

Proof.   From our earlier remarks we know that $\tilde{f}$ is analytic on $\Omega \cup \Omega^*$. It will follow from Lemma 8.2 that $\tilde{f}$ is analytic on $\tilde{\Omega}$ if we show $\tilde{f}$ is continuous at points $z \in \gamma$. To this end let z be a point of γ which belongs to $\tilde{\Omega}$. Given $\epsilon > 0$ there is a $\delta > 0$ such that if $\zeta \in \Omega$ and $|\zeta - z| < \delta$, then $|f(z) - f(\zeta)| < \epsilon$. If $\zeta \in \Omega^*$ and $|\zeta - z| < \delta$, then $|\bar{\zeta} - z| < \delta$ and $|f(z) - f(\bar{\zeta})| < \epsilon$. Because $f(z)$ is real on γ, $|f(z) - f(\bar{\zeta})| = |f(z) - \tilde{f}(\bar{\zeta})|$ and therefore,

$$|\tilde{f}(z) - \tilde{f}(\zeta)| = |f(z) - \tilde{f}(\bar{\zeta})|$$
$$< \epsilon.$$

Since ϵ is arbitrary, $\tilde{f}$ is continuous, and the theorem obtains.

Theorem 8.1 will be placed in a more general (and natural) setting. Ω will be a region contained "on one side of" a disk U_1; that is, Ω lies either inside or outside U_1. If γ_1 denotes the bounding circle of U_1, there will be given an arc γ of γ_1 which forms part of the boundary of Ω. If $*$ denotes reflection in γ_1 and $\Omega^* = \{z^* \mid z \in \Omega\}$, then $\tilde{\Omega}$ will be the interior of the set

$$\Omega \cup \gamma \cup \Omega^*.$$

It is possible that $\tilde{\Omega}$ contains the point ∞.

Suppose now that γ_2 is another circle (or straight line) and that f is analytic on Ω, continuous on $\Omega \cup \gamma$, with values $f(z) \in \gamma_2$ if $z \in \gamma$. Then we can state

Theorem 8.2.   *On $\tilde{\Omega}$ define*

$$\tilde{f}(z) = \begin{cases} f(z), & z \in \Omega \cup \gamma \\ f^*(z^*), & z \in \Omega^*, \end{cases}$$

where f^* denotes reflection in γ_2. Then $\tilde{f}(z)$ is meromorphic in $\tilde{\Omega}$.

REMARK.   If for some $z \in \Omega$, $f(z)$ is the center of γ_2, then $\tilde{f}(z^*) = f^*(z) = \infty$, and at z^* $\tilde{f}$ will have a pole.

Proof. Let S, T be linear fractional transformations which map the real line onto γ_1, γ_2, respectively. Then

$$h(z) = T^{-1}f(Sz),$$

which is defined on $\Omega_0 = S^{-1}\Omega$, satisfies the hypotheses of Theorem 8.1 if Ω, γ there be replaced by Ω_0, $\gamma_0 = S^{-1}\gamma$. Define $\tilde{h}$ on $\tilde{\Omega}_0$ by Theorem 8.1. We claim

(8.2) $$\tilde{f}(w) = T\tilde{h}(S^{-1}w)$$

from which the theorem will follow immediately. If $w \in \Omega \cup \gamma$, (8.2) is immediate. If $w \in \Omega^*$, then

$$\begin{aligned}
T\tilde{h}(S^{-1}w) &= T\overline{\tilde{h}(\overline{S^{-1}w})} \\
&= (T\tilde{h}(S^{-1}w^*))^* \\
&= \tilde{f}(w^*)^* \\
&= \tilde{f}(w),
\end{aligned}$$

where the second equality follows from symmetry.

The next chapter will be devoted in large part to establishing the existence of analytic mappings of one region onto another. The following, an amusing application of the Schwarz reflection principle, proves the *non-existence* of such mappings in a certain situation.

In preparation of Theorem 8.3 suppose V is an annulus in the plane with inner boundary the unit circle $|z| = 1$ and outer boundary the circle $|z| = R$, $R > 1$. Let $V^{(1)}$ be the region $V \cup \gamma \cup V^*$, where $\gamma = \{|z| = 1\}$ is the inner circle and V^* denotes reflection in γ. Having defined annuli $V^{(1)}$, $V^{(2)}$, . . . , $V^{(n)}$ with inner circles $\gamma^{(1)}$, . . . , $\gamma^{(n)}$ and common outer circle $|z| = R$, let $V^{(n+1)} = V^{(n)} \cup \gamma^{(n)} \cup V^{(n)*}$, where reflection is in $\gamma^{(n)}$. If r_n is the radius of $\gamma^{(n)}$, then by (5.1)

$$r_{n+1} = \frac{r_n^2}{R},$$

and so $\lim\limits_{n \to \infty} r_n = 0$.

Now, let V_1, V_2 be annuli centered at 0 with inner radius $|z| = 1$, outer radii $|z| = R_1$, $|z| = R_2$, respectively. Suppose there is a one-to-one analytic function f mapping V_1 onto V_2 with the inner circle mapping continuously onto itself and the outer circle $|z| = R_1$ mapping continuously onto $|z| = R_2$. If $V_1^{(n)}$, $V_2^{(n)}$ are as in the previous paragraph, the function f can be extended by Theorem 8.2 to a mapping of $V_1^{(1)}$ onto $V_2^{(1)}$. Now f is successively extended by Schwarz reflection from a mapping of $V_1{}^{(n)}$ onto $V_2{}^{(n)}$ to a mapping of $V_1{}^{(n+1)}$ onto $V_2{}^{(n+1)}$. Thus, f becomes defined in the region $0 < |z| < R_1$ mapping onto $0 < |w| < R_2$. By Riemann's removable singularities theorem f can be defined at 0. Of course, it must be that $f(0) = 0$, and so f becomes a mapping of $|z| < R_1$ onto $|z| < R_2$ which takes 0 into 0. By a similar construction f^{-1} is defined for $|z| < R_2$ with range $|z| < R_1$. Since $f(0) = 0 = f^{-1}(0)$, we have from Schwarz's lemma $|f(z)| \leq (|z|/R_1)R_2$ and $|f^{-1}(z)| \leq (|z|/R_2)R_1$. Taking $|z| = 1$, in which case $|f(z)| = 1 = |f^{-1}(z)|$, gives $R_1/R_2 \geq 1$ and $R_2/R_1 \geq 1$. Thus $R_1 = R_2$.

REMARK. The mapping $Tz = R_1/z$ puts V_1 in one-to-one correspondence with itself interchanging the boundary circles. If the function $f(z)$ of the preceding paragraph interchanges the inner and outer boundaries of V_1 and V_2, a preliminary application of T reduces us to the situation just covered.

Theorem 8.3. *Let V_1, V_2 be annuli in the plane with inner and outer radii (r_1, R_1), (r_2, R_2), respectively. There is a one-to-one analytic mapping*[1] *of V_1 onto V_2 if, and only if, $r_1/R_1 = r_2/R_2$.*

Proof. If a_1, a_2 are the centers of V_1, V_2, respectively, then

$$T_1z = \frac{z - a_1}{r_1}$$

$$T_2z = \frac{z - a_2}{r_2}$$

map V_1, V_2 onto annuli W_1, W_2 centered at 0 with inner radii 1 and outer radii R_1/r_1, R_2/r_2. For V_1 and V_2 to be analytically equivalent it is necessary and sufficient that W_1 and W_2 be analytically equivalent, and the latter holds by the remarks preceding if, and only if, $R_1/r_1 = R_2/r_2$.

Problems

1. The following is a fact about harmonic functions: If $u(z)$ is (real valued and) continuous on a region Ω, and if for each $z_0 \in \Omega$ the equality

$$u(z_0) = \frac{1}{2\pi} \int_{-\pi}^{\pi} u(z_0 + re^{i\theta})\, d\theta$$

[1] Strictly speaking it must be assumed that the outer and inner circles are put in continuous correspondence by f, but this assumption is unnecessary as can be shown.

holds for all r sufficiently small, then $u(z)$ is harmonic. Use this fact to prove the following reflection principle: If $u(z)$ is harmonic in a region Ω of the upper half-plane, if $u(z)$ is continuous on $\Omega \cup \gamma$, where γ is an interval of the x axis which comprises part of the boundary of Ω, and if $u(z) = 0$ on γ, then

$$\tilde{u}(z) = \begin{cases} u(x + iy), & z \in \Omega \cup \gamma \\ u(x - iy), & z \in \Omega^* \end{cases}$$

defines a harmonic function on $\tilde{\Omega}$, where $\tilde{\Omega}$ is the interior of $\Omega \cup \gamma \cup \Omega^*$.

2. Use Problem 1 to show that the assumption $f(z)$ real on γ in Theorem 8.1 can be replaced by the evidently weaker $\lim_{z \to \gamma} \operatorname{Im} f(z) = 0$. (In other words no assumption is made about the behavior of $\operatorname{Re} f(z)$ at the boundary.)

3. Does there exist a one-to-one analytic mapping of $1 < |z| < 2$ onto $0 < |z| < 1$?

4. Let f be analytic on a region Ω which is bounded in part by an arc γ of a circle. Letting z^* denote reflection in γ suppose at least one point of γ lies in the interior of $\Omega \cup \gamma \cup \Omega^*$. Then if $f(z) \equiv 0$ on γ, f vanishes identically.

chapter 3

The Mapping Theorems of Riemann and Koebe

1. Analytic Equivalence

Regions Ω_1 and Ω_2 are *analytically equivalent* if there exists a one-to-one analytic function on Ω_1 with range Ω_2. The inverse of such a function is one-to-one and analytic on Ω_2 with range Ω_1. Therefore, the relation of analytic equivalence is symmetric; there is no prejudice as to which region is written first.

An analytic one-to-one correspondence is, in particular, a continuous one-to-one correspondence, meaning that analytic equivalence implies topological equivalence. Therefore, the topological properties of a region, the properties which are preserved under continuous one-to-one mappings of the region, are preserved by analytic equivalence. An important example of such a property is simple connectivity.

In general, it is difficult for regions to be analytically equivalent, even when it is known that they are, as they must be, topologically equivalent. Theorem 8.3 of Chapter 2 provides a wealth of examples. The regions $\Omega_1 = \{z \mid 1 < |z| < 2\}$ and $\Omega_2 = \{z \mid 1 < |z| < 3\}$ are not analytically equivalent because $\frac{1}{2} \neq \frac{1}{3}$. Yet the reader should have no difficulty constructing a continuous one-to-one mapping between the two.

At first blush a theorem which concludes analytic equivalence from topological equivalence would come as a surprise. Yet the Riemann mapping theorem, Theorem 7.2, asserts even more: *Simply connected regions Ω_1 and Ω_2 are analytically equivalent if neither is the plane.* Here topological equivalence is not assumed; indeed, there is no *a priori* reason why simply connected regions should be topologically equivalent. (In fact, the Riemann mapping theorem turns out to be the easiest proof of *topological* equivalence.)

The apparent discrepancy between a very general theorem for simply connected regions and very simple counterexamples for multiply connected regions is best understood in the context of covering surfaces. For this reason we will obtain the Riemann mapping theorem as a consequence of Theorem 7.1, which itself is a special case of the "general uniformization theorem" of P. Koebe. If Ω is an arbitrary *bounded*[1] region, Theorem 7.1 guarantees the existence of a covering $\Delta \overset{f}{\to} \Omega$, where, as usual, Δ denotes the unit disk. When Ω happens to be simply connected, the covering map, f, is one-to-one by Lemma 11.2, Chapter 1. Thus, a bounded simply connected region is analytically equivalent with Δ, which is the same as saying all bounded simply connected regions are analytically equivalent. The case of an unbounded, but still simply connected, region is taken care of by

Lemma 1.1. A simply connected region which is not the plane is analytically equivalent with some bounded simply connected region.

Proof of this lemma is postponed until the end of the section. In Problem 2 the reader will combine Lemma 1.1 with Liouville's theorem in order to prove that the plane is analytically equivalent with no region but itself.

We remark that a couple of problems mentioned in Chapter 1 are solved by Theorems 7.1 and 7.2. In the first place we now know that bounded regions, at least, have universal covering surfaces. Secondly, if a region has a universal covering surface, then the latter, being simply connected, is either the plane or else it is analytically equivalent with Δ; there are really only two universal covering surfaces, $\mathbf{C}$ and Δ. In the next chapter we will see that every region has a universal covering surface, and with the exception of the plane and the plane minus a point, that covering surface can be taken to be Δ.

Regarding the proof of Theorem 7.1, it involves a construction due to Koebe and the application thereto of the results of Sections 2–6. The turning point of the argument is a convergence proof which follows the construction; a point where modern authors usually invoke the theory of "normal families." However, as we will see in Chapter 4, normal families are truly extraneous to the problem at hand. Moreover a "normal families

---

[1] Unbounded regions are treated in Chapter 4, specifically Theorem 2.3.

argument" is necessarily indirect, while a direct argument is available to one willing to make (more) use of the special properties of Koebe's construction. All correct proofs of a theorem are "equal" in principle, however in practice a choice has to be made, and this choice is dictated by taste. Our taste dictates the longer, but more constructive, argument.[2]

Proof of Lemma 1.1.   Simple connectivity, a topological property, is preserved under analytic equivalence. Therefore, if Ω is a simply connected region which is not the plane, it suffices to produce a bounded one-to-one analytic function f on Ω. The region $f(\Omega)$ will then be the region whose existence is asserted.

Let h be a single-valued (analytic) determination of $\sqrt{z-a}$ on Ω, where a is some point not in Ω. The existence of h is guaranteed by the monodromy theorem and the simple connectivity of Ω. We claim (a) h is one-to-one on Ω, and (b) if ζ belongs to the range of h, then $-\zeta$ does not. To see (a) and (b), at once, suppose $h(z) = \pm h(w)$ for a pair z, $w \in \Omega$. Squaring yields $h^2(z) = h^2(w)$ or $z - a = w - a$. Thus, $z = w$, and both (a) and (b) obtain.

The open mapping theorem implies that $h(\Omega)$ and therefore $-h(\Omega) = \{-h(z) \mid z \in \Omega\}$ are open sets. Naturally, by (b) $h(\Omega) \cap -h(\Omega) = \emptyset$. Fix a point $\zeta \in -h(\Omega)$. Because the latter is open, there exists $\delta > 0$ such that if $|w - \zeta| \leq \delta$, then $w \in -h(\Omega)$. Using (b) and the definition of δ, the function

$$f(z) = \frac{1}{h(z) - \zeta}$$

is bounded by $1/\delta$ on Ω. Being the composition of one-to-one functions h and $1/(w - \zeta)$, f is one-to-one. The lemma is proved.

Notation.   If α is a positive real number, the symbol Δ_α will be used to denote the open disk of radius α and center 0. $\Delta_\alpha = \{z \mid |z| < \alpha\}$. When $\alpha = 1$, we continue to drop the α and write simply Δ.

Problems

1. For each of the following pairs Ω_1, Ω_2 construct a one-to-one analytic correspondence between them or else prove that none exists.

Cf. Robert Frost, "The Road not Taken"

> . . . Two roads diverged in a wood, and I—
> I took the one less traveled by,
> And that has made all the difference.

(a) $\Omega_1 = \Delta$, $\Omega_2 = \mathbf{C}$.

(b) $\Omega_1 = \Delta$, $\Omega_2 = \{z \mid -1 < \operatorname{Re} z < 1\}$.
(HINT: Begin with $f(z) = e^{i\pi z}$.)

(c) $\Omega_1 = \{z \mid 1 < |z - i| < 2\}$, $\Omega_2 = \{z \mid 2 < |z - 3| < 3\}$.

(d) $\Omega_1 = \Delta$, $\Omega_2 = \{z \mid z = x + iy; x > 0, y > 0\}$.

(e) $\Omega_1 = \Delta$, $\Omega_2 = \Delta$, less the interval $\{x \mid 0 \le x < 1\}$.
(HINT: In succession consider the mappings $w = 1/z$, $w_1 = \sqrt{w}$, $w_2 = w_1 + 1/w_1$.)

(f) $\Omega_1 = \Delta$, $\Omega_2 = A \cap B$, where $A = \Delta$ and $B = \{z \mid |z - i| < 1\}$.
(HINT: Let ζ be a point of intersection of $C_1 = \{z \mid |z| = 1\}$ and $C_2 = \{z \mid |z - i| = 1\}$. Consider the images of C_1 and C_2 under $1/(z - \zeta)$.)

(g) $\Omega_1 = A_n$, $\Omega_2 = A_m$, n, $m > 0$, where
$A_p = \{z \mid |z| < p, z \ne 0, \pm 1, \ldots, \pm(p - 1)\}$.

2. The plane is not analytically equivalent with any region but itself.

3. Let Ω be a region consisting of the complex plane minus a finite number of points.

(a) A bounded analytic function on Ω reduces to a constant. (HINT: Use the Riemann removable singularities theorem to show that a bounded analytic function on Ω can be defined so as to be entire. Invoke Liouville's theorem.)

(b) Ω is not analytically equivalent with a bounded region.

4. Let $\Delta \xrightarrow{f} \Omega$ be a covering, $f(0) = z_0$. Show that f is a "uniformizer" for any multiple-valued function on Ω. That is, if $[\varphi]_{z_0}$ is a germ which can be continued along any arc from z_0 in Ω, there exists an analytic function ψ on Δ such that $[\varphi]_{z_0} \circ [f]_0 = [\psi]_0$. (The problem of finding such a uniformizer was first solved by Poincaré. In the old days "analytic" functions were not necessarily single valued; those that were were called "uniform." Thus the terminology "uniformization" or "uniformizer.")

2. Local Uniform Convergence

This section concerns sequences of analytic functions. In large measure the proof of Theorem 7.1 consists of establishing the convergence (in a sense to be made precise) of a constructed sequence of analytic functions. In order to complete the argument it is necessary to have some general facts concerning the limits of such sequences. Most important is the knowledge that the limit is analytic.

If in a neighborhood of a point z a function f is the uniform limit of analytic functions, then f is analytic at z. (See below.) Therefore, if $\{f_n\}$ is a sequence of analytic functions such that $\lim_{n \to \infty} f_n(z) = f(z)$ exists for each z in a region Ω, then f will be analytic if the convergence is "locally uniform," uniform in some neighborhood of each point.

Definition 2.1. A sequence $\{f_n\}$ converges *locally uniformly* on a region Ω if for each *closed* disk U in Ω $\lim_{n \to \infty} f_n(z) = f(z)$ exists uniformly on U.

Convergent power series give rise to examples of local uniform convergence. Recall that if $f(z) = \sum_{k=0}^{\infty} a_k(z - z_0)^k$ has radius of convergence $R > 0$, then for each $r < R$ the partial sums

$$f_n(z) = \sum_{k=0}^{n} a_k(z - z_0)^k$$

converge uniformly for $|z - z_0| \leq r$. If U is a *closed* disk contained in the region $\Omega = \{z \mid |z - z_0| < R\}$, then for some $r < R$, U is also contained in $\{z \mid |z - z_0| \leq r\}$. Therefore, $\{f_n\}$ converges uniformly on U, and since U is arbitrary, $\{f_n\}$ converges locally uniformly on Ω.

Illustrative of Theorem 2.1 is the following fact about power series. If f and Ω are as above, then f is analytic on Ω, and for each $m > 0$ the mth derivative of f is represented on Ω by the convergent power series

$$f^{(m)}(z) = \sum_{k=m}^{\infty} a_k(k(k - 1) \cdot \cdot \cdot (k - m + 1))(z - z_0)^{k-m}.$$

From the result of the preceding paragraph it follows that $\{f_n^{(m)}\}$ converges locally uniformly to $f^{(m)}$.

It is useful to note two conditions which are equivalent with local uniform convergence. The first comes from Cauchy's criterion. A sequence converges locally uniformly if for each closed disk U and $\epsilon > 0$ there exists an integer N such that

$$\max_{z \in U} |f_n(z) - f_m(z)| < \epsilon$$

for $m, n \geq N$.

The second equivalent condition is "uniform convergence on compact sets." If K is a compact subset of Ω, then $\lim_{n \to \infty} f_n(z) = f(z)$ should exist uniformly on K. This condition arises from Definition 2.1 by covering K with (the interiors of) finitely many closed disks in Ω (using the Heine-Borel theorem). Details (easy) are left to the reader.

Theorem 2.1. *Given a region Ω and a sequence $\{f_n\}$ of functions analytic on Ω suppose $\lim\limits_{n \to \infty} f_n(z) = f(z)$ exists locally uniformly on Ω. Then f is analytic, and for each $k > 0$ the sequence $\{f_n^{(k)}\}$ converges locally uniformly to $f^{(k)}$.*

Proof. If U is a closed disk of radius r in Ω, $U = \{z \mid |z - z_0| \leq r\}$, there exists a number $\delta > 0$ such that the closed disk $V = \{z \mid |z - z_0| \leq r + \delta\}$ is also contained in Ω. From the known uniform convergence of $\{f_n\}$ on V we will conclude the uniform convergence of $\{f_n^{(k)}\}$ on U. Denote by γ the circle bounding V (natural parametrization), and make note of the inequality $|\zeta - z| \geq \delta$, or

$$(2.1) \qquad \frac{1}{|\zeta - z|} \leq \frac{1}{\delta},$$

valid when $z \in U$ and $\zeta \in \gamma$. For each n, k we represent $f_n^{(k)}(z)$, $z \in U$, as the Cauchy integral

$$(2.2) \qquad f_n^{(k)}(z) = \frac{k!}{2\pi i} \int_\gamma \frac{f_n(\zeta)}{(\zeta - z)^{k+1}} \, d\zeta.$$

Given $\epsilon > 0$, let N be so large that if m, $n \geq N$, then

$$(2.3) \qquad \max_{\zeta \in V} |f_m(\zeta) - f_n(\zeta)| < \epsilon.$$

Using (2.1) and (2.3), we obtain for each k the estimate

$$(2.4) \quad \max_{\substack{z \in U \\ \zeta \in \gamma}} \left| \frac{f_m(\zeta)}{(\zeta - z)^{k+1}} - \frac{f_n(\zeta)}{(\zeta - z)^{k+1}} \right| = \max_{\substack{z \in U \\ \zeta \in \gamma}} \frac{|f_m(\zeta) - f_n(\zeta)|}{|(\zeta - z)|^{k+1}} < \frac{\epsilon}{\delta^{k+1}}.$$

Combining formula (2.2) and inequality (2.4), we get for n, $m \geq N$

$$\max_{z \in U} |f_m^{(k)}(z) - f_n^{(k)}(z)| \leq \frac{k!}{2\pi} \int_\gamma \left| \frac{f_m(\zeta)}{(\zeta - z)^{k+1}} - \frac{f_n(\zeta)}{(\zeta - z)^{k+1}} \right| |d\zeta|$$

$$< \frac{k!}{2\pi} \frac{\epsilon}{\delta^{k+1}} 2\pi(r + \delta)$$

$$= \frac{k!(r + \delta)\epsilon}{\delta^{k+1}}.$$

Since ϵ is arbitrary, $\{f_n{}^{(k)}\}$ converges uniformly on U; since U is arbitrary, $\{f_n{}^{(k)}\}$ converges locally uniformly on Ω. Denoting the limit function by f_k (for $k = 0, f_0 = f$), we have

$$f_k(z) = \frac{k!}{2\pi i} \int_\gamma \frac{f(\zeta)}{(\zeta - z)^{k+1}} \, d\zeta.$$

This formula for $k = 0$ implies that f is analytic.[1] Therefore for $k > 0$, $f_k(z) = f^{(k)}(z)$ by the Cauchy integral formula. The theorem is proved.

Problems

1. (Weierstrass M-test) Let $\{a_k(z)\}$ be a sequence of functions analytic on a region Ω. Suppose for each closed disk $U \subset \Omega$ the sequence of constants $c_k = c_k{}^U = \max\limits_{z \in U} |a_k(z)|$, $k = 1, 2, \ldots$, is such that $\sum\limits_1^\infty c_k < \infty$. Show that $f(z) = \sum\limits_{k=1}^\infty a_k(z)$ is analytic on Ω and $f'(z) = \sum\limits_1^\infty a_k'(z)$.

2. If $\mathrm{Re}\, s > 1$ define $\zeta(s) = \sum\limits_{n=1}^\infty (1/n^s)$. Prove that ζ is analytic, and show that $\zeta'(s) = -\sum\limits_{n=1}^\infty ((\log n)/n^s)$. ($\zeta(s)$ is the *Riemann zeta function*. For more details see Chapter 6.)

3. Consider local uniform convergence as opposed to *uniform* convergence.

   (a) Show by example that the former does not imply the latter, even on bounded regions.

   (b) Show that if $\{f_n\}$ is a sequence of *entire* functions converging *uniformly* to a function f, then for large n $f_n = f + c_n$, where c_n is a constant.

4. If f is analytic on $\Delta = \{z \mid |z| < 1\}$, and if f does not extend to be continuous on $\{z \mid |z| \le 1\}$, then the power series expansion of f about 0 does not converge uniformly on Δ.

---

[1] Indeed if $f(z) = (1/2\pi i) \int_\gamma ((\varphi(\zeta))/(\zeta - z)) \, d\zeta$, where φ is *any* continuous function, then f is analytic. Of course, here $\varphi = f$.

5. If Re $z > 0$ define

$$\Gamma_n(z) = \int_{1/n}^{n} t^{z-1}e^{-t}\,dt, \; n = 1, 2, \ldots .$$

Show

(a) Γ_n is analytic, and

(b) $\lim_{n \to \infty} \Gamma_n(z) = \int_0^{\infty} t^{z-1}e^{-t}\,dt = \Gamma(z)$ locally uniformly.

Therefore, $\Gamma(z)$ is analytic. ($\Gamma(z)$ is the Gamma function of Euler. For more details see Chapter 5, Section 10.)

6. Let $\{f_n\}$ be a sequence of functions analytic and bounded by 1 on Δ. Show that $\{f_n\}$ converges locally uniformly if, and only if, $\lim_{\substack{n \to \infty \\ m \geq n}} d(f_m(z),$ $f_n(z)) = 0$ uniformly on compact sets.

7. Suppose f_n is bounded by $M < \infty$ on Ω. If $\{f_n\}$ converges locally uniformly, and if $\lim_{n \to \infty} |f_n(z_0)| = M$ for some z_0, then $\{f_n\}$ converges locally uniformly to a constant.

3. A Theorem of Hurwitz

Certain statements about individual analytic functions enjoy the property of being "preserved" under local uniform limits. Quite generally, let P denote a statement whose truth can be tested for an analytic function by an application of the argument principle, Chapter 1, Section 7. If $\{f_n\}$ converges locally uniformly to f on a region, and if P is true of f_n for each n, then P is true of f, at least if f is not constant. Such statements as "—is nonzero" or "—is one-to-one" will be cases in point.

Theorem 3.2, which corresponds to "—is nonzero," is due to A. Hurwitz. It could be used as a basis for the other results of this section, however the following theorem (which is equivalent) gives a clearer picture of local uniform convergence.

Theorem 3.1. *Let $\{f_n\}$ be a sequence of analytic functions on a region Ω, and suppose $\{f_n\}$ converges locally uniformly to f. If f is not constant, there exists for each $z \in \Omega$ an integer $n_1 = n_1(z)$ and a sequence $\{z_n\}, n \geq n_1$, such that*

(3.1) $$f_n(z_n) = f(z), \quad n \geq n_1$$

(3.2) $$\lim_{n \to \infty} z_n = z.$$

Proof. Assume f is not constant since otherwise there is nothing to prove. Fix $z \in \Omega$, and set $w = f(z)$. By Theorem 2.1 f is analytic, and because f is not constant, the uniqueness theorem applies. There exists $\delta > 0$ such that if $0 < |\zeta - z| \leq \delta$, then $\zeta \in \Omega$ and $f(\zeta) \neq w$.

For each integer $k > 0$ define γ_k to be the circle of radius δ/k about z, and let $\delta_k = \min_{\zeta \in \gamma_k} |f(\zeta) - w|$. The continuity of f, the compactness of γ_k, and the definition of δ combine to imply $\delta_k > 0$, $k = 1, 2, \ldots$. Using the uniform convergence of $\{f_n\}$ on γ_k, choose n_k so large that if $n \geq n_k$, then

$$\max_{\zeta \in \gamma_k} |f_n(\zeta) - f(\zeta)| < \frac{\delta_k}{2}.$$

Matters can also be arranged so that $n_1 < n_2 < n_3 < \cdots$.

For each k if $n \geq n_k$, and if $\zeta \in \gamma_k$, the inequalities

$$|(f_n(\zeta) - w) - (f(\zeta) - w)| = |f_n(\zeta) - f(\zeta)| < \frac{\delta_k}{2} < \delta_k \leq |f(\zeta) - w|$$

are true. Therefore, by Rouché's theorem, Theorem 7.3, Chapter 1, the functions $(f_n(\zeta) - w)$ and $(f(\zeta) - w)$ have the same number of zeros inside γ_k. By assumption $(f(\zeta) - w)$ has a zero of order at least 1 at z, and therefore there exists at least one point z_n inside γ_k with $f_n(z_n) = w$. Define a sequence $\{z_n\}$, $n \geq n_1$, as follows: if $n_k \leq n < n_{k+1}$, select z_n inside γ_k with $f_n(z_n) = w$. By construction, $\lim_{n \to \infty} z_n = z$, and the theorem is proved.

Theorems 3.2 and 3.3 and their corollaries follow quickly from Theorem 3.1. In the statement of each we will assume $\{f_n\}$ is a sequence of analytic functions converging locally uniformly to a function f.

Theorem 3.2. (Hurwitz)   *If $f_n(z) \neq 0$ for all $z \in \Omega$ and n, then either $f \equiv 0$ or else $f(z) \neq 0$ for all $z \in \Omega$. More generally, if $f_n(z) \neq w$ for all $z \in \Omega$ and n, then either $f \equiv w$ or else $f(z) \neq w$ for all $z \in \Omega$.*

Proof. We prove the second statement which includes the first. If f is constant, the constant either is or is not w. In either case there is nothing to prove. On the other hand, if f is not constant, Theorem 3.1 and especially equation (3.1) apply. An element in the range of f must belong to the range of f_n for large n ($n \geq n_1(z)$). Thus, if w is not in the range of f_n for any n, w cannot be in the range of f. The theorem is proved.

Corollary 3.1.   *If $f_n'(z) \neq 0$ for all $z \in \Omega$ and n, then either f is constant or else $f'(z) \neq 0$ for all $z \in \Omega$.*

Proof. The sequence $\{f_n'\}$ converges locally uniformly to f' by Theorem 2.1. By Theorem 3.2 either $f' \equiv 0$ or else $f'(z) \neq 0$ for all $z \in \Omega$. In the former case f is constant, and the corollary obtains.

Corollary 3.2. *Suppose Ω_0 is a region such that $f_n(\Omega) \subseteq \Omega_0$ for each n. Then either f is constant or else $f(\Omega) \subseteq \Omega_0$.*

Proof. The proof is left to the reader.

Theorem 3.3. *If for each n, f_n is one-to-one on Ω, then unless f reduces to a constant, f is one-to-one.*

Proof. We assume f is not constant since otherwise there is nothing to prove. Suppose $f(z_1) = f(z_2)$ for certain z_1, $z_2 \in \Omega$. We claim $z_1 = z_2$. By Theorem 3.1 if $n \geq \max(n_1(z_1), n_1(z_2))$, there exist points $z_1^{(n)}, z_2^{(n)} \in \Omega$ such that (3.1) and (3.2) hold for z_1 and z_2. That is, $f_n(z_1^{(n)}) = f(z_1) = f(z_2) = f_n(z_2^{(n)})$ and $\lim_{n \to \infty} z_i^{(n)} = z_i$, $i = 1, 2$. Since f_n is one-to-one, it must be that $z_1^{(n)} = z_2^{(n)}$ for each n, and therefore $z_1 = \lim_{n \to \infty} z_1^{(n)} = \lim_{n \to \infty} z_2^{(n)} = z_2$. The theorem is proved.

REMARK. If f is not constant in Theorem 3.3, then because f is one-to-one, f^{-1} is analytic[1] on the region $f(\Omega)$. If $z \in \Omega$, and if $n \geq n_1(z)$, there exists exactly *one* point $z_n \in \Omega$ with $f_n(z_n) = f(z)$. Of course, it must be that $\lim_{n \to \infty} z_n = z$. Thus if $w \in f(\Omega)$, then for large n, $w \in f_n(\Omega)$ and

$$(3.3) \qquad \lim_{n \to \infty} f_n^{-1}(w) = f^{-1}(w).$$

A corollary to this observation is

Theorem 3.4. *Let f_n be one-to-one on Ω for each n, and suppose f is not constant. If U is an open set which belongs to both $f(\Omega)$ and $f_n(\Omega)$ for all n, then on U*

$$\lim_{n \to \infty} f_n^{-1}(w) = f^{-1}(w)$$

holds.

Proof. The proof is immediate from (3.3) and the fact that f_n^{-1} is defined on U for each n.

REMARK. Theorem 3.4 does not assert local uniform convergence on U. Local uniform convergence does hold, and this will be proved (for a special situation) in the next section.

[1] Chapter 1, Section 7, Problem 1.

Problems

1. Prove Corollary 3.2.
2. Let f_n be one-to-one and analytic on Ω for each n. If $z_0 \in \Omega$ is such that $f_n'(z_0) = 1$, $n = 1, 2, \ldots$, and if $\{f_n\}$ converges locally uniformly on Ω to a function f, then f is also one-to-one.
3. (Refer to Problem 5, Section 2.) For $0 \leq t < \infty$ define $\varphi_n(t)$ by

$$\varphi_n(t) = \begin{cases} \left(1 - \dfrac{t}{n}\right)^n, & 0 \leq t \leq n \\ 0, & t > n. \end{cases}$$

It will be shown that the sequence $\{f_n\}$,

$$f_n(z) = \int_0^\infty \varphi_n(t) t^{z-1} \, dt$$

converges locally uniformly to $\Gamma(z)$ for Re $z > 0$. (Chapter 5, Section 12.) It will also be shown that

$$f_n(z) = \frac{n^z n!}{z(z+1) \cdots (z+n)}.$$

Assume these facts, and prove $\Gamma(z) \neq 0$ for Re $z > 0$.

4. Implications of Pointwise Convergence

Our purpose in the following two sections is to demonstrate that certain apparently weak forms of convergence actually imply local uniform convergence. In each instance an assumption of uniform boundedness is made, and without *some* such assumption the theorem can be shown to be false.

Lemma 4.1. Let $\{f_n\}$ be a sequence of functions analytic and bounded by 1 on Δ. If $\lim_{n \to \infty} f_n(z) = f(z)$ exists for each $z \in \Delta$, then $\{f_n\}$ converges locally uniformly, and f is analytic.

Proof. By Theorem 2.1 analyticity will follow from local uniform convergence. Given a closed disk U in Δ and a number $\epsilon > 0$, it will be sufficient to produce an integer N such that if $m, n \geq N$, then

$$\max_{z \in U} d(f_m(z), f_n(z)) < \epsilon.$$

To this end we define U_z for each z to be the open non-Euclidean disk of radius $\epsilon/3$ about z.

$$U_z = \left\{ \varsigma \mid d(z, \varsigma) < \frac{\epsilon}{3} \right\}.$$

Because U is compact, there exist by the Heine-Borel theorem points $z_1, \ldots, z_k \in U$ such that $U \subset U_{z_1} \cup U_{z_2} \cup \cdots \cup U_{z_k}$. What is the same thing, for each $z \in U$ there exists a subscript $i = i(z)$ such that $d(z, z_i) < \epsilon/3$. Since $\{z_1, \ldots, z_k\}$ is a finite set, we can find an integer N such that if $m, n \geq N$, then

$$\max_{1 \leq j \leq k} d(f_m(z_j), f_n(z_j)) < \frac{\epsilon}{3}.$$

Now fix $z \in U$ and $j = j(z)$. From the triangle inequality, the choice of j, and Pick's theorem we obtain for $m, n \geq N$

$$d(f_m(z), f_n(z)) \leq d(f_m(z), f_m(z_j)) + d(f_m(z_j), f_n(z_j)) + d(f_n(z_j), f_n(z))$$

$$\leq d(z, z_j) + \frac{\epsilon}{3} + d(z_j, z) < \frac{\epsilon}{3} + \frac{\epsilon}{3} + \frac{\epsilon}{3} = \epsilon.$$

Since z is an arbitrary point of U, we have $\max_{z \in U} d(f_m(z), f_n(z)) < \epsilon$. It follows (Problem 6, Section 2) that $\{f_n\}$ converges locally uniformly, and the lemma is proved.

Theorem 4.1 is an extension of Lemma 4.1.

Theorem 4.1.   *Let $\{f_n\}$ be a sequence of analytic functions on a disk U which take their values in a fixed disk V. If $\lim_{n \to \infty} f_n(z) = f(z)$ exists for each $z \in U$, then $\{f_n\}$ converges locally uniformly on U.*

Proof.   There exist linear transformations S and T which map Δ onto U and V, respectively. For each n the function $g_n(z) = T^{-1}f_n(Sz)$, $z \in \Delta$, is analytic and bounded by 1 on Δ. Furthermore, because T^{-1} is continuous on the closure of V, and because $\lim_{n \to \infty} f_n(Sz)$ exists for $Sz \in U$, $\lim_{n \to \infty} g_n(z) = g(z)$ exists for each $z \in \Delta$. By Lemma 4.1 $\{g_n\}$ converges locally uniformly on Δ, and since T is continuous on the closure of Δ, $\{Tg_n\}$ converges locally uniformly on Δ. Therefore, because $f_n(z) = Tg_n(S^{-1}z)$, $z \in U$, $\{f_n\}$ converges locally uniformly on U.

The following result is rather special; it is being included because it is used in the proof of Theorem 7.1.

Lemma 4.2. Let $\{f_n\}$ be a sequence of functions analytic and bounded by 1 on Δ. Suppose there exists an r, $0 < r < 1$, such that f_n^{-1} can be defined on Δ_r for each n with values in Δ. Suppose also that $f_n(0) = 0 = f_n^{-1}(0)$. Under these conditions if $\{f_n\}$ converges locally uniformly on Δ, then $\{f_n^{-1}\}$ converges locally uniformly on Δ_{r^2}.

Proof.   Let f be the limit of the sequence $\{f_n\}$. By Problem 4, Section 6, Chapter 2, f_n is one-to-one on Δ_r with range containing Δ_{r^2}, and

$$(4.1) \qquad\qquad \min_{|z|=r} |f_n(z)| \geq r^2.$$

Passing to the limit in (4.1) and taking account of the uniform convergence on Δ_r, it follows that

$$(4.2) \qquad\qquad \min_{|z|=r} |f(z)| \geq r^2.$$

Obviously, $f(0) = 0$, and so f is not constant. By Theorem 3.3 f is one-to-one on Δ_r; by Theorem 7.1, Chapter 1, applied to (4.2) the range of f contains Δ_{r^2}. Next, Theorem 3.4 implies

$$\lim_{n \to \infty} f_n^{-1}(w) = f^{-1}(w)$$

for each $w \in \Delta_{r^2}$, and finally Theorem 4.1 gives us that $\{f_n^{-1}\}$ converges locally uniformly on Δ_{r^2} to f^{-1}.

Problems

1. Let $\{f_n\}$ be a sequence of functions analytic and bounded by 1 on Δ. If $\lim_{n \to \infty} f_n(z)$ exists on a set with accumulation point z_0 *in* Δ, show that $\lim_{n \to \infty} f_n(z_0)$ exists.

2. Generalize Problem 1 to functions in one disk which take their values in another disk.

3. Let f_n be analytic on Δ for each n, and suppose $\mathrm{Im}\, f_n(z) > 0$, $z \in \Delta$. If $\lim_{n \to \infty} f_n(z) = f(z)$ exists for each z (here $f(z) = \infty$ is allowed), then either

   (a) $f(z) \equiv \infty$, or
   (b) $\{f_n\}$ converges locally uniformly to f.

   Using (a) as your guide, devise a definition of "local uniform convergence to ∞." Then show that if (a) holds, $\{f_n\}$ converges locally uniformly to ∞.

4. Prove: There exists a sequence $\{z_n\}$ of points in Δ *without limit point in* Δ such that if f is *any* bounded analytic function on Δ

$$\sup_{z \in \Delta} |f(z)| = \sup_n |f(z_n)|.$$

5. Suppose $\{f_n\}$ is a sequence of functions analytic and bounded by 1 on Δ. If $\lim_{n \to \infty} f_n(0) = 1$, then f_n converges locally uniformly to 1. (Use Pick's theorem to show that $\lim_{n \to \infty} f_n(z) = 1$ for each z.)

5. Implications of Convergence on a Subset

We discuss conditions enabling us to prove a sequence converges locally uniformly on a region when it is known to converge on a subset of that region. The result, Theorem 5.1, will be used to prove the "convergence" of continuations. For example, suppose $\{(f_{j,n}, U_j)\}_{j=1}^2$, $n = 1, 2, \ldots$, is a sequence of continuations. If $\{f_{1,n}\}$ converges locally uniformly on U_1, then $\{f_{2,n}\}$ converges locally uniformly, at least on $U_1 \cap U_2$. If $\{f_{2,n}\}$ is known to be uniformly bounded, Theorem 5.1 will imply that $\{f_{2,n}\}$ converges locally uniformly on U_2. Denoting by f_1 and f_2 the limits of the sequences, it is clear that $f_1 \equiv f_2$ on $U_1 \cap U_2$. Therefore, $\mathfrak{U} = \{(f_j, U_j)\}_{j=1}^2$ is a continuation.

Lemma 5.1. For each n, $n = 1, 2, \ldots$, let f_n be a power series

$$f_n(z) = \sum_{k=0}^{\infty} a_k^{(n)} (z - z_0)^k$$

convergent on $\Omega = \{z \mid |z - z_0| < R\}$. In addition suppose there exists a constant $M < \infty$ such that $|f_n(z)| \le M$ for all $z \in \Omega$ and n. If $\lim_{n \to \infty} a_k^{(n)} = a_k$ exists for each k, then $\{f_n\}$ converges locally uniformly on Ω to $f(z) = \sum_{k=0}^{\infty} a_k(z - z_0)^k$.

Proof. We appeal to Cauchy's estimate from the elementary theory which says (for each k and n)

$$(5.1) \qquad\qquad |a_k^{(n)}| \le \frac{M}{R^k}.$$

Letting $n \to \infty$ gives $|a_k| \le (M/R^k)$, and therefore $f(z) = \sum_{k=0}^{\infty} a_k(z - z_0)^k$

converges on Ω. To see that $\{f_n\}$ converges locally uniformly to f, it suffices to produce for each $r < R$ and $\epsilon > 0$ an integer N such that

$$\max_{|z-z_0|\le r} |f_n(z) - f(z)| < \epsilon$$

if $n \ge N$. To this end fix r and ϵ, and let l be an integer large enough that

$$(5.2) \qquad \frac{MR}{R-r}\left(\frac{r}{R}\right)^l < \frac{\epsilon}{4}.$$

This is possible because $(r/R) < 1$. Next, let N be so large that if $n \ge N$ and if $|z - z_0| \le r$, then

$$(5.3) \qquad \left| \sum_{k=0}^{l-1} (a_k^{(n)} - a_k)(z - z_0)^k \right| < \frac{\epsilon}{2}.$$

For the same values of n and z inequalities (5.1)–(5.3) together with the triangle inequality imply

$$|f_n(z) - f(z)| = \left| \sum_{k=0}^{\infty} (a_k^{(n)} - a_k)(z - z_0)^k \right|$$

$$\le \left| \sum_{k=0}^{l-1} (a_k^{(n)} - a_k)(z - z_0)^k \right| + \left| \sum_{k=l}^{\infty} (a_k^{(n)} - a_k)(z - z_0)^k \right|$$

$$\le \frac{\epsilon}{2} + \sum_{k=l}^{\infty} |a_k^{(n)} - a_k| r^k \le \frac{\epsilon}{2} + 2M \sum_{k=l}^{\infty} \frac{r^k}{R^k}$$

$$= \frac{\epsilon}{2} + \frac{2MR}{R-r}\left(\frac{r}{R}\right)^l < \epsilon.$$

Thus, $\{f_n\}$ converges locally uniformly; the lemma is proved.

To apply Lemma 5.1 suppose $\{f_n\}$ is a sequence of functions analytic and bounded by M on the region Ω of that lemma. If $\{f_n\}$ converges locally uniformly on an open set containing z_0, then a particular consequence of Theorem 2.1 is that

$$\lim_{n\to\infty} f_n^{(k)}(z_0) = c_k$$

exists for each k. By Taylor's theorem we can take $a_k^{(n)} = (f_n^{(k)}(z_0)/k!)$ in the statement of Lemma 5.1. Thus, it follows that $\{f_n\}$ converges locally uniformly on Ω. More generally, we prove

Theorem 5.1.   *If Ω, $\{f_n\}$, and M are as above, and if $\lim\limits_{n \to \infty} f_n(z)$ exists locally uniformly on an open subset of Ω, then $\{f_n\}$ converges locally uniformly on Ω.*

Proof.   If $z_0 \in V$, the theorem follows from the discussion above. Otherwise, let T be a linear transformation of Ω onto itself which takes z_0 into a point of V. The functions $h_n(z) = f_n(Tz)$ converge locally uniformly on the open set $T^{-1}V$ which contains z_0. Therefore, $\{h_n\}$ converges locally uniformly on Ω. It follows that $f_n(z) = h_n(T^{-1}z)$ converges locally uniformly on Ω. The theorem is proved.

As for the convergence of continuations, Theorem 5.1 together with the discussion at the beginning of the section provides the following information.

Theorem 5.2.   *For each n suppose $\mathfrak{U}_n = \{(f_{n,j}, U_j)\}_{j=1}^{m}$ is a continuation sequence. In addition suppose there is a constant M such that $f_{n,j}$ is bounded by M on U_j for all n and j. If $\{f_{n,1}\}$ converges locally uniformly on U_1, then $\{f_{n,j}\}$ converges locally uniformly on U_j. If f_j denotes the limit, $1 \leq j \leq m$, the sequence $\mathfrak{U} = \{(f_j, U_j)\}_{j=1}^{m}$ is also a continuation sequence.*

Proof.   The argument of the first paragraph used successively on $U_2, U_3, \ldots, U_m$ shows that the sequences $\{f_{n,2}\}, \ldots, \{f_{n,m}\}$ converge locally uniformly on $U_2, \ldots, U_m$ to limits $f_2, \ldots, f_m$. Obviously, $f_1 \equiv f_2$ on $U_1 \cap U_2, f_2 \equiv f_3$ on $U_2 \cap U_3, \ldots, f_{m-1} \equiv f_m$ on $U_{m-1} \cap U_m$. $\mathfrak{U} = \{(f_j, U_j)\}_{j=1}^{m}$ is a continuation sequence, and the theorem is proved.

The results obtained thus far will be used to prove in certain situations that the "limit" of a sequence of coverings is itself a covering. Theorem 5.3 will be a valuable aid in Section 7.

Consider a sequence of coverings $\Omega_n \xrightarrow{f_n} \Omega$ having the following properties:

(a) $\Omega_n \subseteq \Delta$ for each n $(\Omega_0 = \Omega)$.

(b) f_n is the restriction to Ω_n of a function analytic and bounded by 1 on Δ.

(c) There exist constants $d_n{}^2$,[1] $0 < d_0{}^2 < d_1{}^2 < \cdots < 1$ such that if $|z| < d_n{}^2$, then $z \in \Omega_n$. In particular, $0 \in \Omega_n$ for each n.

(d) $\lim\limits_{n \to \infty} d_n{}^2 = 1$.

(e) $f_n(0) = 0, n = 1, 2, \ldots$.

(f) $\{f_n\}$ converges locally uniformly on Δ to a function f.

[1] Notation $d_n{}^2$ conforms to that of Section 7.

Theorem 5.3. *If Ω_n, f_n, and f are as above, then $f(z) \in \Omega$ for each $z \in \Delta$, and furthermore $\Delta \xrightarrow{f} \Omega$ is a covering.*

Proof. The disk $\Delta_{d_0{}^2}$ belongs to Ω, and since $\Omega_n \xrightarrow{f_n} \Omega$ is a covering with $f_n(0) = 0$, it is possible for each n to define f_n^{-1} to be analytic on $\Delta_{d_0{}^2}$ with values in Δ and $f_n^{-1}(0) = 0$. Therefore, by Lemma 4.2, $\{f_n^{-1}\}$ converges locally uniformly on $\Delta_{d_0{}^4}$ to f^{-1}. In particular, f is not constant.

If $0 < r < 1$, and if $d_n{}^2 > r$, then by property (c), $f_n(\Delta_r) \subset \Omega$. Since f is not constant, Corollary 3.2 implies that $f(\Delta_r) \subset \Omega$. Letting $r \to 1$ tells us $f(\Delta) \subseteq \Omega$.

We next demonstrate that f^{-1} can be continued along an arbitrary arc from 0 in Ω with values in Δ and initial value 0. Let γ be such an arc, and fix a sequence $U_1, \ldots, U_m$ of disks in Ω admissible for γ. For each n there exists a continuation $\mathfrak{U}_n = \{(h_{j,n}, U_j)\}_{j=1}^m$ of f_n^{-1} along γ with values in Δ and initial value 0. The intersection $U_1 \cap \Delta_{d_0{}^4}$ is nonempty and open, and therefore $\{h_{1,n}\}$ converges locally uniformly on U_1 to f^{-1} by Theorem 5.1. Let h_1 denote f^{-1} restricted to U_1 with $h_1(0) = 0$. By Theorem 5.2 $\{h_{j,n}\}$ converges locally uniformly to a function h_j on U_j, $2 \leq j \leq m$, and $\mathfrak{U} = \{(h_j, U_j)\}_{j=1}^m$ is a continuation along γ. To see that $\mathfrak{U}$ takes values in Δ we note that h_j is not constant on U_j because h_1 is not constant on U_1; also $h_{j,n}(U_j) \subseteq \Delta$ for each n. Again using Corollary 3.2, $h_j(U_j) \subseteq \Delta$. That $\Delta \xrightarrow{f} \Omega$ is a covering is now immediate from Theorem 11.2, Chapter 1.

Problems

1. (Refer to Problem 1, Section 4.) Let $\{f_n\}$ be a sequence of functions analytic and bounded by $M < \infty$ on $\Omega = \{z \mid |z - z_0| < R\}$. Suppose $\lim_{n \to \infty} f_n(z)$ exists on a set E with limit point z_0.

    (a) Prove that $\lim_{n \to \infty} f_n(z_0)$ exists.

    (b) On Ω define $h_n(z) = \begin{cases} \dfrac{f_n(z) - f_n(z_0)}{z - z_0}, & z \neq z_0 \\ f_n{}'(z_0), & z = z_0. \end{cases}$
    Prove that h_n is bounded by $2M/R$.

    (c) Prove that $\lim_{n \to \infty} h_n(z)$ exists for $z \in E$. Thus $\lim_{n \to \infty} f_n{}'(z_0) = \lim_{n \to \infty} h_n(z_0)$ exists by part (a).

    (d) In similar fashion prove that $\lim_{n \to \infty} f_n{}^{(k)}(z_0)$ exists for each k.

    (e) Conclude that $\{f_n\}$ converges locally uniformly on Ω.

2. Let $\{f_n\}$ be as in Problem 1, except now assume only that $\lim_{n \to \infty} f_n(z)$ exists on a set with *some* limit point in Ω. Prove that $\{f_n\}$ converges locally uniformly on Ω.

3. Give an example of a sequence of functions analytic on $\Omega = \{z \mid |z| < 2\}$ which converges locally uniformly on Δ but not on Ω.

6. Approximately Linear Functions—Another Application of Schwarz's Lemma

We first made use of Schwarz's lemma in proving an analytic one-to-one mapping of a disk onto a disk is linear. Here we shall use it (in Pick's form) to prove an analytic function which is "approximately" a one-to-one mapping of a disk onto a disk is "approximately" linear. Before elaborating we need a preliminary result.

The non-Euclidean distance $d(z, w)$ is defined in Chapter 2, Section 7. Given a complex number z let γ be the radius from 0 to z parametrized in the obvious way ($z(t) = tz$, $0 \leq t \leq 1$). If $|z| < R$, a change of variables in (7.6), Chapter 2, yields

$$(6.1) \qquad d\left(0, \frac{z}{R}\right) = \frac{1}{R} \int_\gamma \frac{|d\zeta|}{(1 - |\zeta/R|^2)}.$$

Lemma 6.1. Let h be analytic and bounded by $M < \infty$ on Δ_R. If there exists a number $t > 0$ such that $|h(z)| > t$ for $z \in \Delta_R$, then

$$(6.2) \qquad |h(z) - h(0)| < M\left(1 - \left(\frac{t}{M}\right)^2\right) d\left(0, \frac{z}{R}\right).$$

Proof. By (6.11), Chapter 2, the derivative of h is bounded by

$$(6.3) \qquad |h'(z)| \leq \frac{R}{M} \frac{M^2 - |h(z)|^2}{R^2 - |z|^2} = \frac{M}{R} \frac{1 - (|h(z)|/M)^2}{1 - (|z|/R)^2}.$$

Using the assumption that $|h(z)| \geq t$, inequality (6.3) can be replaced by

$$(6.4) \qquad |h'(z)| \leq \frac{M}{R} \frac{1 - (t/M)^2}{1 - (|z|/R)^2}.$$

If γ is the radius from 0 to z used in (6.1), $h(z) - h(0)$ is given by the integral $\int_\gamma h'(\zeta)\, d\zeta$. Applying (6.4) to this fact yields

$$|h(z) - h(0)| = \left| \int_\gamma h'(\zeta)\, d\zeta \right| \le \int_\gamma |h'(\zeta)|\, |d\zeta| \le M\left(1 - \left(\frac{t}{M}\right)^2\right) d\left(0, \frac{z}{R}\right)$$

as was to be proved.

We shall apply the lemma to the following situation: There are given real numbers a, b, and c, all positive, and a function f such that

(1) f is analytic and bounded by 1 on Δ_a,
(2) $b < a$, and f is one-to-one on Δ_b,
(3) $f(0) = 0$ and $\inf_{|z|=b} |f(z)| = c > 0$.

Define h on Δ_a by

$$h(z) = \begin{cases} \dfrac{f(z)}{z}, & z \ne 0 \\[2mm] f'(0), & z = 0. \end{cases}$$

As usual, h is analytic on Δ_a, and because f is one-to-one on Δ_b, h is nonzero on Δ_b. By property (3) the minimum of $|h(z)|$ on the boundary of Δ_b is

$$\min_{|z|=b} |h(z)| = \min_{|z|=b} \frac{|f(z)|}{|z|} = \frac{c}{b}.$$

The maximum of $|h(z)|$ on the boundary of Δ_b is at most $1/b$ since $|f(z)|/|z| < 1/b$ on $|z| = b$. Applying the maximum principle separately to the functions h and $1/h$, both of which are analytic on Δ_b, yields

$$(6.5) \qquad \frac{c}{b} < |h(z)| < \frac{1}{b}, \quad z \in \Delta_b.$$

(The reader will note that $1/b$ can actually be replaced by the smaller number $1/a$. In our applications a will not be much larger than b, and the formulas turn out to be simpler with b instead of a.)

In the statement of Lemma 6.1 take $R = b$, $M = 1/b$, and $t = c/b$. If $z \in \Delta_b$, we have

$$|h(z) - h(0)| \le \frac{1}{b}(1 - c^2) d\left(0, \frac{z}{b}\right), \quad z \in \Delta_b.$$

Since $h(0) = f'(0)$, the last inequality implies (for $|z| < b$)

$$|f(z) - f'(0)z| = |z|\,|h(z) - h(0)| \le \frac{|z|}{b}(1 - c^2) d\left(0, \frac{z}{b}\right)$$

$$\le (1 - c^2) d\left(0, \frac{z}{b}\right).$$

Collecting results, we have proved

Theorem 6.1. *Let a, b, c, and f enjoy the properties (1)–(3) above. If $z \in \Delta_b$, then*

$$(6.6) \qquad |f(z) - f'(0)z| \leq (1 - c^2)d\left(0, \frac{z}{b}\right).$$

Notice for fixed a and b that the closer c is to 1 the more nearly linear f will be. Had we used $1/a$ rather than $1/b$, inequality (6.6) would read

$$(6.6') \qquad |f(z) - f'(0)z| \leq \frac{b}{a}(1 - c^2)d\left(0, \frac{z}{b}\right)$$

which could be more useful if $a \gg b$.

Continuing with (6.6) we now assume $f'(0) > 0$ and $0 < c < b < a < 1$. The latter inequalities imply $c/b < 1 < 1/b$, while (6.5) implies $c/b < f'(0) < 1/b$. Combining these we find that $|1 - f'(0)| < ((1 - c)/b)$. If $z \in \Delta_b$, (6.6) and this last inequality give rise to

$$
\begin{aligned}
|f(z) - z| &\leq |f(z) - f'(0)z| + |f'(0)z - z| \\
&\leq (1 - c^2)d\left(0, \frac{z}{b}\right) + |z|\left(\frac{1 - c}{b}\right) \\
(6.7) \qquad &\leq (1 - c^2)d\left(0, \frac{z}{b}\right) + (1 - c) \\
&\leq (1 - c)\left\{2d\left(0, \frac{z}{b}\right) + 1\right\}.
\end{aligned}
$$

The relation $1 + c \leq 2$ has been used for the last line of (6.7).

It is useful to have (6.7) in a form involving $d(f(z), z)$. Since by assumption $|f(z)| < 1$ for all $z \in \Delta_a$, Schwarz's lemma implies that $|f(z)| \leq (|z|/a)$, $z \in \Delta_a$. Of course, $(|z|/a) > |z|$ because $a < 1$, and therefore by (7.12), Chapter 2,

$$d(f(z), z) \leq \frac{|f(z) - z|}{1 - (|z|^2/a^2)} = a^2 \frac{|f(z) - z|}{a^2 - |z|^2} \leq \frac{|f(z) - z|}{a^2 - |z|^2}.$$

Substituting this in (6.7), we get

$$(6.8) \qquad d(f(z), z) \leq \frac{1 - c}{a^2 - |z|^2}\left\{2d\left(0, \frac{z}{b}\right) + 1\right\}$$

valid for $z \in \Delta_b$.

The following theorem is crucial to the proof of Theorem 7.1.

Theorem 6.2. *Let f and g be analytic and bounded by 1 on Δ. In addition suppose*

   (a) $f(0) = 0 = g(0)$;
   (b) $f'(0) > 0$, $g'(0) > 0$;
   (c) *A constant r, $0 < r < 1$, is such that f^{-1} can be continued along an arbitrary arc from 0 in $g(\Delta_r)$ with values in Δ and initial value 0;*
   (d) *For the same constant r statement (c) holds with g and f interchanged. Under these circumstances if $z \in \Delta_{r^2}$, the inequality*

$$(6.9) \qquad d(f(z), g(z)) \leq \frac{1 - r^3}{r^2 - |z|^2} \left\{ 2d\left(0, \frac{z}{r^2}\right) + 1 \right\}$$

is true.

Proof.   Assumption (c) means that the germ $[f^{-1}]_0$ is continuable along arcs from 0 in $g(\Delta_r)$. By Chapter 1, Section 10, $[f^{-1}]_0 \circ [g]_0$ can be continued along an arbitrary arc from 0 in Δ_r, and because Δ_r is simply connected, the monodromy theorem implies the existence of a function h_1, analytic on Δ_r (with values in Δ), such that $[h_1]_0 = [f^{-1}]_0 \circ [g]_0$. Similarly, there exists h_2 with $[h_2]_0 = [g^{-1}]_0 \circ [f]_0$.

By Schwarz's lemma $|h_i(z)| \leq (|z|/r)$, $z \in \Delta_r$, $i = 1, 2$, and therefore if $z \in \Delta_{r^2}$, $h_i(z) \in \Delta_r$. The compositions $h_1(h_2(z))$ and $h_2(h_1(z))$ are thus defined on Δ_{r^2}, and analysis of the germs at 0 reveals that $h_1(h_2(z)) = z = h_2(h_1(z))$, $z \in \Delta_{r^2}$. It follows that both h_2 and h_1 are one-to-one on Δ_{r^2}. The range of each contains Δ_{r^3}; for example, if $z \in \Delta_{r^3}$, then $h_2(z) \in \Delta_{r^2}$, and $z = h_1(h_2(z))$ is in the range of h_1. By Problem 4, Section 6, Chapter 2

$$\min_{|z| = r^2} |h_1(z)| \geq r^3.$$

On Δ_r, $f(h_1(z)) = g(z)$ as one sees as before from examining the germs at 0. Thus, if $z \in \Delta_{r^2}$

$$d(f(z), g(z)) = d(f(z), f(h_1(z)) \leq d(z, h_1(z))$$

by Pick's theorem. If $a = r$, $b = r^2$, and $c = r^3$ in (6.8), then because $h_1'(0) = \dfrac{g'(0)}{f'(0)} > 0$, we have

$$d(f(z), g(z)) \leq \frac{1 - r^3}{r^2 - |z|^2} \left\{ 2d\left(0, \frac{z}{r^2}\right) + 1 \right\}, \quad z \in \Delta_{r^2}$$

which was to be proved.

Problems

1. Verify the claims that

   (a) $[h_1]_0 \circ [h_2]_0 = [z]_0$ and
   (b) $[f]_0 \circ [h_1]_0 = [g]_0$.

2. Suppose $r = 1$ in conditions (c) and (d) of Theorem 6.2. Show that $f \equiv g$.

7. A Uniformization Theorem

Returning to the discussion of Section 1, the results of Sections 2–6 will be used to demonstrate that a *bounded* region has the unit disk for a universal covering surface. It will suffice to prove this for regions containing 0 which are themselves contained in Δ, as any bounded region is analytically equivalent with a region of this special form.

Fix for the discussion a region Ω contained in Δ with $0 \in \Omega$. The case $\Omega = \Delta$ is uninteresting, and so we assume $\Omega \neq \Delta$. The number

$$(7.1) \qquad\qquad d^2 = \inf_{z \notin \Omega} |z|$$

satisfies $0 < d^2 < 1$. Furthermore, the minimum (7.1) is actually assumed. That is, there exists a point $d^2 e^{i\theta}$ which does not belong to Ω. (The use of d^2 instead of d will simplify equations to follow.) Later, when Ω will sometimes have a subscript, the same subscript will be attached to d and θ.

REMARK. The choice of θ may not be unique. A canonical choice is the *smallest* θ, $0 \leq \theta < \pi$, such that $d^2 e^{i\theta} \notin \Omega$.

The proof of Theorem 7.1 divides naturally into three steps. The first step is to construct a sequence

$$\to \Omega_{n+1} \xrightarrow{\varphi_n} \Omega_n \to \;\cdot\;\cdot\;\cdot\; \xrightarrow{\varphi_1} \Omega_1 \xrightarrow{\varphi} \Omega$$

of coverings, where the regions Ω_n, subregions of Δ, "swell out" to Δ. The next step is to prove that the sequence $f_n(z) = \varphi_{n-1}(\varphi_{n-2}(\ldots (\varphi(z)) \ldots))$, $n = 1, 2, \ldots$, $(\varphi_0 = \varphi)$, converges locally uniformly on Δ. Finally, the limit, f, is proved to be a covering map of Δ onto Ω.

Step 1. Ω, d^2, and θ are assumed to be as in the paragraph containing (7.1). If φ is an analytic function mapping Δ *onto* Δ, if $\varphi(0) = 0$, and if φ

is not one-to-one, then by Schwarz's lemma

(7.2) $$|\varphi(z)| < |z|, \quad z \neq 0.$$

Define Ω_1 to be the connected component[1] of 0 in the open set $\varphi^{-1}(\Omega) = \{z \mid \varphi(z) \in \Omega\}$. By our assumptions φ maps Δ onto Δ and $\Omega \neq \Delta$. Therefore, there exist points z such that $\varphi(z) \notin \Omega$, and we have $\Omega_1 \neq \Delta$. Associate $d_1{}^2$ and θ_1 with Ω_1. By definition $\varphi(d_1{}^2 e^{i\theta_1}) \notin \Omega$, and so

$$|\varphi(d_1{}^2 e^{i\theta_1})| \geq d^2.$$

Together with (7.2) this implies

(7.3) $$d^2 < d_1{}^2.$$

We will find a function φ such that $\Omega_1 \xrightarrow{\varphi} \Omega$ is a covering. Furthermore, the construction will depend only on d^2 and θ, meaning it can be carried out again for Ω_1, $d_1{}^2$, and θ_1. There arises a second covering $\Omega_2 \xrightarrow{\varphi_1} \Omega_1$ and an obvious iteration procedure.

In order that (7.3) hold, it is necessary to reject one-to-one functions φ. Balancing a desire for simplicity against this rejection, we shall define φ as a two-to-one function.

If S and T are linear transformations of Δ, then

(7.4) $$\psi(z) = S^{-1}(Tz)^2$$

is a two-to-one analytic mapping of Δ onto Δ. (The most general such mapping by Problem 1.) Since $\Omega_1 \xrightarrow{\psi} \Omega$ is to be a covering, it is necessary to choose S and T so that ψ^{-1} can be continued along arcs γ in Ω. Clearly, this will be possible if $\sqrt{w}$ can be continued along arcs $S\gamma$ in $S\Omega$. We therefore choose S so that $Sz \neq 0$, $z \in \Omega$.

A natural point to send into 0 under S is $d^2 e^{i\theta}$. Define

(7.5) $$Sz = \frac{z - d^2 e^{i\theta}}{1 - d^2 e^{-i\theta}z}, \qquad S^{-1}z = \frac{z + d^2 e^{i\theta}}{1 + d^2 e^{-i\theta}z}.$$

It is required that $\psi(0) = 0$, meaning T must be such that $(T0)^2 = -d^2 e^{i\theta}$ $(= S0)$. Define T as

(7.6) $$Tz = \frac{z - ide^{i\theta/2}}{1 + ide^{-i\theta/2}z}.$$

---

[1] The *connected component* B of a point a in an open set A is the set of points $b \in A$ which can be joined to a by an arc in A. B is itself an open set, and being connected by definition, a region.

We compute ψ:

$$\psi(z) = S^{-1}(Tz)^2 = \frac{(Tz)^2 + d^2 e^{i\theta}}{1 + d^2 e^{-i\theta}(Tz)^2}$$

$$= \frac{(z - ide^{i\theta/2})^2 + d^2 e^{i\theta}(1 + ide^{-i\theta/2}z)^2}{(1 + ide^{-i\theta/2}z)^2 + d^2 e^{-i\theta}(z - ide^{i\theta/2})^2}$$

(7.7)

$$= \frac{z^2(1 - d^4) - 2ide^{i\theta/2}z(1 - d^2)}{(1 - d^4) + 2ide^{-i\theta/2}z(1 - d^2)}$$

$$= z \frac{z - ie^{i\theta/2}h}{1 + ie^{-i\theta/2}hz}.$$

In the last expression $h = (2d/(1 + d^2))$ arises by dividing the numerator and denominator of the second-to-last expression by $1 - d^4$.

We normalize ψ by letting $\alpha = ie^{-i\theta/2}$ and defining $\varphi(z) = \psi(\alpha z)$. Then $\varphi'(0) = \alpha\bar{\alpha}h = h > 0$. Using (7.7) one sees that

$$\varphi(z) = z \frac{h - e^{-i\theta}z}{1 - he^{-i\theta}z}.$$

When it is necessary to denote dependence on d and θ we will write

(7.8) $$\varphi(z, d, \theta) = z \frac{h - e^{-i\theta}z}{1 - he^{-i\theta}z}, \quad h = \frac{2d}{1 + d^2}.$$

REMARK. Let $\tilde{\Omega}_1$ and Ω_1 respectively denote the connected components of 0 in $\psi^{-1}(\Omega)$ and $\varphi^{-1}(\Omega)$. By construction $\tilde{\Omega}_1 \xrightarrow{\psi} \Omega$ is a covering, and therefore $\Omega_1 \xrightarrow{\varphi} \Omega$ is a covering because $\Omega_1 = \bar{\alpha}\tilde{\Omega}_1 = \{\bar{\alpha}z \mid z \in \tilde{\Omega}_1\}$.

Associate $d_1{}^2$ and θ_1 with Ω_1, and define $\varphi_1(z) = \varphi(z, d_1, \theta_1)$. If Ω_2 is the connected component of 0 in $\varphi_1^{-1}(\Omega_1)$, then as before, $\Omega_2 \xrightarrow{\varphi_1} \Omega_1$ is a covering. In an obvious way there arises a sequence of coverings

$$\cdots \to \Omega_{n+1} \xrightarrow{\varphi_n} \Omega_n \xrightarrow{\varphi_{n-1}} \cdots \xrightarrow{\varphi_1} \Omega_1 \xrightarrow{\varphi} \Omega$$

where $\varphi_n(z) = \varphi(z, d_n, \theta_n)$ for each n. We note that $d^2 < d_1{}^2 < d_2{}^2 < \cdots$.

Lemma 7.1. $\lim\limits_{n \to \infty} d_n{}^2 = 1$.

Proof. First $\lim\limits_{n \to \infty} d_n{}^2 = t^2$ *exists* because the sequence is monotone and bounded by 1. Of course, $t^2 \le 1$, and we set $s = (2t/(1 + t^2)) = \lim\limits_{n \to \infty} (2d_n/(1 + d_n{}^2))$, noting that $s \le 1$. For each n, Lemma 6.3 of Chapter

2 implies that

$$(7.9) \qquad |\varphi(z, d_n, \theta_n)| \leq |z| \frac{h_n + |z|}{1 + h_n|z|}.$$

If $z = d_{n+1}^2 e^{i\theta_{n+1}}$, then by definition $\varphi(z, d_n, \theta_n) \notin \Omega_n$. In particular, $|\varphi(z, d_n, \theta_n)| \geq d_n^2$. Substituting this in (7.9) we find

$$(7.10) \qquad d_n^2 \leq d_{n+1}^2 \frac{h_n + d_{n+1}^2}{1 + h_n d_{n+1}^2}.$$

Passing to the limit in (7.10),

$$t^2 \leq t^2 \frac{s + t^2}{1 + st^2} \quad \text{or} \quad 1 \leq \frac{s + t^2}{1 + st^2}.$$

Since $0 < s$, $t^2 \leq 1$, the second half of Lemma 6.3, Chapter 2, implies $t^2 = 1$. Therefore, $\lim_{n \to \infty} d_n^2 = 1$, and the lemma is proved.

Step 2. Define $f_n(z) = \varphi_{n-1}(\varphi_{n-2}(\ldots (\varphi(z)) \ldots))$ for $n \geq 3$. $\Omega_n \xrightarrow{f_n} \Omega$ is the composition of n coverings, and therefore by Theorem 11.3, Chapter 1, it is itself a covering. Naturally, $f_n(0) = 0$ for each n and $f_n'(0) = \varphi_{n-1}'(0) \cdots \varphi_1'(0)\varphi'(0) = h_{n-1}h_{n-2} \cdots h > 0$.

If $0 < r \leq d_n^2 < d_m^2$, then by the definitions of d_n^2 and d_m^2 we have the inclusions $f_n(\Delta_r) \subseteq \Omega$ and $f_m(\Delta_r) \subseteq \Omega$. Since f_m and f_n are covering maps, it is possible to continue f_m^{-1} along an arbitrary arc from 0 in $f_n(\Delta_r)$ with values in Δ (indeed, in Ω_m) and initial value 0. A similar statement holds with f_n and f_m interchanged. Theorem 6.2, especially (6.9), implies the inequality (for $z \in \Delta_{r^2}$)

$$d(f_m(z), f_n(z)) < \frac{1 - r^3}{r^2 - |z|^2} \left\{ 2d\left(0, \frac{z}{r^2}\right) + 1 \right\}$$

which, if we take $r = d_n^2$, becomes

$$(7.11) \qquad d(f_m(z), f_n(z)) < \frac{1 - d_n^6}{d_n^4 - |z|^2} \left\{ 2d\left(0, \frac{z}{d_n^4}\right) + 1 \right\}.$$

It is clear from (7.11) and Lemma 7.1 that

$$\lim_{\substack{n \to \infty \\ m \geq n}} d(f_m(z), f_n(z)) = 0$$

locally uniformly on Δ.

Step 3. Denote by f the limit of the sequence $\{f_n\}$. Assumptions (a)–(f) of Theorem 5.3 are satisfied, and therefore

$$\Delta \xrightarrow{f} \Omega$$

is a covering.

Theorem 7.1. *If Ω is a subregion of Δ containing 0, there exists a covering $\Delta \xrightarrow{f} \Omega$ with $f(0) = 0$ and $f'(0) > 0$. Furthermore, with these properties f is unique. More generally, if Ω is analytically equivalent with a bounded region, and if z_0 is a prescribed point of Ω, there exists a unique covering $\Delta \xrightarrow{f} \Omega$ such that $f(0) = z_0$ and $f'(0) > 0$.*

Proof. The first statement has already been proved; uniqueness is a consequence of Problem 2, Section 6. If Ω is analytically equivalent with a bounded region, then given $z_0 \in \Omega$ there exists (Problem 2) a subregion Ω_0 of Δ and a one-to-one analytic mapping φ of Ω onto Ω_0 such that $\varphi(z_0) = 0$ and $\varphi'(z_0) > 0$. By the first part of the theorem there exists a covering $\Delta \xrightarrow{f_0} \Omega_0$ with $f_0(0) = 0$ and $f_0'(0) > 0$. Clearly, $f(z) = \varphi^{-1}(f_0(z))$ is the desired covering map of Δ onto Ω. The uniqueness of f is also left to the reader (Problem 3).

As a corollary we obtain the Riemann mapping theorem:

Theorem 7.2. (Riemann Mapping Theorem) *A simply connected region Ω which is not the plane is analytically equivalent with Δ. In fact, if z_0 is a prescribed point of Ω, there exists a unique one-to-one analytic mapping f of Δ onto Ω with $f(0) = z_0$ and $f'(0) > 0$.*

Proof. By Lemma 1.1 Ω is analytically equivalent with a bounded region. Therefore, there exists a unique covering $\Delta \xrightarrow{f} \Omega$ with $f(0) = z_0$ and $f'(0) > 0$. Since Ω is simply connected, the covering map f is one-to-one, and the theorem is proved.

Problems

1. Let φ be a two-to-one analytic mapping of Δ onto Δ. Show that there exist linear transformations S and T such that $\varphi(z) = S^{-1}(Tz)^2$. (HINT: There exist exactly two numbers z_1, z_2 such that $\varphi(z_1) = \varphi(z_2) = 0$. It is possible that $z_1 = z_2$.

(a) Let ζ denote the non-Euclidean midpoint of the non-Euclidean line joining z_1 to z_2. Define T in such a way that $T\zeta = 0$. Show that $Tz_1 = -Tz_2$.

(b) Define S_0^{-1} to map $(Tz_1)^2 = (Tz_2)^2$ into 0. Show that there exists a constant c such that $S_0^{-1}(Tz)^2 = c\varphi(z)$, and define $Sw = S_0\bar{c}w$.)

2. Let Ω be analytically equivalent with a bounded region. For each $z_0 \in \Omega$ show that there exists a subregion Ω_0 of Δ and a one-to-one analytic mapping φ of Ω onto Ω_0 such that $\varphi(z_0) = 0$ and $\varphi'(z_0) > 0$.

3. Let $\Delta \xrightarrow{f} \Omega$ and $\Delta \xrightarrow{g} \Omega$ be coverings. If $f'(0) > 0$ and $g'(0) > 0$, and if $f(0) = g(0)$, then $f \equiv g$.

4. Let Ω be an arbitrary region. If Ω has a universal covering surface, then this surface is either the plane, or else it is analytically equivalent with the disk.

5. Let $\Delta \xrightarrow{f} \Omega_1$ and $\Delta \xrightarrow{g} \Omega_2$ be coverings. If $\Omega_2 \subseteq \Omega_1$, and if $f(0) = g(0)$, then $|f'(0)| > |g'(0)|$ unless $\Omega_2 = \Omega_1$. In the latter case $|f'(0)| = |g'(0)|$.

6. Let $\Delta \xrightarrow{f} \Omega$ be a covering with $f(0) = 0$ and $f'(0) \geq \epsilon > 0$. If $\Omega \subseteq \Delta$, then Ω contains the disk of radius $(1/\epsilon^2)(1 - \sqrt{1 - \epsilon^2})^2$ about 0. (HINT: By the construction of f, $f'(0) < (2d/(1 + d^2))$.)

7. Construct a covering $\Delta \xrightarrow{f} \Delta_0$, where Δ_0 is the disk minus the point $z = 0$.

8. If Ω is a simply connected region which is not the whole plane, denote by $f_z(\zeta)$, $z \in \Omega$, the unique one-to-one analytic mapping of Ω onto Δ with $f_z(z) = 0$, $f_z'(z) > 0$. Define $G(z_1, z_2)$ by

$$G(z_1, z_2) = \log|f_{z_1}(z_2)|, \quad z_1 \neq z_2.$$

(a) For each pair $z_1, z_2 \in \Omega$

$$|f_{z_1}(z_2)| = |f_{z_2}(z_1)|.$$

Therefore, $G(z_1, z_2) = G(z_2, z_1)$, $z_1 \neq z_2$.

(b) For fixed z_1, $U_{z_1}(z_2) = G(z_1, z_2)$ is harmonic in z_2, $z_2 \neq z_1$.

(c) Let ζ be a boundary point of Ω. Prove that $\lim_{z_2 \to \zeta} G(z_1, z_2) = 0$.

(d) Prove that $G(z_1, z_2) - \log|z_1 - z_2|$ can be defined to be harmonic at $z_2 = z_1$. (Fixed z_1.)

With properties (a)–(d), $G(z_1, z_2)$ is called the *Green's function* of Ω.

9. Suppose Ω is a simply connected region bounded by a piecewise differentiable curve γ. We assume

$$n(\gamma, z) = \begin{cases} 1, & z \in \Omega \\ 0, & z \notin \Omega \cup \gamma. \end{cases}$$

If $U(\zeta)$ is harmonic on Ω and continuous on $\Omega \cup \gamma$, then for each $z \in \Omega$

$$U(z) = \int_\gamma U(\zeta) \frac{\partial G}{\partial n}(z, \zeta)\, ds, \quad ds = |d\zeta|.$$

(Here $\partial G/\partial n$ denotes the derivative of G with respect to the outward normal of γ. You may assume the derivative is piecewise continuous. The differential is given by $(\partial G/\partial n)\, ds = (\partial G/\partial x)\, dy - (\partial G/\partial y)\, dx$.)

10. Compute $G(z_1, z_2)$ for

   (a) $\Omega = \Delta$;
   (b) $\Omega = \{z \mid \operatorname{Im} z > 0\}$.

11. If $U(z)$ is harmonic on an open set containing $\{z \mid |z| \leq 1\}$, then

   (a) $U(z) = \dfrac{1}{2\pi} \displaystyle\int_{-\pi}^{\pi} \operatorname{Re}\left(\dfrac{e^{i\theta} + z}{e^{i\theta} - z}\right) U(e^{i\theta})\, d\theta$ (Poisson)

   and

   (b) $f(z) = \dfrac{1}{2\pi} \displaystyle\int_{-\pi}^{\pi} \dfrac{e^{i\theta} + z}{e^{i\theta} - z} U(e^{i\theta})\, d\theta$ (Herglotz)

   is an analytic function whose real part is U.

The next eleven problems should be done in order. In each it is assumed that $\Delta \xrightarrow{f} \Omega$ is a covering with $f(0) = w_0$, $f'(0) > 0$. Usually, the "uniqueness" statement of Theorem 7.1 will be necessary for the solution.

12. If $\Delta \xrightarrow{f_1} \Omega$ is a second covering with $f_1(0) = w_0$, then for some α, $|\alpha| = 1$, $f_1(z) \equiv f(\alpha z)$. Also $|f_1'(0)| = |f'(0)|$.

13. If $z_0 \in \Delta$ is another point such that $f(z_0) = w_0$, prove (by construction) that there exists a linear transformation T of Δ, $T0 = z_0$, such that $f_1(z) = f(Tz)$ has positive derivative at 0. Conclude that $f_1 \equiv f$. Also

$$|f'(z_0)| = \frac{|f'(0)|}{1 - |z_0|^2}.$$

14. The solutions to $f(z) = w_0$ form a sequence $z_0 = 0, z_1, z_2, \ldots$. For each n define T_n as

   (a) $T_0 z = z$
   (b) $T_n z, n > 0$, is the transformation constructed in Problem 13 cor-

responding to z_n. Prove

(i) the sequence $\{z_n\}$, if infinite, has no limit point in Δ. (Remember $f(z_n) = w_0$, $n = 0, 1, 2, \ldots$.)

(ii) $f(T_n z) \equiv f(z)$, $n = 0, 1, \ldots$.

15. Let Γ denote the set $\{T_n\}$ constructed in Problem 14. If T is a transformation of Δ such that $f(Tz) \equiv f(z)$, prove $T \in \Gamma$.

16. If $m, n \geq 0$ prove $T_m T_n^{-1} \in \Gamma$. (Use Problem 15.) Thus Γ is a *group*. Γ is called the *covering group* associated with $\Delta \xrightarrow{f} \Omega$.

17. If γ is a closed curve from 0 in Ω, denote by $[\gamma]$ the set of closed curves homotopic to γ with respect to Ω. Exhibit a "natural" *one-to-one* correspondence between the distinct classes $[\gamma]$ and the sequence $\{z_n\}$. (Use the monodromy theorem on f^{-1}.) Thus there is a one-to-one correspondence between Γ and the classes $[\gamma]$.

18. If Ω is not simply connected there are infinitely many distinct classes $[\gamma]$. Therefore, Γ is infinite.

19. A mapping $\Omega \xrightarrow{\varphi} \Omega$ is an *analytic automorphism* of Ω if φ is analytic and one-to-one on Ω with range Ω.

   (a) If φ is an analytic automorphism of Ω such that $\varphi(w_0) = w_0$, show that for some α, $|\alpha| = 1$, $\varphi(f(z)) = f(\alpha z)$.

   (b) If α is as in (a), show that $z_n \to \alpha z_n$ gives a permutation of the sequence $\{z_n\}$.

   (c) Using Problem 14(i), show that the set of possible α's is finite unless Ω is simply connected.

   (d) If there are ρ α's in (a), show that there exists one, α_0, such that the others are given by $\alpha_0, \alpha_0^2, \ldots, \alpha_0^{\rho-1}$. The upshot of this problem is that there are not many analytic automorphisms of a region which leave a point fixed. It is possible to show that, unless Γ is abelian ($T_n T_m = T_m T_n$), there are at most finitely many analytic automorphisms of Ω.

20. Let $\zeta_1 \in \Delta$ and $w_1 \in \Omega$ be arbitrary points such that $f(\zeta_1) = w_1$. If $f(z) = w_1$, then $z = T_n \zeta_1$ for some n.

21. Assume Ω is bounded, and refer to Problem 7, Section 6, Chapter 2. By observing that $T_n \zeta_1$, $n = 0, 1, 2, \ldots$, is the sequence of zeros of a bounded analytic function, $f(z) - f(\zeta_1)$, prove that

$$\sum_n \log|T_n \zeta_1| = G(0, w_1), \quad w_1 \neq 0$$

is convergent. Prove that $G(0, w_1)$ depends only upon w_1, and not upon the choice of ζ_1.

22. Fix $w_1, w_2 \in \Omega$, $w_1 \neq w_2$, and $\zeta_1, \zeta_2 \in \Delta$ such that $f(\zeta_i) = w_i$, $i = 1, 2$. Prove that

$$\sum_n \log D(\zeta_1, T_n \zeta_2) = G(w_1, w_2)$$

is convergent, and verify that $G(w_1, w_2)$ is independent of the choice of ζ_1, ζ_2. Prove also that $G(w_1, w_2) = G(w_2, w_1)$.

REMARK. It is not difficult to prove that $G(w_1, w_2)$ is the Green's function for Ω.

8. A Closer Look at the Covering

We fix an arbitrary region Ω for which there exists a covering $\Delta \overset{f}{\to} \Omega$. Let $f(0) = w_0$. If $z \in \Delta$ and $w \in \Omega$ are such that $f(z) = w$, and if Ω contains the disk of radius $\delta > 0$ centered at w, it is possible to define on the unit ζ disk the following function of bound one:

$$h(\zeta) = f^{-1}(w + \delta\zeta), \quad h(0) = z.$$

Formula (6.11) of Chapter 2 implies

(8.1) $$|h'(\zeta)| \leq \frac{1 - |h(\zeta)|^2}{1 - |\zeta|^2}.$$

Setting $\zeta = 0$ and observing that $h'(0) = (\delta/f'(z))$, (8.1) becomes

$$\frac{\delta}{|f'(z)|} \leq 1 - |h(0)|^2 = 1 - |z|^2.$$

Inverting and reversing the sense of the inequality, we find

$$\frac{|f'(z)|}{\delta} \geq \frac{1}{1 - |z|^2}.$$

Suppose γ_w is a piecewise differentiable arc in Ω from 0 to w such that Ω contains the disk of radius δ about *each* point of γ_w. A continuation of f^{-1} along γ_w with initial value 0 gives rise to an arc γ_z in Δ from 0 to a point z, $f(z) = w$. At each point ζ of γ_z,

(8.2) $$\frac{|f'(\zeta)|}{\delta} \geq \frac{1}{1 - |\zeta|^2}$$

by the discussion of the preceding paragraph.

Now the length of γ_w is equal to

$$\int_{\gamma_w} |dw| = \int_{\gamma_z} |f'(z)|\,|dz|.$$

Substituting (8.2) into this, and recalling that $d(0, z) \leq \int_{\gamma_z} (|d\zeta| / (1 - |\zeta|^2))$, we have

(8.3) $$d(0, z) \leq \frac{1}{\delta} \int_{\gamma_w} |dw|.$$

To apply (8.3) define Ω_n, $n = 1, 2, \ldots$, to be the set of points $w \in \Omega$ such that

(a) w can be joined to w_0 by an arc γ_w in Ω of length less than n;

(b) at each point of γ_w, Ω contains the *closed* disk of radius $1/n$ about that point.

Ω_n is open (because a closed disk is required in part (b)) and pathwise connected by definition, i.e., Ω_n is a region. If $w \in \Omega_n$, then both factors $1/\delta$ and $\int_{\gamma_w} |dw|$ are bounded by n in (8.3), and therefore

(8.4) $$d(0, z) \leq n^2.$$

There exists a solution z to $f(z) = w$ inside the non-Euclidean disk of radius n^2 about 0.

It is easy to convert (8.4) to an inequality involving Euclidean distance. Because $d(0, z) = \frac{1}{2} \ln ((1 + |z|)/(1 - |z|))$, (8.4) is equivalent to

$$|z| \leq \frac{e^{2n^2} - 1}{e^{2n^2} + 1}.$$

We have proved

Theorem 8.1.   *The region Ω_n is contained in the region $f(\Delta_{r_n})$, where*

$$r_n = \frac{e^{2n^2} - 1}{e^{2n^2} + 1}.$$

Theorem 8.1 gives us an idea of how "rapidly" Ω is covered by Δ.

9. Boundary Behavior

The remainder of the chapter concerns one-to-one mappings between simply connected regions. Given an analytic equivalence $\Omega_1 \xrightarrow{f} \Omega_2$, we ask if the boundaries of Ω_1 and Ω_2 correspond in some sense. In the case where

Ω_1 is a "Jordan region" and Ω_2 is the unit disk, the answer is particularly nice.

The most general statement which can be made is topological in content; it is so weak as to be rather dull.

Lemma 9.1. Let f be a *continuous* one-to-one mapping between regions Ω_1 and Ω_2. Assume f^{-1} is continuous.[1] If $\{z_n\}$ is a sequence of points in Ω_1 without limit point *in* Ω_1, then $\{f(z_n)\}$ is a sequence of points without limit point *in* Ω_2.

REMARK. The sequence $\{f(z_n)\}$ may of course have limit point *not* lying in the region Ω_2.

Proof. By contradiction. Suppose w is a limit point of $\{f(z_n)\}$ which lies in Ω_2. There exists a subsequence of indices $\{n_k\}$ such that $\lim_{k \to \infty} f(z_{n_k}) = w$. Since f^{-1} is continuous, this implies

$$\lim_{k \to \infty} z_{n_k} = \lim_{k \to \infty} f^{-1}(f(z_{n_k})) = f^{-1}(w)$$

which belongs to Ω_1. However, it has been assumed that $\{z_n\}$ has no limit point in Ω_1. The lemma follows by contradiction.

Without additional assumptions not a great deal can be said about continuity at the boundary. For this reason severe topological assumptions will be made in Section 12.

10. Lindelöf's Lemma

The principal result of Section 12 will rely on an elementary yet ingenious device of E. Lindelöf.

To begin with let U_0 and U_1 be concentric disks centered at a point z_0 with $U_1 \subset U_0$. Ω is to be a region whose intersection with U_0 contains z_0, but Ω shall contain no points of an annular rectangle $ABB'A'$ (Figure 2). Choose an integer $n > 0$ such that the angle α subtended by the arc $A'B'$ (and AB) is greater than $2\pi/n$.

Given on Ω is an analytic function f which is bounded by $M < \infty$. For each boundary point ζ of Ω which lies in U_0 it is assumed that

(10.1) $$\limsup_{z \to \zeta} |f(z)| \leq m.$$

The object of Lindelöf's lemma is to give a bound for $|f(z_0)|$ in terms not only of M but also m and n.

---

[1] In fact f^{-1} is automatically continuous, but we do not prove this. The lemma is stated this way to emphasize that analyticity is unnecessary.

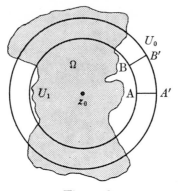

Figure 2.

Define Ω_k, $k = 0, 1, \ldots, n - 1$, to be the subset of Ω consisting of those points which, when rotated by an angle $2\pi k/n$ about z_0, remain in Ω.

$$\Omega_k = \{z \in \Omega \cap U_0 \mid z_0 + e^{2\pi i k/n}(z - z_0) \in \Omega\}.$$

If ζ is a limit point of Ω_k which does not belong to Ω_k, then either

(a) $\zeta \in \Omega$, but $z_0 + e^{2\pi i k/n}(\zeta - z_0) \notin \Omega$; the latter point is a limit point of Ω.

(b) $\zeta \notin \Omega$; ζ is a limit point of Ω.

Let Ω' be the connected component of z_0 in the (open) intersection $\bigcap_{k=0}^{n-1} \Omega_k$. If ζ is a boundary point of Ω', then for some k, $0 \leq k \leq n - 1$, ζ must be a boundary point of Ω_k. Therefore, by (a) and (b), either ζ or $z_0 + e^{2\pi i k/n}(\zeta - z_0)$ is a boundary point of Ω.

We claim $\Omega' \subseteq U_1$. To see this suppose ζ is a point of the annulus between U_0 and U_1. The definition of n in terms of α ensures that for some k, $0 \leq k \leq n - 1$, $z_0 + e^{2\pi i k/n}(\zeta - z_0) \in AA'B'B$, and the latter contains no point of Ω. In other words, for this particular k, $\zeta \notin \Omega_k$, and *a fortiori* $\zeta \notin \Omega'$.

From the last paragraph it follows that every boundary point of Ω' is contained in U_0. We define f_k on Ω', $0 \leq k \leq n - 1$, by

(10.2) $$f_k(z) = f(z_0 + e^{2\pi i k/n}(z - z_0)).$$

The product $F(z) = f_0(z) \cdot f_1(z) \cdots f_{n-1}(z)$ is analytic on Ω'. By (10.2) $f_k(z_0) = f(z_0)$ for each k, and so $F(z_0) = f(z_0)^n$.

If ζ is a boundary point of Ω', then by what has gone before, either ζ is a boundary point of Ω, or for some k, $z_0 + e^{2\pi i k/n}(\zeta - z_0)$ is a boundary point of Ω. In the former case $\lim\limits_{z \to \zeta} \sup |f_0(z)| \leq m$, while in the latter case $\lim\limits_{z \to \zeta} \sup |f_k(z)| \leq m$. In either case, because $|f_j(z)| \leq M$ for all j and $z \in \Omega$, it follows that

$$\lim_{z \to \zeta} \sup |F(z)| \leq M^{n-1} m$$

for each ζ on the boundary of Ω'. From the maximum principle we conclude that if $z \in \Omega'$, then $|F(z)| \leq M^{n-1} m$. Setting $z = z_0$ and taking nth roots, this becomes

Lemma 10.1. (Lindelöf) With notation fixed as above

(10.3) $$|f(z_0)| \leq \left(\frac{m}{M} \right)^{1/n} M.$$

A useful corollary to Lindelöf's lemma is

Theorem 10.1. *If f is as above, and if $m = 0$, then $f(z) \equiv 0$. By the same token if $\lim\limits_{z \to \zeta} f(z) = \alpha$ for some constant α and each $\zeta \in U_0$ which is a boundary point of Ω, then $f(z) \equiv \alpha$.*

Proof. If $m = 0$, then $f(z_0) = 0$ by (10.3). We will show in fact that $f(z) = 0$ on a set with accumulation point z_0, and the theorem will follow from the uniqueness theorem for analytic functions. The second half of the theorem follows from the first by considering the function $f(z) - \alpha$.

Let U_0' be a disk centered at z_0 and contained strictly between U_1 and U_0 (Figure 3). If the disks U_1 and U_0' are simultaneously translated

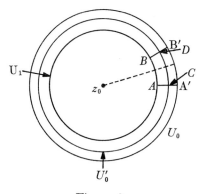

Figure 3.

along the radius bisecting $A'B'$, the rectangle $ABDC$ will continue to contain no points of Ω. For sufficiently small translations U_0' and U_1 will be contained in U_0, and therefore the conditions of Lemma 7.1 will continue to be met by U_0' and U_1. It follows from the first line of this proof that $f(z) = 0$, where z is the new center of U_0'. Thus, f vanishes on a set with accumulation point in Ω. The theorem is proved.

Problem

1. Let f be bounded and analytic in the region $\Omega = \{z \mid x_0 < \operatorname{Re} z < x_1\}$. If ζ is a point on $\operatorname{Re} z = x_0$ or $\operatorname{Re} z = x_1$, assume $\limsup\limits_{z \to \zeta} |f(z)| \leq m$. Show that $|f(z)| \leq m$ for each $z \in \Omega$. (HINT: Let M denote $\sup\limits_{z \in \Omega} |f(z)|$. Fix $z_0 \in \Omega$, and use Lindelöf's lemma cleverly to show that $|f(z_0)| \leq m^{1/3} M^{2/3} \leq M$.)

11. Facts from Topology

In what follows we shall state some definitions and theorems from topology. No proofs will be given for the latter since this would take us too far afield. The interested reader can consult, for example, Newman, *The Topology of Plane Sets of Points.*

Definition 11.1. An arc γ which is the continuous one-to-one image of a closed interval is called a *Jordan arc* or *Jordan curve*. If γ is the continuous one-to-one image of a circle, γ is a *closed Jordan arc*. A bounded region Ω whose boundary is a closed Jordan curve is called a *Jordan region* or *Jordan domain*.

Theorem 11.1. (Jordan Curve Theorem) *If γ is a closed Jordan curve, then γ separates the plane into two open connected sets, a bounded component called the "inside" of γ and an unbounded component called the "outside" of γ. Furthermore, the inside of γ is a simply connected region.*

Theorem 11.2. *Let Ω be a Jordan domain with w a point on the boundary of Ω. If $\{w_{n_k}\}$, $\{w_{m_k}\}$ are sequences of points in Ω such that $\lim\limits_{k \to \infty} w_{n_k} = w = \lim\limits_{k \to \infty} w_{m_k}$, there is a sequence $\{\gamma_k\}$ of Jordan arcs in Ω with the following two properties:* (a) *for each k γ_k has end points w_{n_k}, w_{m_k}, and* (b) *given $\epsilon > 0$ there is an integer k_0 such that if $k > k_0$ and $\zeta \in \gamma_k$, then $|\zeta - w| < \epsilon$.*

One speaks of the sequence $\{\gamma_k\}$ in Theorem 11.2 as *converging uniformly* to w. We remark that if Ω is a convex region, that is, a region which contains a line segment as soon as it contains its end points, then Theorem 11.2 is trivial, as the reader can verify.

Theorem 11.3.   *Let ζ_1, ζ_2 be points of the boundary of a Jordan region Ω. There exists a Jordan arc with end points ζ_1, ζ_2 each point of which, save ζ_1 and ζ_2, belongs to Ω.*

Theorem 11.4.   *Let γ' be the subarc of the boundary of a Jordan region Ω. There exist disks U_0 and U_1, centered at a point $z_0 \in \Omega$, with the properties*

(a) $U_1 \subset U_0$;
(b) $\Omega \cap U_0$ *satisfies the hypotheses of Lemma 10.1*;
(c) *the only boundary points of Ω which lie in U_0 are points of γ'.*

12. Continuity at the Boundary

In preparation of Lemma 12.1 we make some remarks which are purely topological.

In Figure 4 denote by l_1 the union of the radii OA and OB and by l_2 the union of OB and OD. There is given in Δ a Jordan arc η parametrized

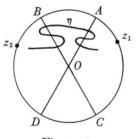

Figure 4.

by $z(t)$, $0 \le t \le 1$, such that $z(0)$ lies in the interior of triangle OAC, $z(1)$ lies in the interior of OBD, and η does not contain 0. We wish to observe in the following that there is a "last point" t for which $z(t) \in l_1$ and after t a "first point" s with $z(s) \in l_2$. The image of the interval $[t, s]$ will be a Jordan arc, δ, which lies entirely in one of the sectors OAB or OCD.

The open interval $0 < t' < 1$ cannot be expressed as the disjoint union of two nonempty open subsets because it is connected. Let U be the set of points t' such that $z(t')$ lies in the interior of OAC, while V is the set of

t' such that $z(t')$ lies in the interior of $OCDA$. Each is open because $z(t)$ is continuous, and each is nonempty by continuity and the assumption on $z(0)$, $z(1)$. Therefore, there exists at least one t', $0 < t' < 1$, which belongs to neither U nor V, and consequently the set

$$A = \{t' \mid z(t') \in l_1\}$$

is nonempty. If t_0 is a limit point of A, then by continuity $z(t_0) \in l_1$, and $t_0 \in A$. Define t by

$$t = \sup_{t' \in A} t'.$$

Then $t \in A$, i.e., $z(t) \in l_1$. The assumption on η is such that $z(t) \neq 0$ and therefore $z(t)$ lies on only one, say OA, of OA and OC.

The arc $z(t')$, $t \leq t' \leq 1$, joins the point $z(t) \in l_1$ to the point $z(1)$ in the interior of OBD. By a connectedness argument similar to the above the set

$$B = \{t' > t \mid z(t') \in l_2\}$$

can be shown to be nonempty and, again by continuity, closed. Define $s = \inf_{t' \in B} t'$. As before for t, s belongs to B and $z(s) \in l_2$.

We claim in fact that $z(s) \in OB$ and $z(t')$ lies in the interior of OAB for $t < t' < s$. By definition of t, s $z(t')$ cannot lie in l_1 or l_2 for any t' strictly between t and s. Therefore, for each t', $t < t' < s$, $z(t')$ must lie in one of the following four open sets: the interior of (a) OAC, (b) OAB, (c) OBD, or (d) ODC. It cannot be that (a) is ever true because then there would exist $t'' > t$ with $z(t'') \in l_1$ contradicting the definition of t. However, for t' sufficiently close to t, the continuity of $z(t')$ implies that $z(t')$ is in (a) or (b), and therefore in (b). Again using the connectedness of an interval, this time $t < t' < s$, we conclude that $z(t')$ is in the interior of OAB for each t', $t < t' < s$, and by continuity $z(s) \in OB$.

Denote by δ the arc $z(t')$, $t \leq t' \leq s$. We associate with δ a closed Jordan curve ϵ which is the union of three Jordan curves joined end-to-end: the radial segment connecting 0 to $z(t)$, the Jordan arc δ, and the radial segment joining $z(s)$ to 0.

With these preliminaries it is possible to prove

Lemma 12.1.   If $f(w)$ is a one-to-one analytic mapping of a Jordan region Ω onto Δ, and if $\{w_n\}$ is a sequence of points in Ω convergent to a boundary point w of Ω, then $\lim_{n \to \infty} f(w_n) = z$ exists for some z, $|z| = 1$.

REMARK.   Of course, $|z| = 1$ holds by Lemma 9.1.

Proof. By contradiction. Assume $\lim\limits_{n \to \infty} f(w_n)$ does not exist. The sequence $\{f(w_n)\}$ is bounded and must therefore have at least one limit point by the Bolzano-Weierstrass theorem. Since $\lim\limits_{n \to \infty} f(w_n)$ is assumed not to exist, there must in fact be at least two limit points w_1 and w_2. Let $\{w_{n_k}\}$ and $\{w_{m_k}\}$ be suitably chosen subsequences of $\{w_n\}$ such that $z_1 = \lim\limits_{k \to \infty} f(w_{n_k})$ and $z_2 = \lim\limits_{k \to \infty} f(w_{m_k})$. Without loss of generality we can assume z_1, z_2 are situated as in Figure 12.1, and by discarding at most finitely many k we can also assume that $f(w_{n_k})$ is in the interior of OAC while $f(w_{m_k})$ is in the interior of OBD.

Using Theorem 11.2 let γ_k for each k be a Jordan arc connecting w_{n_k} to w_{m_k} such that γ_k lies in Ω and the sequence $\{\gamma_k\}$ converges uniformly to w. Let $\eta_k = f(\gamma_k)$. Because f is one-to-one, η_k will also be a Jordan arc, and after again discarding at most finitely many k it can be assumed that $0 \notin \eta_k$. Since η_k satisfies for each k the hypotheses of our prefatory remarks, we can associate with it arcs δ_k, ϵ_k as constructed in those remarks. It may be that δ_k does not always lie in the same region OAB or OCD, so we select a subsequence δ_{k_l}, ϵ_{k_l} such that δ_{k_l} lies in, say, OAB for each l. Now we reletter and assume the original sequence was such that δ_k lies in OAB for each k. Theorem 11.1 implies that ϵ_k has an inside which we denote by Ω_k.

An application of Lemma 9.1 will now give us that the arcs $f(\gamma_k)$ converge uniformly to the boundary of Δ in the following sense: If $0 < r < 1$, there is a k_0 such that if $k \geq k_0$ and $\zeta \in \gamma_k$, then $|f(\zeta)| > r$. Indeed suppose for each l there is a $k = k_l \geq l$ and $\zeta = \zeta_l \in \gamma_{k_l}$ such that $|f(\zeta_l)| \leq r$. The infinite sequence $\{f(\zeta_l)\}$ would have, by the Bolzano-Weierstrass theorem, a limit point z, and of course $|z| \leq r$ because $|f(\zeta_l)| \leq r$ for each l. But $\lim\limits_{l \to \infty} \zeta_l = w \notin \Omega$, because $\{\gamma_k\}$ converges uniformly to w, and this contradicts Lemma 9.1.

While it may seem a fine point, it must be stated that if z lies in the interior of OAB, and if for each $\zeta \in \gamma_k$, $|f(\zeta)| > |z|$, then $z \in \Omega_k$. As in Section 11 this will be left unproved.

Let $a = \frac{1}{3}|A - B|$, and select any point $z_0 \in \Delta$ satisfying the following three inequalities: $|z_0 - A| > a$, $|z_0 - B| > a$, and $|z_0| > 1 - (a/2)$. The remarks of the preceding two paragraphs imply that for k sufficiently large $z_0 \in \Omega_k$. If U_0, U_1 are the disks of radius a, $a/2$, respectively about z_0, each has an arc lying outside Δ and, in particular, outside of Ω_k. Thus, if $z_0 \in \Omega_k$, the region $\Omega_k \cap U_0$ will satisfy the hypotheses of Lemma 10.1. Given $\epsilon > 0$, assume k is also large enough that if $\zeta \in \gamma_k$, then $|\zeta - w| < \epsilon$. Our choice of a implies that the only boundary points z of Ω_k lying in U_0 are points of δ_k, and for each of these $|f^{-1}(z) - w| < \epsilon$.

Applying Lindelof's lemma to the function $f^{-1}(z) - w$ gives

(12.1) $$|f^{-1}(z_0) - w| < \left(\frac{\epsilon}{M}\right)^{1/n} M$$

where M, n depend only on Ω, z_0, respectively. Letting $\epsilon \to 0$ in (12.1) gives $f^{-1}(z_0) = w$ which contradicts the fact that $f^{-1}(z_0) \in \Omega$. Therefore, $\lim_{n \to \infty} f(w_n)$ must exist, and the lemma is proved.

Theorem 12.1. *Let $f(z)$ be a one-to-one analytic mapping of a Jordan region Ω onto Δ. It is possible to define $f(w)$ for each boundary point w of Ω in such a way that f is continuous on $\bar{\Omega}$.*

Proof. Fix w and let $\{w_n\}$ be any sequence of points in Ω convergent to w. By Lemma 12.1 $\lim_{n \to \infty} f(w_n) = z$ exists. Furthermore, the value z is independent of the particular sequence chosen. To see this let $\{w_n'\}$ be another sequence convergent to w with $\lim_{n \to \infty} f(w_n') = z'$. By interleaving these two sequences a third sequence $\{w_n''\}$ is defined as

$$w_{2n+1}'' = w_n,$$
$$w_{2n+2}'' = w_n'.$$

Since $\lim_{n \to \infty} w_n'' = w$, the limit $z'' = \lim_{n \to \infty} f(w_n'')$ exists again by Lemma 12.1. The limit of a sequence is equal to the limit of any subsequence, so it must be that $z = z'' = z'$, and $f(w)$ is well defined.

We must now prove that f is continuous on Ω. If $w \in \Omega$, then f is continuous at w because f is analytic. If w is a boundary point of Ω, we must show that given $\epsilon > 0$ there is a $\delta > 0$ such that if $\zeta \in \bar{\Omega}$ and $|\zeta - w| < \delta$, then $|f(w) - f(\zeta)| < \epsilon$. Suppose for some w and $\epsilon > 0$ no such $\delta > 0$ exists. For each n there would exist $\zeta_n \in \bar{\Omega}$ with $|\zeta_n - w| < 1/n$, but $|f(\zeta_n) - f(w)| \geq \epsilon$. It is possible to associate with ζ_n a point $w_n \in \Omega$ such that $|\zeta_n - w_n| < 1/n$ and $|f(\zeta_n) - f(w_n)| < 1/n$. Then $\lim_{n \to \infty} w_n = \lim_{n \to \infty} \zeta_n = w$, and by the first part of this theorem $\lim_{n \to \infty} f(w_n) = f(w)$. However, $\lim_{n \to \infty} f(\zeta_n) = \lim_{n \to \infty} f(w_n)$, and so for large n $|f(\zeta_n) - f(w)| < \epsilon$, contradicting the choice of ζ_n. This completes the proof that f is continuous on $\bar{\Omega}$.

Let us remark here that when $f(w)$ is extended to $\bar{\Omega}$ by Theorem 12.1, f maps $\bar{\Omega}$ onto $\bar{\Delta}$. In fact, if $|z| = 1$ and if $z_n \in \Delta$, $\lim_{n \to \infty} z_n = z$, the sequence $\{f^{-1}(z_n)\}$ must have at least one limit point w, and for this point $f(w) = z$.

Theorem 12.2. *The function f, when extended to $\bar{\Omega}$, is a (continuous) one-to-one mapping of $\bar{\Omega}$ onto $\bar{\Delta}$. Furthermore, f^{-1} is continuous on $\bar{\Delta}$.*

Proof. Suppose $f(w_1) = f(w_2)$ for certain w_1, $w_2 \in \bar{\Omega}$. If $w_1 \in \Omega$, then $w_2 \in \Omega$ by Lemma 9.1, and $w_1 = w_2$ because f is one-to-one on Ω. If w_1 is on the boundary of Ω, then $|f(w_1)| = 1 = |f(w_2)|$, and w_2 also is on the boundary of Ω. By Theorem 11.3 there is a Jordan arc γ in Ω joining w_1 to w_2. The image η of γ under f is a closed Jordan arc with but one point, $f(w_1)$, on the boundary of Δ. If U is the inside of η, then $f^{-1}(U)$ is a Jordan region part of whose boundary is a subarc γ' of the boundary of Ω. By Theorem 11.4 there are disks U_0, U_1 centered at a point z_0 of $f^{-1}(U)$ such that the hypotheses of Lemma 10.1 are satisfied, and such that the only boundary points of Ω inside U_0 are points of γ'. At each $w \in \gamma'$, $f(w) = f(w_1)$, and so by Theorem 10.1 $f \equiv f(w_1)$, a contradiction from which the theorem follows.

To see that f^{-1} is continuous on $\bar{\Delta}$, it will be sufficient to show that if $\{z_n\}$ is a sequence in Δ with $\lim_{n \to \infty} z_n = z$, $|z| = 1$, then $\lim_{n \to \infty} f^{-1}(z_n) = w$ exists. For then an argument exactly as in Theorem 12.1 gives continuity. If $\lim_{n \to \infty} f^{-1}(z_n)$ does not exist, then the sequence $\{f^{-1}(z_n)\}$ must have at least two limit points w_1, w_2, and of course $f(w_1) = f(w_2)$. This is impossible because f is one-to-one, and hence $\lim_{n \to \infty} f^{-1}(z_n)$ does exist. The theorem is proved.

13. A Theorem of Fejér

Let f be an analytic one-to-one mapping of Δ onto a Jordan region Ω. Theorem 12.1 implies that f extends to be continuous on $\{z \mid |z| \leq 1\}$, and since this set is compact, f is uniformly continuous. Therefore, denoting the boundary values of f by $f(e^{i\theta})$, we have $f(e^{i\theta}) = \lim_{r \to 1} f(re^{i\theta})$, the limit existing uniformly in θ. The question to which we direct our attention is the following: Consider the power series expansion

$$(13.1) \qquad f(z) = \sum_{n=0}^{\infty} a_n z^n$$

of f about 0. Is it possible to interchange the order of $\lim_{r \to 1}$ and $\sum_{n=0}^{\infty}$ to conclude that

$$(13.2) \qquad f(e^{i\theta}) = \sum_{n=0}^{\infty} a_n e^{in\theta}$$

with this sum converging uniformly in θ? The answer, which is affirmative, is due to Fejér; its proof involves methods from the theory of "summation." The proof of Fejér's theorem breaks into two steps. First, using the properties of f as a mapping, we shall establish a growth estimate on the coefficients a_n. Secondly, using this growth estimate and the fact that $f(e^{i\theta}) = \lim_{r \to 1} f(re^{i\theta})$, we prove (13.2). The growth estimate is called a "Tauberian condition," the theorem itself a "Tauberian theorem."

Think of f as a transformation between points (x, y) and (u, v), where $u = u(x, y)$ and $v = v(x, y)$ are the real and imaginary parts of f. Since f is one-to-one, the area of Ω, the image of f, is given by the calculus as

$$(13.3) \qquad \iint_\Delta \left| \frac{\partial(u, v)}{\partial(x, y)} \right| dx\, dy = \iint_\Omega du\, dv.$$

Here, $\dfrac{\partial(u, v)}{\partial(x, y)} = \det \begin{pmatrix} u_x & u_y \\ v_x & v_y \end{pmatrix}$ is the Jacobian of the transformation. Using the Cauchy-Riemann equations ($u_x = v_y$ and $u_y = -v_x$) we find $\partial(u, v)/\partial(x, y) = u_x{}^2 + v_x{}^2 = |f'(z)|^2$.

Ω is a bounded region and therefore has finite area. It follows that the integrals (13.3) are finite. We compute the left-hand integral in polar coordinates, $z = re^{i\theta}$:

$$(13.4) \qquad \iint_\Delta \frac{\partial(u, v)}{\partial(x, y)}\, dx\, dy = \iint_\Delta |f'(z)|^2\, dx\, dy = \iint_\Delta |f'(re^{i\theta})|^2 r\, dr\, d\theta$$

$$= \int_0^1 r\, dr \int_{-\pi}^{\pi} |f'(re^{i\theta})|^2\, d\theta.$$

Now, if $0 \le r < 1$,

$$(13.5) \qquad |f'(re^{i\theta})|^2 = \left\{ \sum_{n=1}^{\infty} n a_n r^{n-1} e^{i(n-1)\theta} \right\} \left\{ \sum_{m=1}^{\infty} m \bar{a}_m r^{m-1} e^{-i(m-1)\theta} \right\}$$

$$= \sum_{k=1}^{\infty} \sum_{m+n=k} mn a_n \bar{a}_m r^{m+n-2} e^{i(n-m)\theta},$$

the interchange being justified by the absolute convergence of the series. Using the relation

$$\int_{-\pi}^{\pi} e^{i(n-m)\theta}\, d\theta = 2\pi \delta_{mn}, \quad \delta_{mn} = \begin{cases} 1, & m = n \\ 0, & m \ne n \end{cases}$$

and the fact that (13.5) converges uniformly in θ, we have

$$\int_{-\pi}^{\pi} |f'(re^{i\theta})|^2 \, d\theta = 2\pi \sum_{n=1}^{\infty} n^2 |a_n|^2 r^{2n-2}$$

valid for $0 \leq r < 1$. The integral (13.4) can be written as a limit

$$\lim_{\substack{s \to 1 \\ s < 1}} \int_0^s r \, dr \int_{-\pi}^{\pi} |f'(re^{i\theta})|^2 \, d\theta = \lim_{\substack{s \to 1 \\ s < 1}} 2\pi \int_0^s \sum_{n=1}^{\infty} n^2 |a_n|^2 r^{2n-1} \, dr$$

$$= \lim_{s \to 1} 2\pi \sum_{n=1}^{\infty} \frac{n^2 |a_n|^2}{2n} s^{2n}.$$

The limit is finite as we have already observed, and since the terms of the sum are *positive* we conclude

$$(13.6) \qquad \sum_{n=1}^{\infty} n |a_n|^2 < \infty.$$

Equation (13.6) is our Tauberian condition.

Theorem 13.1.   *The boundary function $f(e^{i\theta})$ is represented by the series*

$$(13.7) \qquad f(e^{i\theta}) = \sum_{n=0}^{\infty} a_n e^{in\theta},$$

which converges uniformly in θ.

Proof.   If $0 < r < 1$, and if N is an integer, the triangle inequality implies

$$\left| f(e^{i\theta}) - \sum_{n=0}^{N} a_n e^{in\theta} \right| \leq |f(e^{i\theta}) - f(re^{i\theta})| + \left| f(re^{i\theta}) - \sum_{n=0}^{N} a_n e^{in\theta} \right|.$$

The idea of the proof is to choose for each N a particular value of r, $r = r_N$, such that $r_N \to 1$ and

$$(13.8) \qquad \lim_{N \to \infty} \left| f(r_N e^{i\theta}) - \sum_{n=0}^{N} a_n e^{in\theta} \right| = 0$$

uniformly in θ. Since we know for any such sequence $\{r_N\}$ that

$$\lim_{N \to \infty} |f(e^{i\theta}) - f(r_N e^{i\theta})| = 0$$

uniformly in θ, it will follow that (13.7) is true uniformly in θ.

Set $r_N = 1 - (1/N)$. If $a \le b \le \infty$ are integers or ∞, define

$$\epsilon(a, b) = \sum_{n=a}^{b} n |a_n|^2.$$

Because of (13.6), $\lim\limits_{\substack{a \to \infty \\ b \ge a}} \epsilon(a, b) = 0$.

Given $\epsilon > 0$, let k be so large that $\epsilon(k, \infty) < \epsilon^2$. Note that if $m \ge k$, then $\epsilon(m, \infty) \le \epsilon(k, \infty) < \epsilon^2$. For $N > k$, we have by the triangle inequality

$$\left| f(re^{i\theta}) - \sum_{n=0}^{N} a_n e^{in\theta} \right| = \left| \sum_{n=0}^{\infty} a_n r^n e^{in\theta} - \sum_{n=0}^{N} a_n e^{in\theta} \right|$$

$$\le \left| \sum_{n=0}^{k} a_n r^n e^{in\theta} - \sum_{n=0}^{k} a_n e^{in\theta} \right|$$

(13.9)

$$+ \left| \sum_{n=k+1}^{N} a_n r^n e^{in\theta} - \sum_{n=k+1}^{N} a_n e^{in\theta} \right| + \left| \sum_{n=N+1}^{\infty} a_n r^n e^{in\theta} \right|$$

$$\le \sum_{n=0}^{k} (1 - r^n) |a_n| + \sum_{n=k+1}^{N} (1 - r^n) |a_n| + \sum_{n=N+1}^{\infty} r^n |a_n|.$$

The three quantities on the right of (13.9) will be estimated separately. In the first quantity let N be chosen so large that if $r = r_N$, then

(13.10)

$$\sum_{n=0}^{k} (1 - r^n) |a_n| < \epsilon.$$

As for the second term, observe first that $(1 - r^n) = (1 - r)(1 + r + \cdots + r^{n-1}) \le n(1 - r)$. Substituting $r = r_N = 1 - (1/N)$ and using Schwartz's inequality we find

$$\sum_{n=k+1}^{N} (1 - r^n) |a_n| \le (1 - r) \sum_{n=k+1}^{N} n |a_n|$$

(13.11)

$$= \frac{1}{N} \sum_{n=k+1}^{N} \sqrt{n} \sqrt{n} |a_n| \le \frac{1}{N} \left(\sum_{n=k+1}^{N} n \right)^{1/2} \left(\sum_{n=k+1}^{N} n |a_n|^2 \right)^{1/2}$$

$$\le \frac{1}{N} \left\{ \frac{N(N + 1)}{2} \right\}^{1/2} \epsilon(k, \infty)^{1/2} \le \epsilon(k, \infty)^{1/2} < \epsilon.$$

We have used the inequality $\displaystyle\sum_{n=k+1}^{N} n \le \sum_{n=0}^{N} n = \frac{N(N + 1)}{2} \le N^2.$

Finally, we estimate the third term in (13.8) for $r = r_N$:

$$\sum_{n=N+1}^{\infty} |a_n| r^n = \sum_{n=N+1}^{\infty} \sqrt{n}\, |a_n| \frac{r^n}{\sqrt{n}}$$

(13.12)

$$\leq \epsilon(N+1, \infty)^{1/2} \left(\sum_{n=N+1}^{\infty} \frac{r^{2n}}{n} \right)^{1/2}$$

$$< \epsilon \left(\frac{r^{2(N+1)}}{N+1} \sum_{n=0}^{\infty} r^{2n} \right)^{1/2} < \epsilon \left(\frac{1}{N+1} \sum_{n=0}^{\infty} r^n \right)^{1/2}$$

$$= \epsilon \left(\frac{N}{N+1} \right)^{1/2} < \epsilon.$$

Inequalities (13.9)–(13.12) combine to give for large N

$$\left| f(r_N e^{i\theta}) - \sum_{n=0}^{N} a_n e^{in\theta} \right| < \epsilon + \epsilon + \epsilon = 3\epsilon.$$

Since ϵ was arbitrary, the theorem is proved.

chapter 4

The Modular Function

1. Exceptional Values

A complex number λ is an *exceptional value* of a complex function f if λ does not belong to the range of f. Much of the discussion to follow is devoted to analytic functions with exceptional values.

It can be difficult, even impossible, for analytic functions to have exceptional values. For example, by the fundamental theorem of algebra a nonconstant polynomial has no exceptional values. As we will see, this result generalizes to arbitrary entire functions, albeit with a weaker conclusion. The "first theorem" of Picard asserts that a nonconstant entire function omits at most one complex value. Since e^z is never zero, Picard's theorem represents the strongest result obtainable for entire functions with exceptional values.

The proof of Picard's theorem follows a simple outline. If $\Omega_{a,b}$, $a \neq b$, denotes the plane minus points a and b, one proves the existence of a covering $\Delta \xrightarrow{\varphi} \Omega_{a,b}$. If f is an entire function omitting the values a and b, it is possible to define an entire version h of $\varphi^{-1}(f)$. Continuations of φ^{-1} take values in Δ, which means that h is bounded by 1. By Liouville's theorem h is constant, and it follows that $f = \varphi(h)$ is constant.

It is clear from the argument just outlined why a nonconstant entire function may omit one complex value. It is the *plane* and not Δ which is the universal covering surface of the plane minus one point.

Let us first note that Theorem 7.1 of Chapter 3 does not imply the existence of a covering $\Delta \xrightarrow{\varphi} \Omega_{a,b}$. $\Omega_{a,b}$ is not analytically equivalent with a bounded region. (Chapter 3, Section 1, Problem 3.) It will be our first (and principal) problem to prove a version of Koebe's theorem for $\Omega_{a,b}$.

126

It is sufficient to construct a covering $\Delta \overset{\varphi}{\rightarrow} \Omega_{0,1}$ since $\Omega_{a,b}$, $a \neq b$, is analytically equivalent with $\Omega_{0,1}$. We will follow a construction, first indicated by E. Lindelöf, which uses for its primary tools the Riemann mapping theorem and the Schwarz reflection principle. A rough description follows.

A circular arc triangle ABC is inscribed in the unit disk, its sides being perpendicular to the unit circle (Figure 5). The sides of ABC are non-

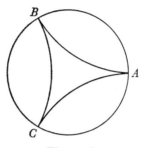

Figure 5.

Euclidean straight lines which meet "at infinity." A version of the Riemann mapping theorem allows one to map ABC one-to-one and analytically onto the upper half-plane. Furthermore, the boundary arcs of ABC map one-to-one and continuously onto the extended real axis, and matters can be arranged so that $\varphi(A) = 0$, $\varphi(B) = 1$, and $\varphi(C) = \infty$, where φ is the mapping function.

Since φ assumes real values on the arcs AB, BC, and CA, the Schwarz reflection principle gives an extension of φ to the (interior of the) set consisting of ABC, the sides of ABC, and the images of ABC under reflection in its sides. This new region lies inside Δ because the sides of ABC are non-Euclidean straight lines.

Each of the four triangles thus far constructed is mapped by φ in a one-to-one fashion onto either the upper or lower half-plane. At each vertex φ assumes one of the values 0, 1, or ∞. Repeated application of Schwarz reflection leads, as will be shown, to a "triangulation" of Δ and a definition of φ on Δ. It will be established that $\Delta \overset{\varphi}{\rightarrow} \Omega_{0,1}$ is a covering.

Problems

1. Prove that the range of a nonconstant entire function is dense in the plane.
2. If f is entire, and if $f(z)$ is never ≥ 0, then f is constant.

2. The Modular Configuration

The outline of Section 1 will be followed in spirit but not in detail. It is somewhat easier to work with "triangles" in the upper half-plane.

Let A be the subregion of the upper half-plane consisting of those points which are simultaneously exterior to the unit circle and interior to the strip $\{z \mid -1 < \operatorname{Re} z < 1\}$ (Figure 6). A and the images of A under reflections will be called *triangles*.

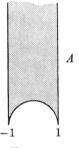

A

-1 1

Figure 6.

Consider the region C_1 obtained through repeated reflection of A and its images in their vertical boundaries (Figure 7). C_1 consists of those points z such that $\operatorname{Im} z > 0$ and $|z - 2n| > 1$, $n = 0, \pm 1, \ldots$.

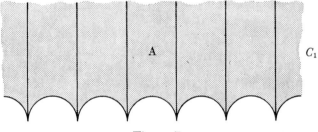

A C_1

Figure 7.

For $n = 0, \pm 1, \ldots$ we denote by $*n$ reflection in the circle $\gamma_n = \{z \mid |z - 2n| = 1\}$. The region $C_1{}^{*n}$ lies within the half-disk $\{z \mid \operatorname{Im} z > 0$ and $|z - 2n| < 1\}$ (Figure 8). We define C_2 to be the interior of the set
$$\bigcup_{n=-\infty}^{\infty} C_1 \cup \gamma_n \cup C_1{}^{*n}.$$
In each strip $2n - 1 < \operatorname{Re} z < 2n + 1$ there are infinitely many bounding semicircles of C_2, these being the images under $*n$ of the upper halves of γ_m, $m \neq n$.

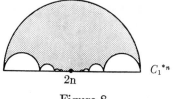

C_1^{*n}

2n

Figure 8.

C_3 is defined to be the interior of the union of C_2, the semicircles bounding C_2, and the images of C_2 under reflection in the latter. C_3 is contained in the upper half-plane and is itself bounded by semicircles.

Continuing in like fashion we obtain a sequence $C_1 \subset C_2 \subset C_3 \subset \cdots$ of regions, each arising from its predecessor through reflection. C_n is naturally decomposed into triangles for each n; each triangle is the image of A under a series of reflections.

Denote by r_n the maximum radius of the semicircles bounding C_n. If γ is a semicircle of radius r bounding C_n, let γ_1 and γ_2 be the images of the vertical tangents to γ under reflection in γ. (See Figure 9.) These are semicircles of radius $r/2$, and those bounding semicircles of C_{n+1} which are contained within γ must lie either in γ_1 or in γ_2. Therefore, $r_{n+1} \leq \frac{1}{2}r_n$. It follows that $\lim\limits_{n \to \infty} r_n = 0$ and $\bigcup\limits_{n=1}^{\infty} C_n = \{z \mid \operatorname{Im} z > 0\}$.

γ_1 γ_2

Figure 9.

Returning to the region A of Figure 6, the transformation $Tz = 1/z$ maps A onto a circular arc triangle PQR (Figure 10). PQR is a Jordan region which by the Riemann mapping theorem can be mapped one-to-

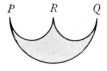

P R Q

Figure 10.

one and analytically onto Δ by a function f. Furthermore, f extends to be continuous and one-to-one on the boundary of PQR. It is a consequence of the argument principle that the counterclockwise order of the points $a = f(P)$, $b = f(Q)$, $c = f(R)$ on the unit circle is just a, b, c. (Otherwise $n(f(\gamma), 0) = -1$, where γ is the boundary of PQR parametrized in the counterclockwise direction.) Thus, if S is a linear transformation such that $Sa = 0$, $Sb = 1$, and $Sc = \infty$, S maps Δ onto the upper half-plane (Problem 1).

Letting S and T be as above we define

$$\varphi(z) = Sf(Tz)$$

for $z \in A$. By construction φ is a one-to-one analytic mapping of A onto the upper half-plane. The boundary of A is put in a one-to-one correspondence with the real numbers, and furthermore $\varphi(-1) = 0$, $\varphi(1) = 1$, and $\varphi(\infty) = \lim_{\mathrm{Im}\, z \to \infty} \varphi(z) = \infty$.

Let $\mathcal{3C}$ denote the upper half-plane. We will now apply the Schwarz reflection principle as indicated in Section 1.

Since φ assumes real values on the vertical boundaries of A, φ can be continued by Schwarz reflection into the images of A under reflection in these half-lines. Repeated reflection enables us to define φ on all of C_1. Each triangle of C_1 is mapped onto either the upper or lower half-plane.

As before $*n$ denotes reflection in $\gamma_n = \{z \mid |z - 2n| = 1\}$. Since φ is real valued on that portion of γ_n bounding C_1, the Schwarz reflection principle implies that

$$\varphi(z) = \begin{cases} \varphi(z), & z \in C_1 \cup \gamma_n \\ \bar{\varphi}(z^{*n}), & z \in C_1^{*n} \end{cases}$$

is analytic on the interior of $C_1 \cup \gamma_n \cup C_1^{*n}$. Making this definition for each n, φ is defined on C_2. Each triangle of C_2 is mapped onto either the upper or the lower half-plane, the vertices going into 0, 1, or ∞.

Repeated application of the Schwarz reflection principle extends φ from C_n to C_{n+1} for $n = 2, 3, \ldots$, and thus φ is defined on all of $\mathcal{3C}$. The construction is such that φ maps each triangle of $\mathcal{3C}$ one-to-one and analytically onto either the upper or lower half-planes. Since φ assumes the values 0 and 1 only at vertices (which lie on the real axis), φ omits the values 0 and 1 on $\mathcal{3C}$. The following two lemmas will enable us to prove that $\mathcal{3C} \xrightarrow{\varphi} \Omega_{0,1}$ is a covering.

Lemma 2.1. Let U be a disk in $\Omega_{0,1}$. If $w \in U$ and $z \in \mathcal{3C}$ are such that $\varphi(z) = w$, there exists a version g of φ^{-1} analytic on U such that $g(w) = z$.

Proof. If U is contained in, say, the upper half-plane, z will lie in a triangle which is mapped one-to-one onto the upper half-plane. Here $g = \varphi^{-1}$ is readily defined. If U intersects the real axis, say, in the interval $(1, \infty)$, then there will exist adjacent triangles A_1 and A_2 such that (a) z belongs to the closure of A_1 and (b) the boundary common to A_1 and A_2 is mapped onto $(1, \infty)$. The interior of $\bar{A}_1 \cup A_2$ ($\bar{A}_1$ denotes the closure of A_1) is mapped one-to-one onto the plane less the interval $(-\infty, 1]$. Again $g = \varphi^{-1}$ is readily defined. The lemma is proved.

REMARK. It is a consequence of the proof of Lemma 2.1 that φ^{-1} takes values in $\mathcal{H}$.

Lemma 2.2. Let γ be an arc in $\Omega_{0,1}$ from a point w. If $z \in \mathcal{H}$ is such that $\varphi(z) = w$, there exists a continuation of φ^{-1} along γ with values in $\mathcal{H}$ and initial value z.

Proof. Let $U_1, \ldots, U_n$ be a sequence in $\Omega_{0,1}$ which is admissible for γ. We define g_1 on U_1 by Lemma 2.3, taking $g_1(w) = z$. Let $w_1 \in U_1 \cap U_2$ be arbitrary, and set $z_1 = g_1(w_1)$. Since $\varphi(z_1) = w_1$, there exists a version g_2 of φ^{-1} on U_2 with $g_2(w_1) = z_1$. Since $[g_1]_{w_1} = [g_2]_{w_1}$, $g_1 \equiv g_2$ on $U_1 \cap U_2$. Similarly, define g_3 on U_3, $\ldots$, g_n on U_n in such a way that $\mathfrak{U} = \{(g_j, U_j)\}_{j=1}^{n}$ is a continuation sequence. By construction $\mathfrak{U}$ has values in $\mathcal{H}$ and initial value z. The lemma is proved.

We have already observed that $\varphi(z) \in \Omega_{0,1}$ for $z \in \mathcal{H}$. Combining this fact with Lemma 2.2 we have

Theorem 2.1. $\mathcal{H} \xrightarrow{\varphi} \Omega_{0,1}$ *is a covering.*

Proof. Immediate.

If $a \neq b$, $\Omega_{a,b}$ is analytically equivalent with $\Omega_{0,1}$. Since also $\mathcal{H}$ is analytically equivalent with Δ, we can state as a consequence of Theorem 2.1

Theorem 2.2. *If $a \neq b$, there exists a covering* $\Delta \xrightarrow{\psi} \Omega_{a,b}$.

It is now a relatively easy task to demonstrate that an arbitrary region Ω has a universal covering surface. If Ω is the plane or the plane minus a point, Ω is covered by the plane. In every other case Ω is covered by Δ.

Theorem 2.3. *If a region Ω is neither the plane nor the plane minus a point, there exists a covering* $\Delta \xrightarrow{f} \Omega$.

Proof. By assumption there exist points a and b, $a \neq b$, neither of which belongs to Ω. What is the same thing, $\Omega \subseteq \Omega_{a,b}$. Let $\Delta \xrightarrow{\psi} \Omega_{a,b}$ be a covering. We fix a pair $z \in \Delta$ and $w \in \Omega$ such that $\psi(z) = w$ and define Ω_0 to be the connected component of z in $\psi^{-1}(\Omega)$.

$\Omega_0 \xrightarrow{\psi} \Omega$ is a covering. To see this fix an arc γ in Ω from w. The image of γ under a continuation of ψ^{-1} lies in $\psi^{-1}(\Omega)$, and if the initial value is z, this image lies in the connected component of z. Therefore, there exists a continuation of ψ^{-1} along γ with values in Ω_0 and initial value z. By Theorem 11.2 of Chapter 1, $\Omega_0 \xrightarrow{\psi} \Omega$ is a covering.

Ω_0 is a bounded region. Therefore by Theorem 7.1 of Chapter 3 there exists a covering $\Delta \xrightarrow{g} \Omega_0$. If $f(z) = \psi(g(z))$, $z \in \Delta$, $\Delta \xrightarrow{f} \Omega$ is a covering by Theorem 11.3 of Chapter 1. The theorem is proved.

If $\Delta \xrightarrow{f} \Omega_{0,1}$ is a covering, the covering map f is usually called the *modular function* (and written $\lambda = \lambda(\tau)$ instead of $f = f(z)$). We shall sometimes use this terminology. A version of f^{-1} (or λ^{-1}) will sometimes be denoted by $\tau = \tau(w)$.

REMARK. Let $\mathfrak{IC} \xrightarrow{\varphi} \Omega_{0,1}$ be the covering constructed earlier in this section. Referring to Chapter 3, Section 7, Problems 12–22 for the definition, let Γ be the covering group associated with this covering. It can be shown that Γ is generated by the transformations $Tz = (1/(-z + 2))$ and $Sz = z + 4$. In other words every element of Γ is a product of the form $T^{n_1}S^{m_1}T^{n_2}S^{m_2} \cdots T^{n_k}S^{m_k}$, where n_i, m_i, $1 \leq i \leq k$, are integers, positive, negative, or zero. The matrices associated with T and S are

$$T = \begin{pmatrix} 0 & 1 \\ -1 & 2 \end{pmatrix} \quad \text{and} \quad S = \begin{pmatrix} 1 & 4 \\ 0 & 1 \end{pmatrix},$$

each of which has integer entries and determinant 1. Thus the matrix of an arbitrary element of Γ has integer entries and determinant 1. Γ is isomorphic to a subgroup of the group $SL(2, \mathbf{Z})$ of integer matrices with determinant 1, the latter being called the *modular group*. The modular function derives its name from this relationship. The reader interested in learning more about the function, the group, or the origin of the term "modular" should consult a text on "elliptic" functions.

Problems

1. Let a, b, and c be points of the unit circle whose counterclockwise order is a, b, c. If S is a linear transformation such that $Sa = 0$, $Sb = 1$, $Sc = \infty$, S maps Δ onto the upper half-plane.

2. Prove Picard's theorem by the argument outlined in Section 1.
3. If f is entire, and if f assumes real values on the real axis, then unless f is constant, f can have no nonreal exceptional values.
4. If f is entire and periodic, f has a fixed point. (f is *periodic* if there exists an $\alpha \neq 0$ such that $f(z + \alpha) \equiv f(z)$.)

3. The Landau Radius

If f is analytic on Δ_R, $R > 0$, with exceptional values 0 and 1, and if $f'(0) \neq 0$, we will see that R is bounded from above by a number which depends solely upon $a_0 = f(0)$ and $a_1 = f'(0)$. In what follows $\Delta \xrightarrow{\lambda} \Omega_{0,1}$ is a covering.

Since $a_0 \neq 0$ or 1, there exists $z_0 \in \Delta$ with $\lambda(z_0) = a_0$. The germ $[\tau]_{a_0}$ of λ^{-1} at a_0 can be continued along an arbitrary arc from a_0 in $\Omega_{0,1}$. Therefore from Section 10 of Chapter 1 we conclude that $[\tau]_{a_0} \circ [f]_0$ can be continued along an arbitrary arc from 0 in Δ_R. By the monodromy theorem there exists an analytic function h on Δ_R such that $[h]_0 = [\tau]_{a_0} \circ [f]_0$, and naturally $h(z) \in \Delta$ for each z.

Theorem 3.1. (Landau) *With notations fixed as above*

$$(3.1) \qquad R \leq \frac{1 - |\tau(a_0)|^2}{|\tau'(a_0)| \, |a_1|}.$$

Furthermore (3.1) *is the best bound possible. Given a_0 and a_1, there exists an f such that equality holds in* (3.1).

Proof. Let h be the version of $\lambda^{-1}(f)$ constructed before the theorem. By Pick's theorem, equation (6.11) of Chapter 2,

$$|\tau'(a_0)| \, |a_1| = |h'(0)|$$

$$(3.2) \qquad \begin{aligned} &\leq \frac{1}{R} \frac{1 - |h(0)|^2}{1 - (0/R)^2} \\ &= \frac{1 - |\tau(a_0)|^2}{R} \end{aligned}$$

or

$$R \leq \frac{1 - |\tau(a_0)|^2}{|\tau'(a_0)| \, |a_1|}$$

which is (3.1).

Toward proving that (3.1) is the best bound possible we first note, again by Pick's theorem, that if equality holds in (3.2), then h is a linear mapping of Δ_R onto Δ. Thus, f has the form $\lambda(h)$ for a certain linear mapping of Δ_R onto Δ.

Set $R = R(a_0, a_1)$, where

$$R(a_0, a_1) = \frac{1 - |\tau(a_0)|^2}{|\tau'(a_0)|\, |a_1|}$$

and define

$$h(z) = \frac{z + R\tau(a_0)}{R + \bar{\tau}(a_0)z}.$$

We know from Chapter 2 that h gives a linear mapping of Δ_R onto Δ. Note also that $h(0) = \tau(a_0)$ and $h'(0) = [(1 - |\tau(a_0)|^2/R] = |\tau'(a_0)|\, |a_1|$. We define $f_0(z) = \lambda(h(z))$, $z \in \Delta_R$. By construction f_0 omits the values 0 and 1, and $f_0(0) = a_0$. To compute $f_0'(0)$, we use the chain rule:

$$f_0'(0) = \lambda'(h(0))h'(0)$$

$$= \frac{1}{\tau'(a_0)} \cdot |\tau'(a_0)|\, |a_1|.$$

Thus $|f_0'(0)| = |a_1|$. Let θ be such that $e^{i\theta}f_0'(0) = a_1$. Then $f(z) = f_0(e^{i\theta}z)$, which still omits 0 and 1, has $f(0) = a_0$, $f'(0) = a_1$. The theorem is proved.

The number $R = R(a_0, a_1)$ is called the *Landau radius*. Notice (Problem 3) that $[(1 - |\tau(a_0)|^2)/|\tau'(a_0)|]$ is independent of the choice of $\tau(a_0)$. (Compare with Problem 13, Section 7, Chapter 3.)

Problems

1. If a, b, $a \neq b$, are complex numbers, and if f is analytic on Δ_R with exceptional values a and b, then

$$R \le R\left(\frac{a_0 - a}{b - a}, \frac{a_1}{b - a}\right),$$

   where $a_0 = f(0)$ and $a_1 = f'(0) \neq 0$.
2. Use Problem 1 to prove Picard's theorem.
3. Prove that $R(a_0, a_1)$ is independent of the version of λ^{-1} chosen at a_0.

4. Schottky's Theorem

We shall denote by $\mathfrak{F}_{a,b} = \mathfrak{F}_{a,b}(\Omega)$ the collection of analytic functions on a region Ω which have the exceptional values a and b. Schottky's theorem, which has to do with the set $\mathfrak{F}_{0,1}(\Delta_R)$, sheds much light on the set $\mathfrak{F}_{a,b}$. It will be particularly useful in the proof of Montel's theorem (Section 6).

For $0 < \epsilon < \frac{1}{2}$ define A_ϵ to be the set of points z satisfying the inequalities $\epsilon < |z| < 1/\epsilon$ and $|z - 1| > \epsilon$ (Figure 11). Let $\Delta \xrightarrow{\lambda} \Omega_{0,1}$ be a covering, set $w_0 = \lambda(0)$, and define Ω_n as in Section 8 of Chapter 3. Obviously, if n is large enough, $A_\epsilon \subseteq \Omega_n$. Therefore by Theorem 8.1 of Chapter 3 there exists an r, $0 < r < 1$, such that $A_\epsilon \subseteq \lambda(\Delta_r)$.

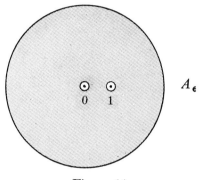

Figure 11.

Select a number s satisfying $r < s < 1$. The choice of s is unimportant, however we note that it can be made in such a way that $d(r, s)$ is arbitrarily large. Finally, let $\delta > 0$ be any number such that the inclusions

(4.1) $$A_\delta \supseteq \lambda(\Delta_s) \supseteq \lambda(\Delta_r) \supseteq A_\epsilon$$

are true.

If $f \in \mathfrak{F}_{0,1}(\Delta_R)$ for some $R > 0$, there exists on Δ_R an analytic version h of $\lambda^{-1}(f)$, as was observed in Section 3. By Pick's theorem h satisfies the inequalities

(4.2) $$d(h(z), h(w)) \leq d\left(\frac{z}{R}, \frac{w}{R}\right)$$

for $z, w \in \Delta_R$.

Set $K = d(r, s)$. If z and w are such that $h(z) \in \Delta_r$ and $d(z/R, w/R) < K$, it must be that $h(w) \in \Delta_s$. For otherwise $d(h(z), h(w)) \geq d(r, s) = K$ contradicting (4.2).

Theorem 4.1. (Schottky) *For every $\epsilon > 0$ and $K < \infty$ there exists a number $\delta > 0$ such that the following statement is true. If $f \in \mathfrak{F}_{0,1}(\Delta_R)$ and $z \in \Delta_R$ are such that $f(z) \in A_\epsilon$, then $f(w) \in A_\delta$ for $d(z/R, w/R) < K$.*

Proof. Let ϵ and r be as above and choose $s \in (r, 1)$ in such a way that $d(r, s) = K$. Then let $\delta > 0$ be small enough that (4.1) is true. If $f(z) \in A_\epsilon$, there exists a version h of $\lambda^{-1}(f)$ having $h(z) \in \Delta_r$. For this version the discussion preceding the theorem implies that $h(w) \in \Delta_s$ if $d(z/R, w/R) < K$. For these values of w, $f(w) = \lambda(h(w))$ belongs to A_δ, again by (4.1). The theorem is proved.

The argument of Theorem 4.1 works just as well to show that if $f(z) \notin A_\delta$, then $f(w) \notin A_\epsilon$ for $d(z/R, w/R) < K$. If $U = \{w \mid d(z/R, w/R) < K\}$, and if $f(z) \notin A_\delta$, the connected set $f(U)$ must lie in the complement of A_ϵ. Since the latter has three connected components, $f(U)$ must lie in one of them. We have

Theorem 4.2. (Schottky) *For every $\epsilon > 0$ and $K < \infty$ there exists a number $\delta > 0$ such that the following statement is true. If $f \in \mathfrak{F}_{0,1}(\Delta_R)$ and $z \in \Delta_R$ are such that*

(a) $|f(z)| \leq \delta$, *then* $|f(w)| \leq \epsilon$ *for* $d\left(\dfrac{z}{R}, \dfrac{w}{R}\right) \leq K$;

(b) $|f(z) - 1| \leq \delta$, *then* $|f(w) - 1| \leq \epsilon$ *for* $d\left(\dfrac{z}{R}, \dfrac{w}{R}\right) \leq K$;

(c) $|f(z)| \geq \dfrac{1}{\delta}$, *then* $|f(w)| \geq \dfrac{1}{\epsilon}$ *for* $d\left(\dfrac{z}{R}, \dfrac{w}{R}\right) \leq K$.

The following simple consequence of Theorem 4.2 will be used in Section 6.

Theorem 4.3. *Suppose that $\{f_n\}$ is a sequence from $\mathfrak{F}_{0,1}(\Delta_R)$ such that for some $z \in \Delta_R$, $\lim\limits_{n \to \infty} f_n(z) = 0$. Then $\{f_n\}$ converges locally uniformly to 0 on Δ_R. A similar statement is true if $\lim\limits_{n \to \infty} f_n(z) = 1$ or ∞.*

Proof. If V is a closed disk in Δ_R, there exists a number $K < \infty$ such that V is contained in the set $U = \{w \mid d(z/R, w/R) \leq K\}$. We are to prove that if $\epsilon > 0$ is given, there exists n_0 such that if $n \geq n_0$, then $|f_n(w)| \leq \epsilon$ for $w \in V$. To this end let $\delta > 0$ be chosen by Theorem 4.2 (part (a)) depending upon K and ϵ. Since $\lim\limits_{n \to \infty} f_n(z) = 0$ is assumed, there exists n_0 such that if $n \geq n_0$, then $|f_n(z)| \leq \delta$. By Theorem 4.2(a), $|f_n(w)| \leq \epsilon$ for $w \in U$ and *a fortiori* for $w \in V$. The main statement of the theorem is proved. The cases $\lim_{n \to \infty} f_n(z) = 1$ or ∞ can be treated by similar arguments.

Problems

1. Supply the missing arguments in Theorem 4.3. ($\{f_n\}$ converges locally uniformly to ∞ if for every closed disk U and number $M < \infty$ there exists an n_0 such that $\min_{w \in U} |f_n(w)| \geq M$ for $n \geq n_0$.)
2. For every $K < \infty$ and $M < \infty$, there exists $N < \infty$ such that the following is true. If $f \in \mathcal{F}_{0,1}(\Delta_R)$ and $z \in \Delta_R$ are such that $|f(z)| \leq M$, then $|f(w)| \leq N$ for $d(z/R, w/R) < K$.
3. Let $\{f_n\}$ be a sequence of elements from $\mathcal{F}_{0,1}(\Delta_R)$. If $\lim_{n \to \infty} f_n(z) = f(z)$ exists for each $z \in \Delta_R$, then $\{f_n\}$ converges locally uniformly on Δ_R.

5. Normal Families

The notion of a normal family is an example of an extension of the notion of compactness à la Bolzano-Weierstrass to a space whose "points" are functions. Normal families were first introduced by P. Montel.

Definition 5.1. Let $\mathcal{F}$ be a collection of analytic functions on a region Ω. $\mathcal{F}$ is a *normal family* if every sequence $\{f_n\}$ of elements of $\mathcal{F}$ contains a subsequence $\{f_{n_k}\}$ which converges locally uniformly on Ω. The limit is to be everywhere finite or else identically infinite.

The following lemma exhibits a line of reasoning which is frequently encountered in the theory of normal families.

Lemma 5.1. Let $\{f_n\}$ be a sequence of functions from a normal family $\mathcal{F}$. If $\{f_n\}$ does *not* converge locally uniformly, there exist two subsequences of $\{f_n\}$ which converge locally uniformly to different limits.

Proof. To say that $\{f_n\}$ does not converge locally uniformly on Ω is to say that there exists a closed disk $U \subset \Omega$ upon which $\{f_n\}$ does not converge uniformly, either to ∞ or to a finite limit. To say that $\{f_n\}$ does not converge uniformly on U is to say that there exists an $\epsilon > 0$ and for each n an $m_n > n$ such that

$$(5.1) \qquad\qquad \max_{z \in U} |f_n(z) - f_{m_n}(z)| \geq \epsilon.$$

Since $\{f_n\}$ does not converge uniformly to ∞ on U, there exists an $M < \infty$ and a subsequence $\{f_{n_k}\}$ such that for each k $\inf_{z \in U} |f_{n_k}(z)| \leq M$. For convenience, set $g_k = f_{n_k}$ and $h_k = f_{m_{n_k}}$ for each k. By (5.1) $\max_{z \in U} |g_k(z) - h_k(z)| \geq \epsilon$. $\mathfrak{F}$ is normal, and so there exists a subsequence $\{g_{k_l}\}$ of $\{g_k\}$ converging locally uniformly on Ω to a limit g. Since $\inf_{z \in U} |g(z)| \leq M$, g is not identically infinite. Also $\max_{z \in U} |g(z) - h_{k_l}(z)| \geq \epsilon/2$ for large l. If h is the limit of a locally uniformly convergent subsequence of $\{h_{k_l}\}$, then whether h is finite or not, $\max_{z \in U} |g(z) - h(z)| \geq \epsilon/2$. Thus $g \neq h$, and the lemma is proved.

For a general sort of application of Lemma 5.1 suppose P is a property which is held by at most one function on a region Ω. If $\{f_n\}$ is a sequence from a normal family $\mathfrak{F}$, and if it is somehow known that the limit of any subsequence of $\{f_n\}$ has property P, then $\{f_n\}$ must converge locally uniformly. For otherwise by Lemma 5.1 there would exist at least two functions having property P. An illustration of the principle which has been outlined is *Vitali's theorem*.

Theorem 5.1.   *Let $\{f_n\}$ be a sequence from a normal family $\mathfrak{F}$. If $\lim_{n \to \infty} f_n(z)$ exists for each z in a set E with accumulation point in Ω, then $\{f_n\}$ converges locally uniformly on Ω.*

Proof.   If $\{f_n\}$ does not converge locally uniformly, there exist convergent subsequences of $\{f_n\}$ with distinct limits f and g. However, since $f(z) = g(z)$ for $z \in E$, the uniqueness theorem requires that $f \equiv g$. The theorem follows by contradiction.

Definition 5.2.   Let $\mathfrak{F}$ be a family of functions analytic on a region Ω. $\mathfrak{F}$ is *locally normal* if for each open disk U in Ω, the set $\mathfrak{F}_U$, consisting of the functions of $\mathfrak{F}$ restricted to U, is normal.

Lemma 5.2.   Let $\mathfrak{F}$ be a locally normal family of functions on a region Ω. If $\{f_n\}$ is a sequence of elements from $\mathfrak{F}$ which converges locally uniformly on a given disk $U \subseteq \Omega$, then $\{f_n\}$ converges locally uniformly on Ω.

Proof. Let V be an open disk in Ω. If $\{f_n\}$ does not converge locally uniformly on V, then by Vitali's theorem and the fact that $\mathfrak{F}_V$ is normal, $\{f_n\}$ converges locally uniformly on no open subset of V. Denote by Θ_1 the set of points $z \in \Omega$ such that $\{f_n\}$ converges locally uniformly on a disk containing z. It follows that Θ_1 and its complement in Ω, Θ_2, are both open sets. Since Ω is connected, and since by assumption $\Theta_1 \neq \emptyset$, we have $\Theta_1 = \Omega$.

It is a consequence of the preceding paragraph that $\{f_n\}$ converges locally uniformly on each open disk in Ω. Since an arbitrary closed disk in Ω is contained in some open disk in Ω, $\{f_n\}$ converges uniformly on every closed disk in Ω. The lemma is proved.

From our lemma follows:

Theorem 5.2. *A locally normal family is normal.*

Proof. Suppose $\mathfrak{F}$ is locally normal, and let $\{f_n\}$ be a sequence from $\mathfrak{F}$. Then fix a disk U in Ω. Because $\mathfrak{F}_U$ is normal there exists a subsequence $\{f_{n_k}\}$ which converges locally uniformly on U. By Lemma 5.2, $\{f_{n_k}\}$ converges locally uniformly on Ω, and the theorem is proved.

In order to apply the theory of normal families it is necessary first to have criteria for deciding whether a family is normal (or locally normal). For this purpose it is virtually impossible not to appeal at some point to the Cantor-Hilbert "diagonal procedure."

Lemma 5.3. Let $\{a_{mn}\}$ be a doubly infinite sequence of complex numbers having the property that for each n there is a constant $A_n < \infty$ such that $\sup_m |a_{mn}| \leq A_n$. There exists a sequence of subscripts $m_1 < m_2 < \cdots$ such that for each n

$$\lim_{k \to \infty} a_{m_k n} = a_n$$

exists. Of course, $|a_n| \leq A_n$.

Proof. For fixed n the Bolzano-Weierstrass theorem implies the existence of a subsequence $\{a_{m_k n}\}$ such that $\lim_{k \to \infty} a_{m_k n} = a_n$ exists. What has to be proved is that the sequence $\{m_k\}$ can be chosen simultaneously for all n.

Select first a sequence $m_{11} < m_{21} < \cdots$ of indices such that $\lim_{k \to \infty} a_{m_{k1}1} = a_1$ exists. Then select a subsequence $m_{12} < m_{22} < \cdots$ of $\{m_{k1}\}$ such that $\lim_{k \to \infty} a_{m_{k2}2} = a_2$ exists. Notice that by the choice of $\{m_{k2}\}$

as a subsequence of $\{m_{k1}\}$, it is still true that $\lim_{k \to \infty} a_{m_{k2}1} = a_1$. Proceeding in like fashion we obtain sequences

$$
\begin{array}{cc}
m_{11} & m_{21} \quad \cdots \\
m_{12} & m_{22} \quad \cdots \\
m_{13} & m_{32} \quad \cdots \\
\cdot & \cdot \\
\cdot & \cdot \\
\cdot & \cdot
\end{array}
$$

each a subsequence of its predecessor, such that $\lim_{k \to \infty} a_{m_{k_j}j} = a_j$ exists for each j. If we set $m_k = m_{kk}$, $k = 1, 2, \ldots$, then for each j, $m_j, m_{j+1}, \ldots$ is a subsequence of $\{m_{kj}\}$. Thus $\lim_{k \to \infty} a_{m_{k}j} = a_j$ exists for each j, and the lemma is proved.

Denote by $\mathfrak{F}_M = \mathfrak{F}_M(\Delta_R)$ the collection of functions analytic and bounded by M on Δ_R. ($R > 0$ and $M < \infty$.)

Theorem 5.3. $\mathfrak{F}_M(\Delta_R)$ *is a normal family.*

Proof. If $\{f_m\}$ is a sequence from $\mathfrak{F}_M$, we represent f_m for each m by its Taylor series:

$$ f_m(z) = \sum_{n=0}^{\infty} a_{mn} z^n. $$

By Cauchy's estimate we have

$$ |a_{mn}| \leq \frac{M}{R^n} $$

for each m and n. Taking $A_n = M/R^n$ in the preceding lemma, let $\{m_k\}$ be a sequence of indices such that

$$ \lim_{k \to \infty} a_{m_k n} = a_n $$

exists for each n. Lemma 5.1 of Chapter 3 implies that $\{f_{m_k}\}$ converges locally uniformly on Δ_R to the function f whose power series is $f(z) = \sum_{n=0}^{\infty} a_n z^n$. The theorem is proved.

Definition 5.3.   A collection $\mathfrak{F}$ of analytic functions is *locally bounded* on a region Ω if there exists for each closed disk $U \subset \Omega$ a constant $M = M(U) < \infty$ such that $\sup_{z \in U} |f(z)| \leq M$ for each $f \in \mathfrak{F}$.

Lemma 5.4. If $\mathcal{F}$ is locally bounded on Δ_R, then $\mathcal{F}$ is normal on Δ_R.

Proof. Let $M = M(\Delta_{R/2})$. If $f \in \mathcal{F}$, the restriction of f to $\Delta_{R/2}$ belongs to $\mathcal{F}_M(\Delta_{R/2})$, a normal family by Theorem 5.3. If $\{f_n\}$ is a sequence of elements from $\mathcal{F}$, there exists a subsequence $\{f_{n_k}\}$ which converges locally uniformly on $\Delta_{R/2}$. By Vitali's theorem $\{f_{n_k}\}$ converges locally uniformly on Δ_r for each $r < R$. If U is a closed disk in Δ_R, then $U \subset \Delta_r$ for some $r < R$. Therefore $\{f_{n_k}\}$ converges uniformly on U. Thus $\mathcal{F}$ is normal, and the lemma is proved.

By combining Lemma 5.4 with Theorem 5.2 we obtain

Theorem 5.4. *Let $\mathcal{F}$ be a collection of analytic functions on a region Ω. If $\mathcal{F}$ is locally bounded, $\mathcal{F}$ is normal.*

Proof. The restriction of $\mathcal{F}$ to an open disk $U \subset \Omega$ is locally bounded on U and therefore normal by Lemma 5.4. (The fact that Δ_R was centered at 0 played no role in Lemma 5.4.) Thus $\mathcal{F}$ is locally normal on Ω. By Theorem 5.2 $\mathcal{F}$ is normal. The theorem is proved.

Problems

1. If Ω is a region, and if U is an open disk, define $\mathcal{G}_U = \mathcal{G}_U(\Omega)$ to be the collection of functions f analytic on Ω such that $f(z) \notin U$, $z \in \Omega$. Prove that $\mathcal{G}_U$ is normal.
2. Denote by $\mathcal{F}^+ = \mathcal{F}^+(\Omega)$ the collection of functions f analytic on Ω such that $f(z) \notin [0, \infty)$ for each z. Prove that $\mathcal{F}^+$ is normal. (HINT: For each $f \in \mathcal{F}^+$ it is possible to define $f^{1/2}$ because $w^{1/2}$ can be defined on $\mathcal{C} - \{[0, \infty)\}$.)
3. Use the theory of normal families (as outlined below) to prove the Riemann mapping theorem. If Ω is a simply connected region which is not the plane, fix a point $z_0 \in \Omega$. Define $\mathcal{F}_{z_0} = \mathcal{F}_{z_0}(\Omega)$ to be the collection of functions f, $f(z_0) = 0$ and $f'(z_0) > 0$, which are analytic, one-to-one, and bounded by 1 on Ω.

    (i) $\mathcal{F}_{z_0}$ is normal.
    (ii) $\mathcal{F}_{z_0}$ is nonempty.
    (iii) $\rho = \sup_{f \in \mathcal{F}_{z_0}} f'(z_0)$ is finite.
    (iv) There exists $f \in \mathcal{F}_{z_0}$ with $f'(z_0) = \rho$. (Here you must use (i).)
    (v) Prove that f maps Ω one-to-one *onto* Δ. (HINT: Let $\Omega_0 = f(\Omega)$. If $\Omega_0 \neq \Delta$, define d_0^2 and θ_0 as in Section 7 of Chapter 3. Make use of $\varphi(z, d_0, \theta_0)^{-1}$.)

4. Let Ω be a subregion of Δ containing 0, and let P be the property: f has property P if $\Delta \xrightarrow{f} \Omega$ is a covering with $f(0) = 0$, $f'(0) > 0$. If $\{f_n\}$ is the sequence constructed in Section 7 of Chapter 3, prove that the limit of any convergent subsequence of $\{f_n\}$ has property P. Conclude that $\{f_n\}$ itself converges. Thus in a sense normal families are extraneous to the proof of the convergence of $\{f_n\}$.

5. If $\mathfrak{F}$ is a normal family, define $\mathfrak{F}'$ to be the collection of functions consisting of the derivatives of functions in $\mathfrak{F}$.

   (a) If $\mathfrak{F}$ is locally bounded, $\mathfrak{F}'$ is normal.
   (b) $\mathfrak{F}'$ need not be normal. (HINT: Consider $f_n(z) = n^n + z^n$ on $\Omega = \mathbf{C}$.)

6. Let f be analytic and bounded by $M < \infty$ in a sector $S(\alpha) = \{z \mid -\alpha < \arg z < \alpha\}$, $\alpha > 0$. If $\lim_{\substack{x \to 0 \\ x > 0}} f(x) = a$ exists, and if $\alpha_0 < \alpha$, then $\lim_{\substack{z \to 0 \\ z \in S(\alpha_0)}} f(z) = a$ exists. (HINT: Let $f_n(z) = f(z/n)$, $n = 1, 2, \ldots$ Use Vitali's theorem.)

7. Let $\mathfrak{F}$ be a normal family. If the limit of any convergent sequence from $\mathfrak{F}$ is finite, $\mathfrak{F}$ is locally bounded.

6. Montel's Theorem

A celebrated theorem concerning exceptional values is Montel's theorem which asserts that $\mathfrak{F}_{a,b}(\Omega)$ is a normal family. We shall prove this theorem by first establishing that $\mathfrak{F}_{0,1}(\Omega)$ is locally normal.

Theorem 6.1. (Montel) $\mathfrak{F}_{0,1}(\Delta_R)$, $R > 0$, *is a normal family. In fact, if U is an arbitrary open disk, $\mathfrak{F}_{0,1}(U)$ is a normal family.*

Proof. The second statement follows from the first since there is a linear mapping of Δ_R onto U. Let $\{f_n\}$ be a sequence from $\mathfrak{F}_{0,1}(\Delta_R)$. If for some z there exists a subsequence $\{f_{n_k}\}$ such that $\lim_{k \to \infty} f_{n_k}(z) = 0$ (or 1 or ∞), then by Theorem 4.3, $\{f_{n_k}\}$ converges locally uniformly to 0 (or 1 or ∞). Since there is then nothing to prove, let us assume no such z exists. In other words, we assume that for each $z \in \Delta_R$ there exists $\epsilon = \epsilon(z) > 0$ such that $f_n(z) \in A_\epsilon$, $n = 1, 2, \ldots$, where A_ϵ is as in Section 4. We will prove that $\{f_n\}$ is locally bounded.

Let $\epsilon = \epsilon(0)$ be such that $f_n(0) \in A_\epsilon$, $n = 1, 2, \ldots$. If U is a closed disk in Δ_R, there exists $K < \infty$ such that $d(0, w/R) < K$, $w \in U$. By Theorem 4.1 there exists $\delta > 0$ depending upon ϵ and K such that if $f \in \mathfrak{F}_{0,1}(\Delta_R)$ and if $f(0) \in A_\epsilon$, then $f(w) \in A_\delta$ for $d(0, w/R) < K$. Applying this to $\{f_n\}$ and U we have $f_n(w) \in A_\delta$ for all $w \in U$ and n. In particular $\max_{w \in U} |f_n(w)| \leq 1/\delta$. Since U is arbitrary, $\{f_n\}$ is locally bounded.

According to Lemma 5.4 the sequence $\{f_n\}$, being locally bounded, is a normal family. Therefore, there exists a subsequence $\{f_{n_k}\}$ which converges locally uniformly on Δ_R. This completes the proof that $\mathfrak{F}_{0,1}(\Delta_R)$ is normal.

Suppose a and b, $a \neq b$, are complex numbers, and let $\{f_n\}$ be a sequence from $\mathfrak{F}_{a,b}(\Delta_R)$. Then defining $g_n(z) = [(f_n(z) - a)/b - a]$ the sequence $\{g_n\}$ belongs to $\mathfrak{F}_{0,1}(\Delta_R)$. Since the latter is normal, there exists a subsequence $\{g_{n_k}\}$ which converges locally uniformly on Δ_R. The local uniform convergence of $\{g_{n_k}\}$ implies the same for $f_{n_k} = (b - a)g_{n_k} + a$. Therefore $\mathfrak{F}_{a,b}(\Delta_R)$ is normal. We have

Theorem 6.1'. *If U is an open disk, and if $a \neq b$, $\mathfrak{F}_{a,b}(U)$ is normal.*

Theorem 6.1' implies that $\mathfrak{F}_{a,b}(\Omega)$, $a \neq b$, is locally normal for any region Ω. Therefore we have by Theorem 5.2

Theorem 6.2. (Montel) *If Ω is an arbitrary region, and if a and b, $a \neq b$, are complex, then $\mathfrak{F}_{a,b}(\Omega)$ is normal.*

Problems

1. Set $f_n(z) = e^{nz}$, $n = 1, 2, \ldots$. The sequence $\{f_n\}$ is not normal on $\Omega = \mathbf{C}$, and thus Montel's theorem cannot be extended to families with one exceptional value.
2. Let $\{f_n\}$ be a sequence of analytic functions on a region Ω. If there is no subsequence of $\{f_n\}$ which converges locally uniformly, then
$$\Lambda = \bigcap_{n=1}^{\infty} \bigcup_{m \geq n} f_m(\Omega)$$
is the plane or the plane minus one point.
3. Let $\{f_n\}$ and Ω be as in Problem 2. Prove there exists a sequence of closed disks U_k, $k = 1, \ldots$ such that

   (a) $U_1 \supseteq U_2 \supset \cdots$;

   (b) $\bigcap_{k=1}^{\infty} U_k = \{z\}$ is one point;

   (c) $\Lambda_k = \bigcap_{n=1}^{\infty} \bigcup_{m=n}^{\infty} f_m(U_k)$ is the plane or the plane minus one point.

   (Since $\Lambda_{k+1} \subseteq \Lambda_k$, if a point is omitted, it is always the same point.)

4. Let $\{f_n\}$ and Ω be as in Problems 2 and 3. There exists a point $z \in \Omega$ such that for any open set U containing z, $\Lambda(U) = \overset{\infty}{\underset{n=1}{\cap}} \overset{\infty}{\underset{m=n}{\cup}} f_m(U)$ is the plane or the plane minus one point.

5. Let f be an entire function which is not a polynomial.

   (a) Prove that $\{f_n\}$ is not normal where $f_n(z) = f(2^n z), n = 0, 1, \ldots$.
   (b) There exists a value θ_0 such that for every $\epsilon > 0$, f has at most one exceptional value in the sector $\theta_0 - \epsilon < \arg z < \theta_0 + \epsilon$. The ray $\arg z = \theta_0$ is called a *line of Julia*.
   (c) Strengthen (b). With at most one exception f assumes each value *infinitely often* in the sector $\theta_0 - \epsilon < \arg z < \theta_0 + \epsilon$.

7. Picard's Second Theorem

If f is analytic on a punctured disk $U_r = \{z \mid 0 < |z| < r\}$, there are from the elementary theory three possibilities for the behavior of f at 0.

   (a) If $0 < s < r$, then f is bounded on U_s. In this case $\lim\limits_{z \to 0} f(z) = a$ exists; the function $\bar{f}(z) = \begin{cases} f(z), & z \neq 0 \\ a, & z = 0 \end{cases}$ is analytic on Δ_r. (Riemann's removable singularities theorem.)
   (b) For some $k > 0$, $z^k f(z)$ is bounded on U_s, $0 < s < r$. If k is the least such, f has a *pole* of order k at 0.
   (c) There is no k such that $z^k f(z)$ is bounded near zero. In this case f has an *essential singularity* at 0.

Picard's second or "great" theorem has to do with the behavior of f in case (c). This behavior is already known to be complicated; the *Casorati-Weierstrass theorem* asserts that $f(U_r)$ is a dense subset of the plane.

Theorem 7.1.   (Picard) *Let f be analytic on U_r with an essential singularity at 0. Then for each s, $0 < s < r$, f has at most one exceptional value on U_s.*

Proof.   (Compare with Problem 5 of the preceding section.) Suppose for some s, $0 < s < r$, f has exceptional values a and b, $a \neq b$, on U_s. We define $h(z) = [(f(z) - a)/(b - a)]$ noting that both h and $1/h$ have essential singularities at 0 and exceptional values 0 and 1 on U_s.

For $n = 0, 1, 2, \ldots$ set up on U_s the function

$$h_n(z) = h\left(\frac{z}{2^n}\right).$$

The sequence $\{h_n\}$ is contained in $\mathfrak{F}_{0,1}(U_s)$ and therefore has a convergent subsequence $\{h_{n_k}\}$. Let H be the limit of $\{h_{n_k}\}$.

Suppose first that H is finite. Then $\lim_{k \to \infty} h_{n_k}(z) = H(z)$ holds uniformly on the circle of radius $s/2$ about 0. Let

$$M = \sup_k \max_{|z| = s/2} |h_{n_k}(z)|.$$

Of course, $M < \infty$. Furthermore, since $h_{n_k}(z) = h(z/2^{n_k})$, we have

$$\sup_k \max_{|z| = \frac{s}{2^{n_k+1}}} |h(z)| = M.$$

Thus by the maximum principle (applied to the regions $\{z \mid s/2^{n_k+1} < |z| < s/2\}$) $|h(z)| \leq M$ for $z \in U_{s/2}$. But this contradicts the assumption that h has an essential singularity at 0.

It must be that H is infinite. However the same argument as above, when applied to the sequence $\{1/h_{n_k}\}$, shows that $1/h$ cannot have an essential singularity at 0. The theorem follows by contradiction.

Problem

1. (Refer to Problem 5, Section 6.) Let f be analytic on U_r with an essential singularity at 0. There exists a θ_0 such that for every $\epsilon > 0$, f has at most one exceptional value on the region consisting of those points of U_r such that $\theta_0 - \epsilon < \arg z < \theta_0 + \epsilon$.

8. The Koebe-Faber Distortion Theorem

Throughout the present section $\mathfrak{F}$ denotes the family of one-to-one analytic functions f on Δ which are such that $f(0) = 0$ and $f'(0) = 1$. Suitable application of Montel's theorem will show that $\mathfrak{F}$ is normal.

If $f \in \mathfrak{F}$, then $f(\Delta) \neq \mathbf{C}$. (Why?) Therefore, there exists a point $a \notin f(\Delta)$, and a can be chosen to have minimum absolute value. Since f/a has the exceptional value 1, and since Δ is simply connected, there exists on Δ an analytic version h of $(1 - f/a)^{1/2}$. Letting h be such that $h(0) = 1^{1/2} = -1$, we claim h omits the value 1. For if $h(z) = 1$, then $h^2(z) = h^2(0)$, meaning hat $f(z) = f(0)$. Since obviously $z \neq 0$, this is in contradiction of the ssumption that $f \in \mathfrak{F}$. Thus h is never 1, and since h is also never 0, $\in \mathfrak{F}_{0,1}(\Delta)$.

In the manner described above we associate with each $f \in \mathfrak{F}$ an $h \in \mathfrak{F}_{0,1}(\Delta)$. While h may not be unique, it can be chosen *uniquely* by requiring that $a = |a|e^{i\theta}$ have as small an argument θ as possible in the interval $0 \leq \theta < 2\pi$. The collection of functions h which arise will be denoted by $\mathcal{3C}$. By construction $\mathcal{3C} \subset \mathfrak{F}_{0,1}(\Delta)$, and therefore by Montel's theorem $\mathcal{3C}$ is normal.

Let us note as a consequence of Schwarz's lemma that the number a associated with an $f \in \mathfrak{F}$ is of absolute value at most 1. Indeed if f is one-to-one on Δ with $f(0) = 0$, and if $\Delta_{1+\epsilon} \subseteq f(\Delta)$ for some $\epsilon > 0$, then f^{-1}, being bounded by 1 on $\Delta_{1+\epsilon}$, has a derivative at 0 whose absolute value is less than $(1/(1 + \epsilon))$. It follows that $|f'(0)| \geq 1 + \epsilon$, and $f \notin \mathfrak{F}$.

Theorem 8.1. $\mathfrak{F}$ *is a normal family.*

Proof. If $\{f_n\}$ is a sequence from $\mathfrak{F}$ we let $\{h_n\}$ be the associated sequence from $\mathcal{3C}$. Since $\mathcal{3C}$ is normal, there exists a subsequence $\{h_{n_k}\}$ which converges locally uniformly on Δ, either to a finite limit or to ∞. Because $\lim_{k \to \infty} h_{n_k}(0) = -1$, the limit, which we denote by h, is finite.

Since $\{h_{n_k}\}$ converges locally uniformly to a finite limit, the sequence whose elements are $1 - h_{n_k}^2 = f_{n_k}/a_{n_k}$ must also converge to a finite limit. By Theorem 2.1 of Chapter 3 the sequence $\{f_{n_k}'/a_{n_k}\}$ of first derivatives converges locally uniformly (to a finite limit), and in particular

$$\lim_{k \to \infty} \frac{f_{n_k}'(0)}{a_{n_k}} = \lim_{k \to \infty} \frac{1}{a_{n_k}}$$

$$= \frac{1}{a}$$

exists and is finite. By the remark preceding the lemma $|a| \leq 1$. It now follows from the convergence of $\{a_{n_k}\}$ to a and the local uniform convergence of $\{f_{n_k}/a_{n_k}\}$ that $\{f_{n_k}\}$ converges locally uniformly on Δ. Therefore $\mathfrak{F}$ is normal, and the theorem is proved.

REMARK. If f is the limit of the sequence $\{f_{n_k}\}$ above, then $f(0) = 0$ and $f'(0) = 1$. By the second equation f is not constant, and therefore Theorem 3.3 of Chapter 3 implies f is one-to-one. Thus $f \in \mathfrak{F}$; $\mathfrak{F}$ is "closed" under local uniform convergence.

The following lemma is the basis of the Koebe-Faber distortion theorem. The constant a whose existence is asserted is *Koebe's constant;* its actual value is $\frac{1}{4}$, as was proved by Bieberbach.

Lemma 8.1. There exists an absolute constant $a > 0$ such that for each $f \in \mathfrak{F}$, $\Delta_a \subseteq f(\Delta)$.

Proof. If the lemma were false there would exist for each $n > 0$ an $f_n \in \mathfrak{F}$, such that the number a_n defined above has absolute value less than $1/n$. However by the proof of Theorem 8.1 there exists a subsequence of $\{a_n\}$ which does not converge to 0. This is a contradiction, and the lemma follows from it.

Definition 8.1. Let a be the *largest* number such that $\Delta_a \subseteq \bigcap_{f \in \mathfrak{F}} f(\Delta)$. (It can be shown that $a = \frac{1}{4}$ and $\Delta_a = \bigcap_{f \in \mathfrak{F}} f(\Delta)$. An $f \in \mathfrak{F}$ for which $a = \frac{1}{4}$ is $f(z) = z/(1 + e^{i\theta}z)^2$.) We refer to a as *Koebe's constant*.

REMARK. If f is any one-to-one analytic function on Δ, then $g(z) = (f(z)/f'(0)) - (f(0)/f'(0))$ defines an element of $\mathfrak{F}$. Since $g(\Delta)$ contains Δ_a, the region $f(\Delta)$ must contain the disk of radius $|f'(0)| \cdot a$ about $f(0)$. Using this observation we shall prove the *Koebe-Faber distortion theorem*.

If $f \in \mathfrak{F}$, and if $w = f(z) \in f(\Delta)$, denote by $d(w)$ the distance from w to the boundary of $f(\Delta)$. By Section 8 of Chapter 3 we have

$$|f'(z)| \geq \frac{d(w)}{1 - |z|^2}.$$

We now prove

Theorem 8.2. (Koebe-Faber Distortion Theorem) *Let a be the absolute constant of Definition* 8.1. *If $f \in \mathfrak{F}$, and if $f(z) = w$, then*

$$(8.1) \qquad |f'(z)| \leq \frac{1}{a}\frac{d(w)}{1 - |z|^2}.$$

Proof. Let $T\zeta = (\zeta + z)/(1 + \bar{z}\zeta)$, and define $h(\zeta) = f(T\zeta)$. By the remark above, $h(\Delta)$ contains the disk of radius $|h'(0)| \cdot a$ about $h(0) = f(z)$. What is the same thing $f(\Delta)$ contains the disk of radius $(1 - |z|^2)|f'(z)| \cdot a$ about $f(z)$, meaning by definition that $d(w) \geq (1 - |z|^2)|f'(z)| \cdot a$, or

$$|f'(z)| \leq \frac{1}{a}\frac{d(w)}{1 - |z|^2}$$

as was to be proved.

We will pursue (8.1) a bit further. If $f \in \mathfrak{F}$, we have already observed that $d(0) \leq 1$. Therefore, if $w = f(z)$, $d(w) \leq 1 + |w|$. Letting $|dw| =$

$|f'(z)| \, |dz|$ and substituting this last inequality in (8.1) yields

$$(8.2) \qquad \frac{|dw|}{1 + |w|} \leq \frac{1}{a} \frac{|dz|}{1 - |z|^2} \qquad (w = f(z)).$$

We fix $z_0 \in \Delta$ and $w_0 = f(z_0)$ and let γ be the radius from 0 to z_0. Then if $\eta = f(\gamma)$, (8.2) implies

$$\int_\eta \frac{|dw|}{1 + |w|} \leq \frac{1}{a} \int_\gamma \frac{|dz|}{1 - |z|^2}$$

$$= \frac{1}{a} d(0, z_0).$$

The left side is at least as large as $\ln(1 + |w_0|)$. Therefore, we have

$$(8.3) \qquad \ln(1 + |w_0|) \leq \frac{1}{a} \frac{1}{2} \ln \frac{1 + |z_0|}{1 - |z_0|}.$$

We now will *assume it known* that $a = \frac{1}{4}$. Doing so and exponentiating (8.3) gives rise to the inequality

$$1 + |w_0| \leq \left(\frac{1 + |z_0|}{1 - |z_0|} \right)^2$$

or

$$(8.4) \qquad |w_0| \leq \frac{4|z_0|}{(1 - |z_0|)^2}.$$

Define $M_{\mathfrak{F}}(r) = \sup_{f \in \mathfrak{F}} \max_{|z| = r} |f(z)|$. As a consequence of (8.4) we have

Theorem 8.3.

$$M_{\mathfrak{F}}(r) \leq \frac{4r}{(1 - r)^2}.$$

Problems

1. Let f be one-to-one and analytic on Δ. If $|f'(0)| = \alpha$, then

$$\max_{|z| = r} |f(z)| \leq |f(0)| + \frac{4\alpha r}{(1 - r)^2}.$$

2. Prove that $f(z) = z/(1 - z)^2$ belongs to $\mathfrak{F}$, and observe that $-\frac{1}{4} \notin f(\Delta)$.
3. Let f be one-to-one and analytic on Δ with $f(0) = 0$. If $1 \notin f(\Delta)$, then $|f'(0)| \leq 4$. (Assume $a = \frac{1}{4}$.)
4. If $0 < \alpha < \infty$, define $\mathfrak{F}_\alpha$ to be the collection of one-to-one mappings of Δ such that $f(0) = 0$ and $|f'(0)| \leq \alpha$. Prove that $\mathfrak{F}_\alpha$ is locally bounded and hence normal.

9. Bloch's Theorem

From Theorem 8.2 follows a remarkable theorem of Bloch. We will state this theorem after a preliminary lemma.

Lemma 9.1. Let f be analytic on a disk U centered at a point z_0. Suppose the inequality

$$(9.1) \qquad |f'(z) - f'(z_0)| < |f'(z_0)|$$

holds on U. Then f is one-to-one on U.

Proof. It will suffice to prove $|f(z_2) - f(z_1)| > 0$ for $z_1 \neq z_2$. To this end let γ be the line segment joining z_1 to z_2. The quantity $|f(z_2) - f(z_1)|$ is given by $\left| \int_\gamma f'(\zeta) \, d\zeta \right|$. Therefore by the triangle inequality

$$
\begin{aligned}
(9.2) \quad |f(z_2) - f(z_1)| &= \left| \int_\gamma \{f'(\zeta) - f'(z_0) + f'(z_0)\} \, d\zeta \right| \\
&\geq |(z_2 - z_1)f'(z_0)| - \int_\gamma |f'(\zeta) - f'(z_0)| \, |d\zeta|.
\end{aligned}
$$

Using (9.1) the integral in the second line of (9.2) is strictly less than $|f'(z_0)| \, |z_2 - z_1|$. Therefore $|f(z_2) - f(z_1)| > 0$ which was to be proved.

In what follows a will denote Koebe's constant, defined in Section 8.

Theorem 9.1. (Bloch) *Let f be analytic on Δ_s for some $s > 1$, and suppose $f'(0) = 1$. If $b = a/6$, there exists a disk U in Δ upon which f is one-to-one, such that $f(U)$ contains a disk of radius b.*

Proof. Define for $0 \leq r \leq 1$, $\psi(r) = \max_{|z|=r} |f'(z)|$. Naturally, ψ is continuous, as is $\varphi(r) = (1 - r)\psi(r)$. Since $\varphi(0) = 1$ and $\varphi(1) = 0$, there exists a number r_0 such that $\varphi(r_0) = 1$ and $\varphi(r) < 1$ for $r > r_0$.

Choose z_0, $|z_0| = r_0$, such that $|f'(z_0)| = 1/(1 - r_0)$. This is possible because $\varphi(r_0) = 1$. Then let U_0 be the disk of radius $\rho_0 = (1 - r_0)/2$

about z_0. Since $U_0 \subset \Delta_{(1+r_0)/2}$, the maximum principle implies $|f'(z)| \leq \psi((1+r_0)/2)$, $z \in U_0$. Since $r_0 < (1+r_0)/2$, the choice of r_0 in turn implies

$$\psi\left(\frac{1+r_0}{2}\right) < \frac{1}{1-(1+r_0)/2}$$

$$= \frac{1}{\rho_0}.$$

Therefore if $z \in U_0$,

$$|f'(z) - f'(z_0)| < |f'(z)| + |f'(z_0)|$$

$$\leq \frac{1}{\rho_0} + \frac{1}{2\rho_0}$$

$$= \frac{3}{2\rho_0}.$$

We apply Schwarz's lemma to obtain

(9.3) $$|f'(z) - f'(z_0)| \leq \frac{|z - z_0|}{\rho_0} \cdot \frac{3}{2\rho_0}$$

for $z \in U_0$.

Let U be the disk of radius $\rho = \rho_0/3$ about z_0. If $z \in U$, then by (9.3)

$$|f'(z) - f'(z_0)| < \frac{1}{2\rho_0}$$

$$= |f'(z_0)|.$$

By Lemma 9.1, f is one-to-one on U.

Define $g(z) = f(z_0 + \rho z)$, $z \in \Delta$. Since g is one-to-one on Δ, $g(\Delta)$ contains the disk of radius $a|g'(0)| = a\rho|f'(z_0)|$ about $f(z_0)$. By definition $\rho|f'(z_0)| = \frac{1}{6}$, and therefore $g(\Delta)$ contains the disk of radius $a/6$ about $f(z_0)$. What is the same thing, $f(U)$ contains the disk of radius $a/6$ about $f(z_0)$. The theorem is proved.

If f is analytic on Δ with $f'(0) = 1$, then for each α, $0 < \alpha < 1$, $f_\alpha(z) = f(\alpha z)/\alpha$ satisfies the hypotheses of Theorem 9.1. Therefore, there exists a disk U in Δ upon which f_α is one-to-one such that $f_\alpha(U)$ contains a disk of radius $a/6$. What is the same, $f(\alpha U) = \{f(z) \mid z = \alpha\zeta, \zeta \in U\}$ contains a disk of radius $\alpha a/6$. Thus if $b < a/6$, Theorem 9.1 holds for f analytic on Δ with b replacing $a/6$.

Definition 9.1.   Let B be the largest number such that if $b < B$, and if f is analytic on Δ with $f'(0) = 1$, then there exists $U \subset \Delta$ upon which f is one-to-one such that $f(U)$ contains a disk of radius b. B is called *Bloch's constant.*

The exact value of B is unknown. By our arguments $B \geq a/6 (= 1/24)$.

Problem

1. Let $f(z) = z + a_2 z^2 + \cdots$ be analytic on Δ. If $\displaystyle\sum_{2}^{\infty} n|a_n| < 1$, then f is one-to-one on Δ.

chapter 5

The Hadamard Product Theorem

1. Infinite Products

Of central importance in the chapter to follow is the representation of a nonconstant entire function as a product, $f = Ph$, of entire functions P and h. The zeros of P coincide with those of f, while h, defined in terms of f/P, has no zeros. The representation is extremely useful, one reason being that the construction of P depends only upon the zeros of f.

The initial sections of the chapter are devoted to a discussion of infinite products, first of complex numbers, then of analytic functions. Later on, the factor P mentioned above will be defined as an infinite product.

If $\{\alpha_n\}$ is a sequence of complex numbers, a naive definition for convergence of the product of these numbers would require simply that the limit

(1.1)
$$\lim_{N \to \infty} \prod_{n=1}^{N} \alpha_n = \alpha$$

exist. Such a definition is inadequate, primarily for the following two reasons:

(a) The limit (1.1) can be zero without any of the terms α_n being zero (e.g., $\alpha_n = 1/n$). One desires of an infinite product that, as for a finite product, it vanish only if one of its factors does.

(b) If one factor happens to be zero, the product converges regardless of the other factors. A "correct" definition of convergence should prevent such a situation from occurring. *Convergence ought to depend on all of the factors* (or at least all but finitely many).

152

For a subtler approach we shall consider the situation for infinite series. Cauchy's criterion for the series $\sum_{n=1}^{\infty} a_n$ says that $\sum_{n=1}^{\infty} a_n = \lim_{N \to \infty} \sum_{n=1}^{N} a_n$ exists if, and only if, there is for every $\epsilon > 0$ an integer N such that $\left| \sum_{n=n_1}^{n_2} a_n \right| < \epsilon$ whenever $n_2 \geq n_1 \geq N$.

Suppose $\alpha_n = e^{a_n}$ for each n. Then *formally* the product $\prod_{n=1}^{\infty} \alpha_n$ is equal to the exponential $e^{\sum_{n=1}^{\infty} a_n}$, and the exponential is meaningful if $\sum_{n=1}^{\infty} a_n$ exists. Supposing this is so, we apply Cauchy's criterion and the inequality $|e^z - 1| \leq e^\epsilon - 1$, valid for $|z| \leq \epsilon$, to obtain the condition: For every $\epsilon > 0$ there exists an integer N such that if $n_2 \geq n_1 \geq N$, then

$$(1.2) \qquad \left| \prod_{n=n_1}^{n_2} \alpha_n - 1 \right| = \left| e^{\sum_{n=n_1}^{n_2} a_n} - 1 \right|$$
$$\leq e^\epsilon - 1.$$

REMARK. Equation (1.2) does not imply that $\sum_{n=1}^{\infty} a_n$ exists. (For example take $a_n = 2\pi i$ for each n.) However, with an appropriate convention (which in the latter example says take $a_n = 0$ instead of $2\pi i$) convergence of the product and the sum will be seen to be equivalent.

Definition 1.1. The product of an infinite sequence $\{\alpha_n\}$ is *convergent* if for each $\epsilon > 0$ there is an integer N such that

$$(1.3) \qquad \left| \prod_{n=n_1}^{n_2} \alpha_n - 1 \right| < \epsilon$$

for $n_2 \geq n_1 \geq N$.

For a convergent product $\lim_{n \to \infty} \alpha_n = 1$. To see this simply let $n_2 = n_1 = n$ in (1.3). Therefore at most finitely many of the terms α_n can be zero. Just as $\lim_{n \to \infty} a_n = 0$ is necessary but not sufficient for the convergence of $\sum_{n=1}^{\infty} a_n$, the condition $\lim_{n \to \infty} \alpha_n = 1$ is necessary but not sufficient for the existence of the infinite product. For example, take $\alpha_n = e^{a_n}$ where $\{a_n\}$ is such that $\lim\limits_{n \to \infty} a_n = 0$ but $\sum\limits_{n=1}^{\infty} a_n$ does not exist.

As yet no value has been defined for the product of infinitely many numbers. The most natural value to take is that given by (1.1), provided the limit exists. As we will see shortly, the limit does exist, and so we define the *value* of a convergent infinite product to be the quantity (1.1).

Theorem 1.1.   *The product of a sequence $\{\alpha_n\}$ is convergent if, and only if,*

$$\text{(1.4)} \qquad \alpha^{(m)} = \lim_{N \to \infty} \prod_{n=m}^{N} \alpha_n$$

exists and is nonzero for at least one value of m.

REMARK.   If $\alpha^{(m)}$ exists, then so will $\alpha^{(k)}$ for $k \leq m$. In particular (1.1) will exist. If $\alpha^{(m)}$ exists and $\alpha^{(m)} \neq 0$, then $\alpha^{(n)}$ exists and is not zero for $n \geq m$. In fact, if $n = m + k$, then

$$\text{(1.5)} \qquad \alpha^{(m+k)} = \frac{\alpha^{(m)}}{\alpha_m \alpha_{m+1} \, \cdots \, \alpha_{m+k-1}}.$$

It follows from (1.5) and (1.4) that

$$\lim_{n \to \infty} \alpha^{(n)} = \frac{\alpha^{(m)}}{\alpha^{(m)}} = 1.$$

Proof of Theorem 1.1.   Suppose $\alpha^{(m)}$ exists and $\alpha^{(m)} \neq 0$. Given $\epsilon > 0$ fix $\delta > 0$ with $2\delta/(1 - \delta) < \epsilon$. By the remark preceding, there exists an integer N such that if $n \geq N$, then $|\alpha^{(n)} - 1| < \delta$. If $n_2 \geq n_1 \geq N$, the last inequality taken with (1.5) implies

$$\left| \prod_{n=n_1}^{n_2} \alpha_n - 1 \right| = \left| \frac{\alpha^{(n_1)}}{\alpha^{(n_2+1)}} - 1 \right|$$

$$= \left| \frac{1}{\alpha^{(n_2+1)}} \right| \left| \alpha^{(n_1)} - \alpha^{(n_2+1)} \right|$$

$$\leq \frac{2\delta}{1 - \delta}$$

$$< \epsilon.$$

The condition of Definition 1.1 being satisfied, the product is convergent.

Suppose conversely that $\prod_{n=1}^{\infty} \alpha_n$ is convergent. Taking $\epsilon = \frac{1}{2}$ in Definition 1.1 there exists an integer N such that

$$\left| \prod_{n=n^-}^{n_2} \alpha_n - 1 \right| < \frac{1}{2}$$

or

(1.6)
$$\frac{1}{2} < \left| \prod_{n=n_1}^{n_2} \alpha_n \right| < \frac{3}{2}$$

if $n_2 \geq n_1 \geq N$. The claim is that $\alpha^{(N)}$ exists. If so, $\alpha^{(N)} \neq 0$, because by (1.6), $|\alpha^{(N)}| \geq \frac{1}{2}$. Given $\epsilon > 0$ select $M \geq N$ in such a way that

$$\left| \prod_{n=n_1}^{n_2} \alpha_n - 1 \right| < \epsilon$$

for $n_2 \geq n_1 \geq M$. For such n_1, n_2, (1.6) and our choice of M give rise to the inequality

$$\left| \prod_{n=N}^{n_1} \alpha_n - \prod_{n=N}^{n_2} \alpha_n \right| = \left| \prod_{n=N}^{n_1} \alpha_n \right| \left| 1 - \prod_{n=n_1+1}^{n_2} \alpha_n \right|$$
$$< \frac{3\epsilon}{2}$$

implying that $\alpha^{(N)}$ exists.

If $\prod_{n=1}^{\infty} \alpha_n$ is convergent, then for some N, $\alpha^{(N)}$ exists and is nonzero. Therefore,

$$\alpha = \lim_{M \to \infty} \prod_{n=1}^{M} \alpha_n$$
$$= \lim_{M \to \infty} \prod_{n=1}^{N-1} \alpha_n \prod_{n=N}^{M} \alpha_n$$
$$= \left(\prod_{n=1}^{N-1} \alpha_n \right) \alpha^{(N)}$$

exists. From this we conclude that α, *the value of a convergent infinite product, can be zero only if one of the terms is zero.*

If $\alpha = \prod_{n=1}^{\infty} \alpha_n$ is the value of a convergent product, and if $\alpha \neq 0$, then formally we have the equality

(1.7)
$$\log \alpha = \log \prod_{n=1}^{\infty} \alpha_n$$
$$= \sum_{n=1}^{\infty} \log \alpha_n.$$

Indeed it was in moving from right to left in (1.7) that we were led to Definition 1.1. The difficulty in establishing (1.7) rigorously lies with the definition of the logarithm.

In what follows the expression "$\log z$" ($z \neq 0$) denotes the unique value of the logarithm whose imaginary part (arg z) satisfies $-\pi \leq \arg z < \pi$. For future reference we note that if $\log_1 z$ is any value of the logarithm, then

(1.8)
$$|\log z| \leq |\log_1 z|.$$

Theorem 1.2. *The infinite product $\prod_{n=1}^{\infty} \alpha_n$ is convergent if, and only if, there exists an integer m such that $\sum_{n=m}^{\infty} \log \alpha_n$ exists.*

Proof. If $\sum_{n=m}^{\infty} \log \alpha_n$ exists, then

$$\alpha^{(m)} = \lim_{N \to \infty} \prod_{n=m}^{N} \alpha_n$$
$$= \lim_{N \to \infty} e^{\sum_{n=m}^{N} \log \alpha_n}$$
$$= e^{\sum_{n=m}^{\infty} \log \alpha_n}$$

exists and is not zero. Therefore by Theorem 1.1, $\prod_{n=1}^{\infty} \alpha_n$ is convergent.

Conversely, suppose $\prod_{n=1}^{\infty} \alpha_n$ is convergent. By Theorem 1.1 $\alpha^{(m)}$ exists and is nonzero for some m. Fixing a value of arg $\alpha^{(m)}$, define Log z for each $z \neq 0$ to be the unique value of the logarithm for which

$$\arg \alpha^{(m)} - \pi \leq \arg z < \arg \alpha^{(m)} + \pi.$$

Since Log z is continuous at $z = \alpha^{(m)}$, and since log z is continuous at $z = 1$, we have

$$\lim_{N \to \infty} \text{Log} \prod_{n=m}^{N} \alpha_n = \text{Log } \alpha^{(m)}$$

and

$$\lim_{N \to \infty} \log \alpha_N = \log 1$$
$$= 0.$$

Now both $\text{Log} \left(\prod_{n=m}^{N} \alpha_n \right)$ and $\sum_{n=m}^{N} \log \alpha_n$ are solutions to the equation $e^z = \prod_{n=m}^{N} \alpha_n$. Therefore, there exists an integer β_N such that

(1.9)
$$\sum_{n=m}^{N} \log \alpha_n = \text{Log} \prod_{n=m}^{N} \alpha_n + 2\pi i \beta_N.$$

Let N be so large that the inequalities

$$|\log \alpha_n| < \frac{\pi}{2} \quad n \geq N$$

and

$$\left| \text{Log} \prod_{n=m}^{n_1} \alpha_n - \text{Log} \prod_{n=m}^{n_2} \alpha_n \right| < \frac{\pi}{2}, \quad n_1, n_2 \geq N$$

hold. From these, (1.9), and the triangle inequality follows

$$2\pi|\beta_{M+1} - \beta_M| = \left| \log \alpha_{M+1} + \text{Log} \prod_{n=m}^{M} \alpha_n - \text{Log} \prod_{n=m}^{M+1} \alpha_n \right|$$

$$\leq |\log \alpha_{M+1}| + \left| \text{Log} \prod_{n=m}^{M} \alpha_n - \text{Log} \prod_{n=m}^{M+1} \alpha_n \right|$$

$$< \frac{\pi}{2} + \frac{\pi}{2} = \pi$$

if $M \geq N$. Thus $|\beta_{M+1} - \beta_M| < \frac{1}{2}$ for $M \geq N$, meaning $\beta_M \equiv \beta_N$ for $M \geq N$. Therefore the limit of each term on the right-hand side of (1.9) exists as $N \to \infty$, and from this fact it follows that $\sum_{n=m}^{\infty} \log \alpha_n$ exists. This completes the proof.

In analogy with infinite series we introduce the following notion of absolute convergence for a product.

Definition 1.2. The infinite product $\prod_{n=1}^{\infty} \alpha_n$ *converges absolutely* if $\prod_{m=1}^{\infty} \beta_m$ is convergent for any rearrangement $\beta_m = \alpha_{n_m}$ of $\{\alpha_n\}$.

A convergent *series* $\sum_{n=1}^{\infty} a_n$ is absolutely convergent if $\sum_{m=1}^{\infty} b_m$ is convergent for any rearrangement $b_m = a_{n_m}$ of $\{a_n\}$. This is equivalent with the finiteness of the sum $\sum_{n=1}^{\infty} |a_n|$.

If $\prod_{n=1}^{\infty} \alpha_n$ is convergent, let m be such that $\alpha^{(m)} \neq 0$. Since $\prod_{n=m}^{\infty} \alpha_n$ omits at most finitely many terms, the product $\alpha = \prod_{n=1}^{\infty} \alpha_n$ converges absolutely if, and only if, $\alpha^{(m)}$ does. By Theorem 1.2 a necessary and sufficient condition for the absolute convergence of $\alpha^{(m)}$ is the existence of the infinite sum $\sum_{k=1}^{\infty} \log \beta_k$ where $\beta_k = \alpha_{n_k}$ is any rearrangement of $\alpha_m, \alpha_{m+1}, \ldots$.

In other words, absolute convergence of the series $\sum_{n=m}^{\infty} \log \alpha_n$ is equivalent with the absolute convergence of $\alpha^{(m)}$ and hence of α.

In the following theorem we associate with the given sequence $\{\alpha_n\}$ a sequence $\{a_n\}$, where for each n, $\alpha_n = 1 + a_n$.

Theorem 1.3. *The product* $\displaystyle\prod_{n=1}^{\infty} \alpha_n$ *is absolutely convergent if, and only*

if, the sum $\displaystyle\sum_{n=m}^{\infty} |\log \alpha_n|$ *is finite for some m. This is equivalent to saying that*

$\displaystyle\sum_{n=1}^{\infty} |a_n|$ *should be finite.*

Proof. The first statement has already been proved. Let $\log(1 + z)$ be the branch of the logarithm on $|z| < 1$ with $\log 1 = 0$. By definition of the derivative at $z = 0$,

$$\lim_{z \to 0} \frac{\log(1 + z)}{z} = 1.$$

Therefore, given $\epsilon > 0$ ($\epsilon < 1$), there is a $\delta > 0$ such that if $|z| \le \delta$, then

$$(1 - \epsilon) \le \left| \frac{\log(1 + z)}{z} \right| \le 1 + \epsilon$$

or

$$(1.10) \qquad (1 - \epsilon)|z| \le |\log(1 + z)| \le (1 + \epsilon)|z|.$$

Now fix any such ϵ, δ. (Say, $\epsilon = \frac{1}{2}$.) If $\displaystyle\sum_{n=1}^{\infty} |a_n| < \infty$, then $|a_n| \le \delta$ for all large n, say, for all $n \ge m$. By the right-hand inequality of (1.10), $\displaystyle\sum_{n=m}^{\infty} |\log(1 + a_n)| < \infty$. Conversely, if $\displaystyle\sum_{n=m}^{\infty} |\log(1 + a_n)| < \infty$, the left-hand inequality of (1.10) implies $\displaystyle\sum_{n=1}^{\infty} |a_n| < \infty$.

REMARK. If $\alpha = \displaystyle\prod_{n=1}^{\infty} \alpha_n$ is absolutely convergent, then for any re-arrangement, $\beta_m = \alpha_{n_m}$, we claim

$$\alpha = \prod_{m=1}^{\infty} \beta_m.$$

If $\alpha = 0$, the statement is trivial since one of the terms is zero. If $\alpha \ne 0$, then due to the absolute convergence of $\displaystyle\sum_{n=1}^{\infty} \log \alpha_n$, we have

$$\alpha = \prod_{n=1}^{\infty} \alpha_n$$

$$= e^{\displaystyle\sum_{n=1}^{\infty} \log \alpha_n}$$

$$= e^{\displaystyle\sum_{m=1}^{\infty} \log \beta_m}$$

$$= \prod_{m=1}^{\infty} \beta_m$$

as claimed.

Problems

1. For each sequence below, determine the convergence or divergence of $\displaystyle\prod_{n=1}^{\infty} \alpha_n$.

   (a) $\alpha_n = 1 - \dfrac{1}{n+1}.$

   (b) $\alpha_n = 1 - \dfrac{1}{n^2+1}.$

   (c) $\alpha_n = \cos \pi n.$

   (d) $\alpha_n = \cos \dfrac{\pi}{n}.$

   (e) $\alpha_n = e^{2\pi i n}.$

2. Show that

   (a) $(1 - \frac{1}{4})(1 - \frac{1}{9})(1 - \frac{1}{16}) \cdots$ converges absolutely.

   (b) $(1 - \frac{1}{2})(1 + \frac{1}{2})(1 - \frac{1}{3})(1 + \frac{1}{3})(1 - \frac{1}{4}) \cdots$ converges, but not absolutely.

   (c) $\displaystyle\prod_{m=1}^{\infty} \left(1 - \frac{1}{m}\right) e^{1/m}$ converges absolutely.

3. For each z, let $P(z) = \displaystyle\prod_{\substack{n=-\infty \\ n\neq 0}}^{\infty} \left(1 - \frac{z}{n}\right) e^{z/n}$.

(a) Prove absolute convergence for each z.

(b) Prove $\displaystyle\lim_{k\to\infty} \prod_{n=-k}^{n=2k} \left(1 - \frac{z}{n}\right) = 2^{-z}P(z)$.

(c) Suppose $i_k \geq j_k > 0$ are such that $\displaystyle\lim_{k\to\infty} j_k = \infty$ and $\displaystyle\lim_{k\to\infty} i_k/j_k = \tau$. Prove

$$\lim_{k\to\infty} \prod_{n=-j_k}^{i_k} \left(1 - \frac{z}{n}\right) = \tau^{-z}P(z).$$

4. Let $\{a_n\}$ be a sequence of complex numbers such that $\displaystyle\sum_{n=1}^{\infty} |a_n| < \infty$. Let f be an analytic function on an open neighborhood U of 0 with $f(0) = 1$, and suppose $\{a_n\} \subset U$. Prove $\displaystyle\prod_{n=1}^{\infty} f(a_n)$ exists.

5. Let p_n denote the nth prime. Prove $\displaystyle\prod_{n=1}^{\infty} (1 - (1/p_n^2))^{-1}$ converges and that

$$\prod_{n=1}^{\infty} \left(1 - \frac{1}{p_n^2}\right)^{-1} = \sum_{m=1}^{\infty} \frac{1}{m^2}.$$

6. Let $\{a_n\}$ be a sequence of real numbers of absolute value less than 1.

(a) Note that $-\log(1 - a_n) = a_n + a_n^2 g(a_n)$, where g is continuous (indeed analytic) in a neighborhood of 0, and $g(0) = \frac{1}{2}$.

(b) If $\displaystyle\sum_{n=1}^{\infty} a_n$ is convergent, then $\displaystyle\prod_{n=1}^{\infty} (1 - a_n)$ is convergent if, and only if, $\displaystyle\sum_{n=1}^{\infty} a_n^2 < \infty$.

(c) Let $b_1 > b_2 > b_3 > \cdots$ be a sequence of real numbers decreasing to 0. Prove $\prod\limits_{n=1}^{\infty} (1 + (-1)^n b_n)$ is convergent if, and only if,

$\sum\limits_{n=1}^{\infty} b_n{}^2 < \infty$. (HINT: Prove $\sum\limits_{n=1}^{\infty} (-1)^n b_n$ is a convergent sum.)

7. Discuss the range of α's, $0 < \alpha < \infty$, for which the following products are divergent, convergent, and absolutely convergent.

$$P = \prod_{n=1}^{\infty} \left(1 + \frac{(-1)^n}{n^\alpha}\right).$$

2. Products of Functions

In the products to be considered the numbers α_n will depend analytically on the variable z. Usually $\alpha_n = \alpha_n(z)$ will be entire for each n, and writing $\alpha_n(z) = 1 + a_n(z)$ it will be assumed that the series $\sum\limits_{n=1}^{\infty} |a_n(z)|$ converges uniformly on every finite disk. For fixed z it follows from Theorem 1.3 that the product

$$(2.1) \qquad P(z) = \prod_{n=1}^{\infty} \alpha_n(z)$$

is absolutely convergent. Letting z vary it will develop that $P(z)$ is itself an entire function.

Our assumption on the sequence $\{a_n(z)\}$ is sufficient to guarantee for every R, $0 \leq R < \infty$, that

$$(2.2) \qquad M_R = \sup_{|z| \leq R} \sum_{n=1}^{\infty} |a_n(z)|$$

be finite. For each N define $P_N(z) = \prod\limits_{n=1}^{N} \alpha_n(z)$. Since $|1 + a_n(z)| \leq e^{|a_n(z)|}$ for all n and z, if follows from (2.2) that if $|z| \leq R$, then

$$\max_{|z| \leq R} |P_N(z)| \leq \max_{|z| \leq R} e^{\sum_{n=1}^{N} |a_n(z)|}$$
$$= e^{M_R}.$$

The family $\{P_N\}$ is therefore locally bounded, and of course for each z

$\lim\limits_{N \to \infty} P_N(z) = P(z)$. From Vitali's theorem, Theorem 5.1 of Chapter 4, follows

Theorem 2.1. *Let $\{\alpha_n(z)\}$ be a sequence of entire functions for which (2.2) holds. Then*

$$(2.3) \qquad P_N(z) = \prod_{n=1}^{N} \alpha_n(z)$$

converges locally uniformly to an entire function $P(z)$. $P(z)$ vanishes at a point z_0 if, and only if, $\alpha_n(z_0) = 0$ for some n.

REMARK. It follows that $P(z) \equiv 0$ only if $\alpha_n(z) \equiv 0$ for some n. The reader should convince himself on this point.

REMARK. The reader should also verify that $\sum\limits_{n=1}^{\infty} |a_n(z)|$ converges uniformly for $|z| \leq R$, if, and only if, for some m, the sum $\sum\limits_{n=m}^{\infty} |\log \alpha_n(z)|$ converges uniformly on the same set. This observation will be useful in succeeding sections.

If we differentiate both sides of (2.3), we obtain the relation

$$P_N'(z) = \alpha_1'(z) \prod_{n=2}^{N} \alpha_n(z) + \alpha_2'(z) \prod_{\substack{n=1 \\ n \neq 2}}^{N} \alpha_n(z) + \cdots + \alpha_n'(z) \prod_{n=1}^{N-1} \alpha_n(z)$$

which, if $P_N(z) \neq 0$, is equivalent to

$$(2.4) \qquad \begin{aligned} P_N'(z) &= \alpha_1'(z) \cdot \frac{P_N(z)}{\alpha_1(z)} + \alpha_2'(z) \frac{P_N(z)}{\alpha_2(z)} + \cdots + \alpha_N'(z) \frac{P_N(z)}{\alpha_N(z)} \\ &= P_N(z) \left\{ \frac{\alpha_1'(z)}{\alpha_1(z)} + \cdots + \frac{\alpha_N'(z)}{\alpha_N(z)} \right\}. \end{aligned}$$

For the logarithmic derivative we obtain the expression (for $P_N(z) \neq 0$)

$$(2.5) \qquad \frac{d}{dz} \log P_N(z) = \frac{P_N'(z)}{P_N(z)} = \frac{\alpha_1'(z)}{\alpha_1(z)} + \cdots + \frac{\alpha_N'(z)}{\alpha_N(z)}.$$

Since $\{P_N\}$ converges locally uniformly to P, the sequence $\{P_N'\}$ of derivatives converges locally uniformly to P'. Therefore, by (2.4) we have for $P(z) \neq 0$,

$$P'(z) = \lim_{N \to \infty} P_N'(z)$$

$$(2.6) \qquad = \lim_{N \to \infty} P_N(z) \left\{ \frac{\alpha_1'(z)}{\alpha_1(z)} + \cdots + \frac{\alpha_N'(z)}{\alpha_N(z)} \right\}$$

$$= P(z) \sum_{n=1}^{\infty} \frac{\alpha_n'(z)}{\alpha_n(z)}.$$

Similarly, $(d/dz) \log P(z)$ is given by

$$(2.7) \qquad \frac{P'(z)}{P(z)} = \sum_{n=1}^{\infty} \frac{\alpha_n'(z)}{\alpha_n(z)}$$

if $P(z) \neq 0$.

Problems

1. Assume for nonintegral z the formula

$$\pi \cot \pi z = \lim_{m \to \infty} \sum_{n=-m}^{m} \frac{1}{z-n}.$$

Define a function $P(z)$ by

$$P(z) = z \prod_{n \neq 0} \left(1 - \frac{z}{n} \right) e^{z/n}.$$

(a) Verify that P is an entire function.
(b) Show that there is an entire function g such that

$$\sin \pi z = e^{g(z)} P(z)$$

holds for all z.
(c) Evaluate $((d/dz) \sin \pi z)/(\sin \pi z)$ in terms of g, P (or more precisely, the factors of P).
(d) Prove that $P(z) = (\sin \pi z)/\pi$.

2. Given complex numbers $a_1, \ldots, a_n$ show that

$$|1 - (1 + a_1)(1 + a_2) \cdots (1 + a_n)| \leq e^{|a_1| + \cdots + |a_n|} - 1.$$

3. Use Problem 2 and the assumption that $\Sigma|a_n(z)|$ converges uniformly on Δ_R to show that

$$\lim_{N \to \infty} P_N(z) = \prod_{n=1}^{N} (1 + a_n(z))$$

exists uniformly on Δ_R.

4. For which of the following sequences $\{a_n(z)\}$ is the product

$$\prod_{n=1}^{\infty} (1 + a_n(z))$$

convergent to an entire function $P(z)$?

(a) $a_n(z) = q^n z, \ |q| < 1.$

(b) $a_n(z) = \dfrac{z}{\log(n + 1)}.$

(c) $a_n(z) = \dfrac{z}{(n + 1)\log^2(n + 1)}.$

3. The Weierstrass Product Theorem

We associate with an arbitrary entire function f, $f \not\equiv 0$, an integer $k \geq 0$ and a sequence (empty, finite, or infinite) $\{z_n\}$ whose descriptions follow. At $z = 0$, f has a zero of order k, where if $f(0) \neq 0$, $k = 0$. The sequence $\{z_n\}$ is composed of the zeros of f distinct from $z = 0$. If f has a zero of order $m > 0$ at $z \ (\neq 0)$, then z should occur exactly m times among the $\{z_n\}$. By the uniqueness theorem $\{z_n\}$ has no finite point of accumulation, meaning that unless the sequence is finite or empty, $\lim_{n \to \infty} z_n = \infty$. We will sometimes arrange matters so that $|z_1| \leq |z_2| \leq \cdots$.

The above paragraph describes the simplest properties of the zeros of an entire function. The "problem of Weierstrass" asks for which integers k and sequences $\{z_n\}$ can one find an entire function f such that k and $\{z_n\}$ describe the zeros of f? If $\{z_n\}$ is empty or finite, and if $k \geq 0$, then

(3.1) $$f(z) = z^k \prod (z - z_n)$$

solves the problem. If $\{z_n\}$ is infinite, the product (3.1) cannot possibly converge. The difficulty with (3.1) for infinite sequences will be resolved by replacing $z - z_n$ with an appropriate entire function $\alpha_n(z)$ and then using Theorem 2.1.

Assume now that $\{z_n\}$ is an infinite sequence with $\lim_{n \to \infty} z_n = \infty$. We wish to represent $P(z)$, a function whose zeros are described by k and $\{z_n\}$, as

$$(3.2) \qquad P(z) = z^k \prod_{n=1}^{\infty} \alpha_n(z).$$

If (3.2) is to fall in the class of products discussed in Section 2, it must be that $\lim_{n \to \infty} \alpha_n(z) = 1$ locally uniformly, and in fact $\sum_{n=1}^{\infty} |1 - \alpha_n(z)|$ must converge locally uniformly.

The first condition is satisfied by $\alpha_n(z) = 1 - z/z_n$, however the second may fail since $\sum_{n=1}^{\infty} |z/z_n|$ need not converge. For such a sequence it is necessary to introduce "convergence factors." That is, for each n, $1 - z/z_n$ is multiplied by a nonvanishing entire function which is chosen carefully to ensure that both conditions be satisfied.

Definition 3.1.   The *Weierstrass primary factor* $E(z, m)$ is

$$(3.3) \qquad E(z, m) = (1 - z)e^{z + z^2/2 + \cdots + z^m/m}.$$

Using (1.15) of Chapter 1 we represent for $|z| < 1$ the branch of $\log(1/(1 - z))$ which has $\log 1 = 0$ by the series

$$\log \frac{1}{1 - z} = \sum_{n=1}^{\infty} \frac{z^n}{n}.$$

In view of this relation it follows for each z, $|z| < 1$, that $\lim_{m \to \infty} E(z, m) = 1$.

If $|z| < 1$, a value of $\log E(z, m)$ is $- \sum_{n=1}^{\infty} z^{n+m}/(n + m)$, and according to (1.8) the absolute value of the branch of $\log E(z, m)$ whose imaginary part lies between $-\pi$ and π is at most $\left| -\sum_{n=1}^{\infty} \frac{z^{n+m}}{n+m} \right|$. Thus,

$$|\log E(z, m)| \leq \sum_{n=1}^{\infty} \frac{|z|^{n+m}}{n+m}$$

(3.4)
$$\leq \frac{|z|^{m+1}}{m+1} \sum_{n=0}^{\infty} |z|^n$$

$$= \frac{|z|^{m+1}}{m+1} \frac{1}{1-|z|}.$$

If $|z| \leq \frac{1}{2}$, inequality (3.4) implies

(3.5)
$$|\log E(z, m)| \leq 2|z|^{m+1}.$$

We now state the *Weierstrass product theorem*.

Theorem 3.1. *Let $k \geq 0$ and $\{z_n\}$ be as described earlier. There exists a sequence $\{m_n\}$ of positive integers (where $m_n = n$ will do) such that*

(3.6)
$$P(z) = z^k \prod_{n=1}^{\infty} E\left(\frac{z}{z_n}, m_n\right)$$

is entire (and $\not\equiv 0$).

Proof. Let $\{m_n\}$ be any sequence such that $\sum_{n=1}^{\infty} |R/z_n|^{m_n+1} < \infty$ for each $R < \infty$. (For example, take $m_n = n$. For each R, $|R/z_n| \leq \frac{1}{2}$ if n is sufficiently large, and so the sum is convergent.) If $|z| \leq R$, and if $|z_n| > 2R$, then (3.5) implies

$$\left| \log E\left(\frac{z}{z_n}, m_n\right) \right| \leq 2 \left| \frac{z}{z_n} \right|^{m_n+1}$$

$$\leq 2 \left| \frac{R}{z_n} \right|^{m_n+1}.$$

Therefore, $\sum_{|z_n|>R} |\log E(z/z_n, m_n)|$ converges uniformly for $|z| \leq R$. By the second remark following Theorem 2.1, $P(z)$ is entire (and $\not\equiv 0$), and the theorem is proved.

Given an entire function f, $f \not\equiv 0$, form $P(z)$ from the associated k and $\{z_n\}$. If $P(z) \neq 0$, then $h(z) = f(z)/P(z)$ is analytic. If z is a zero of f of order m, then z is a zero of P of order m and $h(z) = \lim\limits_{\substack{\zeta \to z \\ P(\zeta) \neq 0}} f(\zeta)/P(\zeta)$ defines h at z to be analytic. Now h is entire and never zero, so there is a single-valued branch $g(z) = \log h(z)$ of the logarithm. We obtain the factorization

$$f(z) = h(z) \cdot P(z)$$
(3.7)
$$= e^{g(z)} \cdot P(z)$$

valid for all z. Thus, the most general entire function has this form.

The representations (3.6) and (3.7) are canonical in form but not in fact. The only requirement on the sequence $\{m_n\}$ has been that $\sum\limits_{n=1}^{\infty} |R/z_n|^{m_n+1} < \infty$ for each R, and this leaves a wide range of possibilities for $\{m_n\}$. For any two such choices, it will be true of the associated products, P_1 and P_2, that

$$P_1(z) = e^{Q(z)} P_2(z)$$

for some entire function Q. This follows easily from the construction in (3.7) and will be left to the reader.

For some integer $m \geq 0$, it may be that the sum

(3.8)
$$\sum_{n=1}^{\infty} \frac{1}{|z_n|^{m+1}}$$

is finite. If this is so, and if m is the least such integer, then an honestly canonical choice of $P(z)$ is

$$P(z) = z^k \prod_{n=1}^{\infty} E\left(\frac{z}{z_n}, m\right).$$

This representation will appear in the context of "functions of finite order."

If $P(z)$ is given by (3.6), then taking equations (2.6) and (2.7) into account we have

$$P'(z) = P(z) \left\{ \sum_{n=1}^{\infty} \left(\frac{1}{z - z_n} + \frac{1}{z_n} + \frac{z}{z_n^2} + \cdots + \frac{z^{m_n-1}}{z_n^{m_n}} \right) + \frac{k}{z} \right\}$$

and

$$\frac{P'(z)}{P(z)} = \frac{k}{z} + \sum_{n=1}^{\infty} \left(\frac{1}{z - z_n} + \frac{1}{z_n} + \cdots + \frac{z^{m_n-1}}{z_n{}^{m_n}} \right)$$

if $P(z) \neq 0$.

Problems

1. Let f be a function which is meromorphic for all z. That is, f is assumed to be analytic except for isolated singularities which are either removable singularities or poles. Using the *Weierstrass product theorem* prove the following theorem: There exist entire functions g and h such that $f(z) = g(z)/h(z)$ whenever f is analytic. (HINT: First construct h from the poles of f, then define $g = f \cdot h$.)

The following two problems are themselves unrelated to infinite products.

2. Let f be meromorphic for all z.

   (a) If a is a pole of f, there is a polynomial $\sum_{q=1}^{n} c_q z^q = P_a(z) (c_n \neq 0)$ such that $f(z) - P_a(1/(z - a))$ has a removable singularity at $z = a$. What is this polynomial? The function $P_a(1/(z - a))$ is called the *principal part* of f at a.

   (b) If the sequence $\{(a_\nu, P_\nu(1/(z - a_\nu))\}$ of poles and principal parts of f is infinite, prove $\lim_{\nu \to \infty} a_\nu = \infty$.

3. (Theorem of Mittag-Leffler) Let there be given a sequence $\{a_\nu\}$ of distinct complex numbers and a sequence $P_\nu(z) = \sum_{q=1}^{n_\nu} c_q{}^\nu z^q, c_{n_\nu}{}^\nu \neq 0$, of polynomials. If $\lim_{\nu \to \infty} a_\nu = \infty$, there is a meromorphic function f with poles $\{a_\nu\}$ and principal parts $\{P_\nu(1/(z - a_\nu))\}$. (HINT:

   (a) First observe that the assumption $a_\nu \neq 0$ for any ν is no loss of generality.

   (b) The function $P_\nu(1/(z - a_\nu))$ is analytic for $|z| < |a_\nu|$. By considering the Taylor expansion of P_ν about the point $z = 0$, show that there is a polynomial $q_\nu(z)$ such that

$$\max_{|z| \le \frac{|a_\nu|}{2}} \left| P_\nu \left(\frac{1}{z - a_\nu} \right) - q_\nu(z) \right| < \frac{1}{2^\nu}.$$

(c) For each R, $0 < R < \infty$, there is an index ν_0 such that the sum

$$\sum_{\nu = \nu_0}^{\infty} \left\{ P_\nu \left(\frac{1}{z - a_\nu} \right) - q_\nu(z) \right\} \quad \text{converges} \quad \text{uniformly} \quad \text{on} \quad \Delta_R =$$

$$\{ |z| \le R \}.$$

(d) Define $f(z) = \sum_\nu \left\{ P_\nu \left(\frac{1}{z - a_\nu} \right) - q_\nu(z) \right\}$, and show that f is the

function desired.)

4. Let $\{a_n\}_{n=1}^{\infty}$ be a sequence of distinct complex numbers with $\lim_{n \to \infty} a_n = \infty$. Show that for *any* sequence $\{c_n\}_{n=1}^{\infty}$ of complex numbers there exists an entire function f with $f(a_n) = c_n$ for each n. (HINT: By the Weierstrass product theorem there is an entire function g with $g(a_n) = 0$, $g'(a_n) \ne 0$, for each n. Using Mittag-Leffler in a clever way define $f = g \cdot h$.)

4. Functions of Finite Order

We focus our attention on a restricted class of entire functions, the functions of finite order. There is a strong correlation between the rate of growth of such a function and the rapidity with which its sequence of zeros (if infinite) tends to infinity. The theorem which makes this correlation precise, the Hadamard product theorem, is difficult, and its proof will occupy the next several sections.

Definition 4.1. An entire function f has *finite order* if for some α, $\alpha \ge 0$, there exist constants A and B such that

(4.1) $$|f(z)| \le A e^{B|z|^\alpha}$$

for all z.

If (4.1) holds and if $\alpha' > \alpha$, then the reader can show that there exist A' and B' such that (4.1) holds for $A = A'$, $B = B'$, and $\alpha = \alpha'$. The following definition is therefore reasonable.

Definition 4.2. If f has *finite order*, the greatest lower bound of the α's which enter into (4.1) is called the *order* of f.

If f has order λ, it does not follow that A and B can be found so that (4.1) holds with $\alpha = \lambda$. For example, a nonconstant polynomial has order $\lambda = 0$, but by Liouville's theorem, (4.1) holds with $\alpha = 0$ only if f is constant. On the other hand, if $\epsilon > 0$ and $\alpha = \lambda + \epsilon$, then A and B can be found.

The reader should verify that the following functions have the orders claimed.

1. $f(z) = e^{P(z)}$, $P(z) = \sum\limits_{n=0}^{N} a_n z^n$ with $a_N \neq 0$. Order $= N$.
2. $f(z) = e^{e^z}$. f does not have finite order.
3. $f(z) = \cos z$. Order $= 1$.
4. $f(z) = \cos \sqrt{z}$. Order $= \frac{1}{2}$.

$$\left(\cos \sqrt{z} = \sum_{k=0}^{\infty} \frac{(-1)^k (\sqrt{z})^{2k}}{(2k)!} = \sum_{k=0}^{\infty} \frac{(-1)^k z^k}{(2k)!} \right)$$

Definition 4.2 is sometimes difficult to work with, and so it is convenient to have equivalent definitions of "order." We shall give two of these, the second of which is particularly useful.

If f has order λ, then for any $\epsilon > 0$ and all large z, the inequality

$$(4.2) \qquad |f(z)| < e^{|z|^{\lambda+\epsilon}}$$

is true. If A and B are chosen in (4.1) corresponding to $\alpha = \lambda + \epsilon/2$, then (4.2) follows from (4.1) and the fact that for large $|z|$, $|z|^{\lambda+\epsilon} > |z|^{\lambda+\epsilon/2}B + |\log A|$.

Let ρ be the greatest lower bound of numbers α such that

$$(4.3) \qquad |f(z)| \leq e^{|z|^{\alpha}}$$

is true for sufficiently large $|z|$. By (4.2) we have $\rho \leq \lambda$.

Recall the definition of $M(r)$ as

$$M(r) = \max_{|z|=r} |f(z)|.$$

For large r we have from (4.3) that

$$(4.4) \qquad M(r) < e^{r^{\rho+\epsilon}}.$$

If f is nonconstant, then $\log M(r) > 1$ for large r, and from (4.4) we get

$$(4.5) \qquad \log \log M(r) < (\rho + \epsilon) \log r.$$

We define $\sigma = \lim\sup_{r \to \infty} (\log \log M(r))/(\log r)$, noting that $\sigma \le \rho$ by (4.5).

So far we have $\sigma \le \rho \le \lambda$. If we can show $\lambda \le \sigma$, we will have proved

Theorem 4.1.   *If $f(z)$ is a nonconstant entire function of order λ, then* $\lambda = \rho = \sigma$.

Proof.   Fix $\epsilon > 0$. Given constants $A > 0$ and $B > 0$, there exists for each n a radius $r_n > n$ such that

$$(4.6) \qquad\qquad M(r_n) > A e^{B r_n^{\lambda - \epsilon}}.$$

Assume $A > e$ and $B > 1$. Taking logarithms of both sides in (4.6) yields

$$\log M(r_n) > \log A + B r_n^{\lambda - \epsilon}$$

$$> r_n^{\lambda - \epsilon}.$$

Therefore

$$\log \log M(r_n) > (\lambda - \epsilon) \log r_n.$$

Dividing by $\log r_n$ and letting $n \to \infty$, we find $\sigma \ge \lambda - \epsilon$. Since ϵ is arbitrary, $\sigma \ge \lambda$, and the theorem is proved.

If f and g are functions of order λ_1 and λ_2, the reader should verify the following properties:

    (a) $f + g$ and $f \cdot g$ have order at most $\max(\lambda_1, \lambda_2)$.
    (b) If $\lambda_1 \ne \lambda_2$, then $f + g$ has order *equal* to $\max(\lambda_1, \lambda_2)$.
    (c) If a and b are constants, $a \ne 0$, and if h is defined as $h(z) = f(az + b)$, then h has order λ_1.
    (d) If k is a real number such that $h(z) = f(z^k)$ can be defined to be entire, then $h(z)$ has order $k\lambda_1$. (Compare with Example 4 above. If f is nonconstant, what are the possible values of k?)

Problems

1. Verify that the functions 1–4 have the orders claimed.
2. Prove statements (a)–(d).
3. Let f have order λ, and suppose for some positive integer k the power series of f about 0 is $f(z) = \sum_{n=0}^{\infty} c_n z^{nk}$. Show that $g(z) = f(z^{1/k})$ has order λ/k.

4. Given a power series $f(z) = \sum\limits_{n=0}^{\infty} a_n z^n$ define

(4.7) $$\mu = \liminf_{n \to \infty} \frac{\log\,(1/|a_n|)}{n \log n}$$

interpreting $\log 1/0$ as $+\infty$. If $\mu > 0$, show that f is an entire function of order at most $1/\mu$.
(HINT:

(a) If $0 < \nu < \mu$, then for all but finitely many n

(4.8) $$|a_n| \le n^{-n\nu}.$$

From this it follows that f is entire.
(b) Using (4.8) estimate the size of $|a_n r^n|$. To do this find the maximum for fixed r of the function

$$h_r(t) = r^t t^{-t\nu}, \quad 0 < t < \infty.$$

The maximum occurs at $t = r^{1/\nu}/e$, and therefore for all n

$$|a_n r^n| \le e^{(\nu/e)r^{1/\nu}}.$$

(c) From (4.8) it is also true that $|a_n r^n| \le (r^{1/\nu}/n)^{n\nu}$. Therefore, setting $s = (2r)^{1/\nu}$, the sum $\sum\limits_{n \ge s} a_n z^n$ is bounded by 1.

(d) If s is as in (c), the sum $\sum\limits_{n < s} a_n z^n$ is less than $(2r)^{1/\nu}e^{(\nu/e)r^{1/\nu}}$. Therefore

$$\limsup_{r \to \infty} \frac{\log \log M(r)}{\log r} \le \frac{1}{\nu}.$$

(e) Let ν increase to μ, and conclude that f has order at most $1/\mu$.)

5. Let $f(z) = \sum\limits_{n=0}^{\infty} a_n z^n$, and define μ as in (4.7). Show that

(4.9) $$\limsup_{r \to \infty} \frac{\log \log M(r)}{\log r} \ge \frac{1}{\mu},$$

and that therefore f has order exactly $1/\mu$. (If $\mu = 0$, then f does not have finite order.)

(HINT:

(a) Let $\nu > \mu$ be arbitrary. By definition of μ, there exist infinitely many n such that

$$|a_n| \geq n^{-\nu n}.$$

(b) Let $r = (2n)^\nu$, and show that

$$|a_n r^n| \geq 2^{(\nu/2)r^{1/\nu}}.$$

(c) From Cauchy's estimate $|a_n| \leq M(r)/r^n$. Use this in (b) to prove (4.9).)

6. Verify the orders claimed for the following functions

(a) $f_\alpha(z) = \displaystyle\sum_{n=1}^{\infty} \frac{z^n}{n^{\alpha n}}, \alpha > 0.$ $\left(\text{Answer: } \dfrac{1}{\alpha}.\right)$

(b) $g_\alpha(z) = \displaystyle\sum_{n=1}^{\infty} \frac{1}{(n!)^\alpha} z^n, \alpha > 0.$ $\left(\text{Answer: } \dfrac{1}{\alpha}.\right)$

(c) $h_\alpha(z) = \displaystyle\sum_{n=1}^{\infty} \frac{1}{n^{\alpha n}} z^n, \alpha > 1.$ $(\text{Answer: } 0.)$

7. If f has order λ, prove f' has order λ.

8. Let $f(z) = \displaystyle\sum_{n=0}^{\infty} a_n z^n$ and $g(z) = \displaystyle\sum_{n=0}^{\infty} b_n z^n$ be functions of orders λ_1 and λ_2. If $h(z) = \displaystyle\sum_{n=0}^{\infty} a_n b_n z^n$, then h has order at most $\lambda_1\lambda_2/(\lambda_1 + \lambda_2)$. (If $\lambda_1 = \lambda_2 = 0$, the order is 0.)

5. Exponent of Convergence

Let g be analytic on an open set containing the disk Δ. If $g(z) \neq 0$ for $z = 0$ or $|z| = 1$, then Jensen's formula (Chapter 2, Section 6, Problem 11) is

$$(5.1) \qquad \frac{1}{2\pi} \int_{-\pi}^{\pi} \log|g(e^{i\theta})| \, d\theta = -\sum_{i=1}^{n} \log|z_i| + \log|g(0)|,$$

where $z_1, \ldots, z_n$ are the zeros of g in Δ. If f is entire, and if for some $r < \infty$, $f(z) \neq 0$ for $z = 0$ or $|z| = r$, then define $g(z) = f(rz)$. Equation (5.1) for g implies for f

$$(5.2) \qquad \frac{1}{2\pi} \int_{-\pi}^{\pi} \log|f(re^{i\theta})|\, d\theta = -\sum_{i=1}^{n} \log\left|\frac{z_i}{r}\right| + \log|f(0)|.$$

Here $z_1, \ldots, z_n$ are the zeros of f in Δ_r.

We now fix a nonconstant entire function f of order λ, and assume $f(0) \neq 0$. As usual $\{z_n\}$ is the sequence of zeros of f, this time arranged so that $|z_n| \leq |z_{n+1}|$ for each n. The case of an empty or finite sequence is uninteresting in what follows, so we shall assume that $\{z_n\}$ is infinite. Our goal is to establish for each $\epsilon > 0$ that $\displaystyle\sum_{n=1}^{\infty} \frac{1}{|z_n|^{(\lambda+\epsilon)}} < \infty$. For this purpose (5.2) will be most useful.

We shall denote by $N(r), 0 \leq r < \infty$, the number of zeros of f of modulus less than or equal to r. $N(r)$ is the largest integer such that $|z_N| \leq r$.

About $N(r)$ we make the following simple observations. First, $N(r) = \lim_{s \to r^+} N(s)$. That is, $N(r)$ is continuous from the right. The difference $N(r) - \lim_{s \to r^-} N(s)$ is just the number of terms of the sequence which have modulus r. Secondly, we make note of the inequality

$$(5.3) \qquad m \leq N(|z_m|)$$

which is strict when $|z_m| = |z_{m+1}|$.

Given $\epsilon > 0$, let $\delta = \epsilon/2$, and choose r_0 so that if $r \geq r_0$, then $M(r) \leq e^{r^{\lambda+\delta}}$. Because f does not vanish identically, r can be chosen so that $f(z) \neq 0$ for $|z| = r$. If $s = r/2$, then

$$\sum_{i=1}^{N(r)} -\log\left|\frac{z_i}{r}\right| \geq \sum_{i=1}^{N(s)} -\log\left|\frac{z_i}{r}\right|$$

$$(5.4) \qquad\qquad\qquad \geq \sum_{i=1}^{N(s)} -\log\frac{1}{2}$$

$$= N(s) \log 2.$$

Using (5.2), (5.4), and the bound on $M(r)$, we obtain the inequality

$$r^{\lambda+\delta} \geq N(s) \log 2 + \log|f(0)|$$

or

$$(5.5) \qquad\qquad N(s) \leq As^{\lambda+\delta} + B,$$

where $A = 2^{\lambda+\delta}/(\log 2)$ and $B = -\log|f(0)|/\log 2$. While (5.5) has been proved for those $s \geq r_0/2$ such that f has no zeros on the circle of radius $2s$, it now follows for all $s \geq r_0/2$ by virtue of the right-hand continuity of $N(s)$.

If $s = |z_m|$, then by (5.3) $m \leq N(s)$. Substituting this fact into (5.5), we obtain

$$m \leq A|z_m|^{\lambda+\delta} + B.$$

Letting $\alpha = 1/A$ and $\beta = -B/A$ we can solve this last equation for $|z_m|^{\lambda+\delta}$:

$$(5.6) \qquad\qquad |z_m|^{\lambda+\delta} \geq \alpha m + \beta.$$

If m is large, then $\alpha m + \beta > 0$, and (5.6) implies

$$(5.7) \qquad\qquad \frac{1}{|z_m|} \leq \frac{1}{(\alpha m + \beta)^{1/(\lambda+\delta)}}.$$

Because $\delta = \epsilon/2$, the inequality $(\lambda + \epsilon)/(\lambda + \delta) > 1$ holds. Therefore the sum $\sum\limits_{\alpha m+\beta>0} (\alpha m + \beta)^{-(\lambda+\epsilon)/(\lambda+\delta)}$ is finite, and from (5.7) we conclude that

$$\sum_{n=1}^{\infty} |z_n|^{-\lambda-\epsilon} < \infty.$$

The restriction $f(0) \neq 0$ is unnecessary. Indeed if f is nonconstant but $f(0) = 0$, then for some $k, f(z) = z^k h(z)$ where $h(0) = 0$. Here h is entire of order λ (why?), and h has the same sequence $\{z_n\}$ as does f. We have proved

Theorem 5.1.   *If f is a nonconstant entire function of order λ, then for each $\epsilon > 0$ the series $\sum\limits_{n=1}^{\infty} 1/|z_n|^{\lambda+\epsilon}$ is convergent.*

REMARK.   If $\{z_n\}$ is empty or finite there is nothing to prove.

Definition 5.1.   *A sequence $\{z_n\}$ has a finite exponent of convergence if for some $\alpha > 0$ the sum $\sum\limits_{n=1}^{\infty} |z_n|^{-\alpha}$ is finite.*

If $\displaystyle\sum_{n=1}^{\infty} |z_n|^{-\alpha} < \infty$, then of course $\displaystyle\sum_{n=1}^{\infty} |z_n|^{-\alpha'} < \infty$ for any $\alpha' \geq \alpha$. If $\{z_n\}$ has finite exponent of convergence, let μ be the greatest lower bound of the nonnegative α's which make $\displaystyle\sum_{n=1}^{\infty} |z_n|^{-\alpha}$ finite. We call μ the *exponent of convergence* of the sequence $\{z_n\}$. The reader should check that μ is the smallest nonnegative number such that $\displaystyle\sum_{n=1}^{\infty} |z_n|^{-\mu-\epsilon} < \infty$ for each $\epsilon > 0$.

The following is a list of sequences with their exponents of convergence.

1. $z_n = n, \quad n = 1, 2, \ldots. \quad \mu = 1.$
2. $z_n = n \log^2 n, \quad n = 2, 3, \ldots. \quad \mu = 1.$
3. $z_n = \log n, \quad n = 2, 3, \ldots. \quad \{z_n\}$ does not have finite exponent of convergence.
4. $z_n = 2^n. \quad \mu = 0.$

It is clear from these examples that $\mu = \alpha$ may or may not make $\displaystyle\sum_{n=1}^{\infty} |z_n|^{-\alpha}$ finite.

Returning to the case of a nonconstant entire function, f, of order λ, let μ be the exponent of convergence of the sequence $\{z_n\}$. In terms of our new definitions, Theorem 5.1 may be restated.

Theorem 5.1′. $\mu \leq \lambda.$

The inequality $\lambda \leq \mu$ is not generally true. For example, if $f(z) = e^z$, then $\mu = 0$ and $\lambda = 1$. (By convention $\mu \geq 0$, even when $\{z_n\}$ is empty.) There appears in the next section a large class of functions for which $\mu = \lambda$.

Problems

1. Verify that the sequences 1–4 have the exponent claimed.
2. Define

$$f(z) = \prod_{n=1}^{\infty} \left(1 - \frac{z}{n}\right) e^{z/n}.$$

Prove that f has order no less than 1.

3. For which of the following sequences is it *possible* that there exists a nonconstant function of finite order with $f(z_n) = 0$?

   (a) $z_n = n^2$.
   (b) $z_n = n \log^2 n$.
   (c) $z_n = \log n$.

4. Let f be an entire function of finite order, and suppose $f(\log n) = n$. What is f?

5. Let $\{z_n\}$ be a sequence of distinct nonzero complex numbers such that $\lim\limits_{n \to \infty} z_n = \infty$. For each n suppose a value w_n of $z_n^{1/2}$ is prescribed. By Problem 4, Section 3, there exists an entire function f with $f(z_n) = w_n$.

   (a) If $\{z_n\}$ has exponent μ, what is the smallest possible order f could have?

   (b) If $\{z_n\}$ does not have finite exponent, can f have finite order?

6. Canonical Products

With a sequence $\{z_n\}$ whose exponent of convergence is μ we associate an integer h as follows:

$$(6.1) \qquad h = \begin{cases} [\mu], & \mu \neq \text{integer}^1 \\ \mu - 1, & \mu = \text{integer}, \ \sum\limits_{n=1}^{\infty} |z_n|^{-\mu} < \infty \\ \mu, & \text{otherwise.} \end{cases}$$

By Theorem 3.1 the product

$$(6.2) \qquad P(z) = \prod_{n=1}^{\infty} E\left(\frac{z}{z_n}, h\right)$$

is entire with zeros $\{z_n\}$. A *priori* there is no reason why P should have finite order, but should it be, say, of order λ, then certainly by Theorem 5.1′, $\lambda \geq \mu$. P does in fact have finite order, and what is more, we shall see that $\lambda \leq \mu$, i.e., $\lambda = \mu$.

Let α be a fixed number between 0 and 1. The following two lemmas will establish bounds on the sums $\sum\limits_{|z/z_n| \geq \alpha} \log|E(z/z_n, h)|$ and $\sum\limits_{|z/z_n| < \alpha} \log|E(z/z_n, h)|$.

---
[1] $[\mu]$ denotes the greatest integer less than or equal to μ.

Lemma 6.1. Given $\epsilon > 0$ there exists a number M such that for any z, $|z| = r$,

$$(6.3) \qquad \sum_{|z/z_n| \geq \alpha} \log \left| E\left(\frac{z}{z_n}, h\right) \right| \leq M r^{\mu + \epsilon}.$$

Proof. Let A be the finite number

$$A = \sup_{t \geq \alpha} \frac{1}{t^h} \left\{ \log(1 + t) + t + \cdots + \frac{t^h}{h} \right\}.$$

Then for any $t \geq \alpha$,

$$(6.4) \qquad \log(1 + t) + t + \cdots + \frac{t^h}{h} \leq A t^h.$$

If $|z/z_n| \geq \alpha$, we let $t = |z/z_n|$ in (6.4) and find

$$\log \left| E\left(\frac{z}{z_n}, h\right) \right| = \log \left| \left(1 - \frac{z}{z_n}\right) e^{z/z_n + \cdots + 1/h(z/z_n)^h} \right|$$

$$(6.5) \qquad \leq \log\left(1 + \left|\frac{z}{z_n}\right|\right) + \left|\frac{z}{z_n}\right| + \cdots + \frac{1}{h}\left|\frac{z}{z_n}\right|^h$$

$$\leq A \left|\frac{z}{z_n}\right|^h.$$

Because $\mu + \epsilon > h$, we also have the inequality

$$\left|\frac{z}{z_n}\right|^h = |z|^{\mu+\epsilon} \left|\frac{z}{z_n}\right|^{h-\mu-\epsilon} |z_n|^{-\mu-\epsilon},$$

$$(6.6)$$

$$\leq |z|^{\mu+\epsilon} \frac{1}{\alpha^{\mu+\epsilon-h}} |z_n|^{-\mu-\epsilon}.$$

The number $M = A/\alpha^{\mu+\epsilon-h} \sum_{n=1}^{\infty} |z_n|^{-\mu-\epsilon}$ is finite because $\{z_n\}$ has exponent of convergence μ. Together, (6.5) and (6.6) imply (6.3). The lemma is proved.

Lemma 6.2. Given $\epsilon > 0$ there exists a constant N such that for any z, $|z| = r$,

$$(6.7) \qquad \sum_{|z/z_n| < \alpha} \log \left| E\left(\frac{z}{z_n}, h\right) \right| \leq N r^{\mu + \epsilon}.$$

Proof.   For $|w| \leq \alpha(<1)$, (3.4) implies the inequality

$$\log|E(w, h)| \leq \frac{1}{1 - \alpha} |w|^{h+1}.$$

Using this with $w = z/z_n$ we find

$$\sum_{|z/z_n|<\alpha} \log\left| E\left(\frac{z}{z_n}, \alpha\right)\right| \leq \frac{1}{1 - \alpha} \sum_{|z/z_n|<\alpha} \left|\frac{z}{z_n}\right|^{h+1}.$$

Because $h + 1 > \mu + \epsilon$, we have the inequality

$$\left|\frac{z}{z_n}\right|^{h+1} = |z|^{\mu+\epsilon} \left|\frac{z}{z_n}\right|^{h+1-\mu-\epsilon} |z_n|^{-\mu-\epsilon}$$

$$\leq |z|^{\mu+\epsilon}\alpha^{h+1-\mu-\epsilon}|z_n|^{-\mu-\epsilon}.$$

As before the number $N = \alpha^{h+1-\mu-\epsilon}/(1 - \alpha) \sum_{n=1}^{\infty} |z_n|^{-\mu-\epsilon}$ is finite, and (6.7) follows. The lemma is proved.

We shall now combine Lemmas 6.1 and 6.2 to obtain

Theorem 6.1.   *If P is defined by equations (6.2) and (6.1), then the order of P is less than or equal to μ.*

Proof.   Let α, M, and N be as in Lemmas 6.1 and 6.2. We estimate $\log M(r)$ by

$$\log M(r) = \max_{|z|=r} \log|P(z)|$$

$$= \max_{|z|=r} \left\{ \sum_{|z/z_n|<\alpha} \log\left| E\left(\frac{z}{z_n}, h\right)\right| + \sum_{|z/z_n|\geq\alpha} \log\left| E\left(\frac{z}{z_n}, h\right)\right| \right\}$$

$$\leq Mr^{\mu+\epsilon} + Nr^{\mu+\epsilon}$$

$$= Kr^{\mu+\epsilon},$$

where $K = M + N$. Thus

$$\frac{\log\log M(r)}{\log r} \leq \frac{\log K}{\log r} + \mu + \epsilon.$$

and letting $r \to \infty$ gives $\lambda \le \mu + \epsilon$. The desired inequality follows by letting $\epsilon \to 0$.

REMARK. As noted earlier, Theorems 5.1′ and 6.1 tell us that $\lambda = \mu$ for canonical products.

Problems

1. Find the order of the following functions.

(a) $f(z) = \displaystyle\prod_{n=0}^{\infty} (1 - q^n z), |q| < 1.$

(b) $f(z) = \displaystyle\prod_{n=0}^{\infty} \left(1 - \frac{z}{n^\alpha}\right) e^{z/n^\alpha}, \frac{1}{2} < \alpha \le 1.$

(c) $f(z) = \displaystyle\prod_{n=0}^{\infty} \left(1 - \frac{z}{n^2 \log n}\right).$

2. Let P and Q be canonical products of orders λ_1 and λ_2. If $h = P/Q$ is entire, let $\lambda = \limsup\limits_{r \to \infty} \max\limits_{|z|=r} (\log \log|h(z)|)/(\log r)$. Prove (a) $\lambda_2 \le \lambda_1$ and $\lambda \le \lambda_1$, and (b) if $\lambda_2 < \lambda_1$, then $\lambda = \lambda_1$.

7. The Borel-Carathéodory Lemma—Another Form of Schwarz's Lemma

If f is a nonvanishing entire function of order λ, $f(z) = e^{g(z)}$, and if $\epsilon > 0$ is given, the inequality $|f(z)| < e^{|z|^{\lambda+\epsilon}}$ holds for all sufficiently large z. Since $|f(z)| = e^{\operatorname{Re} g(z)}$, the latter inequality is equivalent to

(7.1) $$\operatorname{Re} g(z) < |z|^{\lambda+\epsilon}.$$

Entire functions g which satisfy (7.1) for $\epsilon > 0$ and all large $|z|$ will be seen to be polynomials of degree at most λ. This result is a special case of the Hadamard product theorem.

The object of the Borel-Carathéodory lemma is to replace the bound (7.1) on $\operatorname{Re} g(z)$ by a similar bound on $|g(z)|$. The fact that g is a polynomial then follows from the elementary theory.

Let g be an entire function with $g(0) = 0$. For each $r > 0$ define

$$A(r) = \max_{|z|=r} \operatorname{Re} g(z).$$

As usual $M(r)$ is the maximum of $|g(z)|$ over $|z| = r$. The maximum principle, applied to $e^{g(z)}$, implies that $\operatorname{Re} g(z) \leq A(r)$ for $|z| \leq r$, or what is the same thing, $f(\Delta_r) \subset \mathscr{K}_r$, where

$$\mathscr{K}_r = \{w \mid \operatorname{Re} w \leq A(r)\}.$$

Because the points $2A(r)$ and 0 are symmetric with respect to the line $\{w \mid \operatorname{Re} w = A(r)\}$, the transformation

(7.2) $$Tz = \frac{z}{2A(r) - z},$$

which sends 0 into 0, $A(r)$ into 1, and $2A(r)$ into ∞, must map $\mathscr{K}_r$ onto Δ. (A direct verification is easy. See also Problem 4, Section 5, Chapter 2.) If $\varphi(z) = Tg(z)$, then $\varphi(0) = 0$ and $|\varphi(z)| \leq 1$ for $z \in \Delta_r$. By Schwarz's lemma

(7.3) $$\max_{|z|=s} |\varphi(z)| \leq \frac{s}{r}.$$

Next, we substitute $g(z)$ for z in (7.2) and solve for $g(z)$:

(7.4) $$g(z) = \frac{2A(r)\varphi(z)}{1 + \varphi(z)}.$$

Equations (7.4) and (7.3) easily yield

(7.5) $$\begin{aligned} M(s) &= \max_{|z|=s} |g(z)| \\ &\leq \frac{2A(r)s}{r - s}. \end{aligned}$$

We will now adjust what has gone before in order to extend the relationship (7.5) between $M(s)$ and $A(r)$ to functions g with $g(0) \neq 0$.

Lemma 7.1.   If g is analytic on a region containing $\{z \mid |z| \leq r\}$, and if $s < r$, then

(7.6) $$M(s) \leq 2s \frac{A(r) - \operatorname{Re} g(0)}{r - s} + |g(0)|.$$

Proof. If $g(0) = 0$, (7.6) reduces to (7.5). If $g(0) \neq 0$, let $h(z) = g(z) - g(0)$ and apply (7.5) to $h(z)$. We find

$$
\begin{aligned}
M(s) - |g(0)| &= \max_{|z|=s} |g(z)| - |g(0)| \\
&\leq \max_{|z|=s} |g(z) - g(0)| \\
&\leq \frac{2 \max_{|z|=s} \mathrm{Re}\{g(z) - g(0)\} s}{r - s} \\
&= \frac{2\{A(r) - \mathrm{Re}\, g(0)\} s}{r - s},
\end{aligned}
$$

and this implies (7.6).

Using the Cauchy integral formula for the derivatives of g it is easy to see that if $M(r) \leq r^{\alpha}$ for all large r, then $g(z)$ is a polynomial of degree at most α (Problem 1). In fact, it is only necessary to assume $M(r_n) \leq r_n^{\alpha}$ for a sequence r_n with $\lim_{n \to \infty} r_n = \infty$.

REMARK. When confusion might arise, the quantities $M(r)$ and $A(r)$ will be subscripted by the symbols for the functions to which they refer.

Theorem 7.1. *If f is a nonvanishing entire function of order λ, then $f(z) = e^{g(z)}$ for some polynomial g of degree λ.*

Proof. Since f is never zero, there exists an entire version, g, of $\log f(z)$, and we can write $f(z) = e^{g(z)}$. As remarked in the beginning of the section the inequality $M_f(r) \leq e^{r^{\lambda+\epsilon}}$ which is valid for large r implies the inequality

$$ A_g(r) \leq r^{\lambda+\epsilon}. $$

Let $r = 2s$, and substitute in (7.6):

$$ (7.7) \qquad M_g(s) \leq \frac{2\{2^{\lambda+\epsilon} s^{\lambda+\epsilon} - \mathrm{Re}\, g(0)\} s}{s} + |g(0)|. $$

The right side of (7.7) is dominated by $s^{\lambda+2\epsilon}$ for large s, and so for large s, $M_g(s) \leq s^{\lambda+2\epsilon}$. By the remark preceding the theorem g is a polynomial of degree at most $\lambda + 2\epsilon$, and since ϵ is arbitrary, g has degree at most λ. If the degree of g were *less* than λ, the order of f would be less than λ (Problem 1, Section 4). Thus, degree $g = \lambda$, and the theorem is proved.

A further observation based on (7.5) will be useful in Section 9. For fixed $R < \infty$ let f be nonvanishing on Δ_{2R} with $f(0) = 1$. Suppose

$$\max_{|z|=2R} |f(z)| = e^A.$$

It is possible to define on Δ_{2R} a branch $\varphi(z)$ of $\log f$ such that $\varphi(0) = 0$. The image of Δ_{2R} under φ is contained in $\mathcal{H}_A = \{w \mid \operatorname{Re} w \leq A\}$, and therefore (7.5) implies

$$|\varphi(z)| \leq \frac{2A|z|}{2R - |z|}.$$

In Section 9 $|z|$ will vary between $R/2$ and $3R/2$. For such values the last inequality implies

$$|\varphi(z)| \leq 6A,$$

and

(7.8) $$-6A \leq \operatorname{Re} \varphi (= \log|f(z)|) \leq 6A.$$

Problems

1. Let g be an entire function, and suppose there exists an $\alpha > 0$ and a sequence $\{r_n\}$ of radii tending to infinity such that $M(r_n) \leq r_n{}^\alpha$ for each n. Then g is a polynomial of degree at most α.
2. Let $f_n(z) = u_n(z) + iv_n(z)$, $v_n(0) = 0$, be analytic for each n, and suppose that $\lim_{n \to \infty} u_n(z)$ exists locally uniformly. Then $\lim_{n \to \infty} f_n(z)$ exists locally uniformly. In particular, the locally uniform limit of harmonic functions is harmonic.

8. A Lemma of H. Cartan

If f is entire of order λ, we construct from the zeros (including 0) of f a canonical product P of order $\mu \leq \lambda$ (Sections 5 and 6). As before there is the factorization $f(z) = P(z)e^{g(z)}$ for some entire function g, and what is necessary to complete the Hadamard product theorem is some precise information on g. To get this information we will obtain estimates on the function

$$m(r) = \min_{|z|=r} |P(z)|.$$

The desired estimates will be obtained with the help of a combinatorial lemma of H. Cartan.

We make note of the inequality

(8.1)
$$\frac{n!}{n^n} \geq \frac{1}{e^n}, \quad n \geq 1$$

which follows from exponentiating the obvious relation

$$\sum_{k=0}^{n-1} \frac{1}{n} \log\left(1 - \frac{k}{n}\right) \geq \int_0^1 \log(1 - t)\, dt$$

$$= -1.$$

Lemma 8.1. (H. Cartan) Let $z_1, \ldots, z_n$ be fixed points in the plane. Given $H > 0$, there exist disks $D_1, \ldots, D_m$ ($m \leq n$), the sum of whose radii is $2H$, such that if $z \notin D_1 \cup \cdots \cup D_m$, then

(8.2)
$$|z - z_1|\, |z - z_2| \cdots |z - z_n| > \left(\frac{H}{e}\right)^n.$$

Proof. Suppose there happens to be one closed disk of radius H which contains all the points. Let D_1 be the concentric disk of radius $2H$. If $z \notin D_1$, then $|z - z_k| \geq H$ for $1 \leq k \leq n$, and in this case $\prod_{k=1}^{n} |z - z_k| \geq H^n \geq (H/e)^n$.

In general there will be no such disk, but there will be a largest integer, k, for which the following statement is true: There is a closed disk of radius $(k/n)H$ which contains at least k of the given points. The integer k exists because the statement is certainly true for $k = 1$. The assumption $k = n$ was made in the preceding paragraph. Set $k = k_1$.

Choose a closed disk C_1 of radius $(k_1/n)H$ containing at least k_1 of the given points. C_1 cannot contain *more* than k_1 of the points, for if it did the concentric disk of radius $((k_1 + 1)/n)H$ would contain at least $k_1 + 1$ points contradicting the definition of k_1.

For the remaining $n - k_1$ points we choose in similar fashion an integer $k = k_2$, $1 \leq k_2 \leq n - k_1$, and a closed disk C_2 of radius $(k_2/n)H$ containing k_2 of the remaining points. Of course, $k_2 \leq k_1$.

The process is repeated for the remaining $n - k_1 - k_2$ points and so on, until after m steps the points $z_1, \ldots, z_n$ have been covered by disks $C_1, \ldots, C_m$. The radius of C_j is $(k_j/n)H$ for each j, and $k_1 \geq k_2 \geq \cdots \geq k_m$. Since $k_1 + k_2 + \cdots + k_m = n$, the total radius of these disks is H.

Define D_j for each j, $1 \le j \le m$, to be the closed disk of radius $2(k_j/n)H$ concentric with C_j. Fixing $z \notin D_1 \cup \cdots \cup D_m$ we renumber $z_1, \ldots, z_n$, if necessary, to ensure that

(8.3) $$|z - z_1| \le |z - z_2| \le \cdots \le |z - z_n|.$$

If $1 \le i \le n$, we claim

(8.4) $$|z - z_i| > \frac{i}{n} H.$$

The proof is by contradiction. Suppose for some i that $|z - z_i| \le (i/n)H$, and let j be the largest integer for which $k_j \ge i$. (Certainly $k_1 \ge i$, because the disk C of radius $(i/n)H$ about z contains $z_1, \ldots, z_i$.)

If $p \le i$ and $q \le j$, it cannot be that $z_p \in C_q$. Indeed since $k_q \ge i$, it would then be true that $z \in D_q$, and the contrary has been assumed. All of the points $z_1, \ldots, z_i$ lie outside of $C_1 \cup \cdots \cup C_j$. Since $|z - z_i| \le (i/n)H$, it follows from (8.3) that there is a disk of radius $(i/n)H$ containing $z_1, \ldots, z_i$. Thus $k_{j+1} \ge i$, contradicting the definition of j.

Therefore (8.4) holds for all i as claimed. Equations (8.4) and (8.1) imply

$$\prod_{i=1}^{n} |z - z_i| > \frac{n!}{n^n} H^n$$

$$> \left(\frac{H}{e}\right)^n,$$

and the lemma is proved.

Problem

1. Verify inequality (8.1).

9. The Hadamard Product Theorem

If f is a nonconstant entire function of order λ, the results obtained thus far enable us to write

(9.1) $$f(z) = z^k P(z) e^{g(z)}$$

where $k \ge 0$ is an integer, P is a canonical product of order $\mu \le \lambda$, and g is entire. Our final task is to estimate the order of $e^{g(z)}$ from which estimate it will follow that g is a polynomial. As mentioned earlier it is necessary to estimate

$$(9.2) \qquad m(r) = \min_{|z|=r} |P(z)|,$$

for certain r, and the estimate obtained will allow us to make statements regarding $e^{g(z)}$. The point is to show that (9.2) is not too *small* for a sequence of values of r tending to infinity.

Lemma 9.1. Let P be a canonical product of order μ. For each $\epsilon > 0$ the following statement is true for arbitrarily large values of R: There exists an r, $R/2 < r < 3R/2$, such that

$$(9.3) \qquad m(r) > e^{-r^{\mu+\epsilon}}.$$

Proof. We introduce an auxiliary function Q. If $0 < R < \infty$, and if $z_1, \ldots, z_n$ are nonzero numbers of modulus less than $2R$, define

$$Q(z) = \left(\prod_{j=1}^{n} \frac{2R(z - z_j)}{(2R)^2 - \bar{z}_j z} \right) \frac{(-2R)^n}{z_1 \cdots z_n}.$$

Note that $Q(0) = 1$, and for real θ

$$(9.4) \qquad |Q(2Re^{i\theta})| = \frac{(2R)^n}{|z_1 \cdots z_n|} \geq 1.$$

Suppose P has no zeros on $\{|z| = 2R\}$, and let $z_1, \ldots, z_n$ be the zeros of P inside Δ_{2R}. In view of (5.5), R can be assumed so large[1] that

$$(9.5) \qquad n = N(2R) < (2R)^{\mu+\epsilon/2}.$$

There is an entire function $S(z)$ which has no zeros for $|z| \leq 2R$ such that $P(z) = S(z)Q(z)$. Of course, $S(0) = 1$, and from (9.4)

$$\max_{|z|=2R} |S(z)| = \max_{|z|=2R} \frac{|P(z)|}{|Q(z)|}$$

$$\leq \max_{|z|=2R} |P(z)|.$$

R can be assumed so large that $\max_{|z|=2R} |P(z)| \leq e^{(2R)^{\mu+\epsilon/2}}$, and therefore $\max_{|z|=2R} |S(z)| \leq e^{(2R)^{\mu+\epsilon/2}}$. If $R/2 \leq |r| \leq 3R/2$, then (7.8) implies

$$\min_{|z|=r} \log|S(z)| \geq -6(2R)^{\mu+\epsilon/2}.$$

---

[1] Throughout the proof occur statements like "R can be assumed so large." At each of these R is also assumed large enough that all previous statements remain true.

If we replace $\mu + \epsilon/2$ by the larger number $\mu + \epsilon$, R can also be assumed so large that $-6(2R)^{\mu+\epsilon/2} \geq -\frac{1}{2}(R/2)^{\mu+\epsilon}$ and

$$(9.6) \qquad \log|S(z)| \geq -\frac{1}{2}\left(\frac{R}{2}\right)^{\mu+\epsilon}.$$

Next, it is necessary to estimate $\log|Q(z)|$. If $|z| \leq 2R$, then

$$(9.7) \qquad \left| \prod_{k=1}^{n} ((2R)^2 - \bar{z}_k z) \right| \leq 8^n R^{2n}.$$

Fix α, $0 < \alpha < \frac{1}{2}$, and $H = \alpha R < R/2$. By Cartan's lemma there are disks $D_1, \ldots, D_m$ of total radius $2H < R$ such that if $z \notin D_1 \cup \cdots \cup D_m$, then

$$(9.8) \qquad \left| \prod_{k=1}^{n} 2R(z - z_k) \right| \geq (2R)^n \left(\frac{H}{e}\right)^n.$$

Since $2H < R$, there will exist an r, $R/2 < r < 3R/2$, such that no point z, $|z| = r$, lies in $D_1 \cup \cdots \cup D_m$. If we combine (9.7) and (9.8), we find that

$$\min_{|z|=r} |Q(z)| \geq (2R)^n \left(\frac{H}{e}\right)^n \frac{1}{8^n R^{2n}} = \left(\frac{\alpha}{4e}\right)^n.$$

If $|z| = r$, therefore, $\log|Q(z)| \geq n \log(\alpha/4e)$. This equation, the fact that $\log(\alpha/4e) < 0$, and (9.5) give us

$$\log|Q(z)| \geq \log\left(\frac{\alpha}{4e}\right)(2R)^{\mu+\epsilon/2}.$$

Replacing $\mu + \epsilon/2$ by $\mu + \epsilon$ and taking R large enough we find

$$(9.9) \qquad \min_{|z|=r} \log|Q(z)| \geq -\frac{1}{2}\left(\frac{R}{2}\right)^{\mu+\epsilon}.$$

Finally (9.6), (9.9), and the fact that $|P(z)| = |S(z)|\,|Q(z)|$ yield

$$\begin{aligned}
\log m(r) &= \min_{|z|=r} \log|P(z)| \\
&\geq \min_{|z|=r} \log|S(z)| + \min_{|z|=r} \log|Q(z)| \\
&\geq -\frac{1}{2}\left(\frac{R}{2}\right)^{\mu+\epsilon} - \frac{1}{2}\left(\frac{R}{2}\right)^{\mu+\epsilon} \\
&\geq -r^{\mu+\epsilon}.
\end{aligned}$$

Equation (9.3) follows by exponentiation.

Returning to (9.1) we write for $P(z) \neq 0$

$$e^{g(z)} = \frac{f(z)}{z^k P(z)}.$$

If $r \geq 1$ is such that both (9.3) and $\max_{|z|=r} |f(z)| < e^{r^{\lambda+\epsilon}}$ are true, then

$$\max_{|z|=r} |e^{g(z)}| \leq e^{2r^{\lambda+\epsilon}}.$$

(Remember $\mu \leq \lambda$.) There is a sequence r_n of such r's with $\lim_{n \to \infty} r_n = \infty$. The discussion of Section 7 therefore implies that g is a polynomial of degree at most $\lambda + \epsilon$, and letting $\epsilon \to 0$, we obtain

Theorem 9.1. (Hadamard Product Theorem) *Let f be a nonconstant entire function of order λ. Then f can be written as a product of three factors*

$$f(z) = z^k P(z) e^{g(z)},$$

where

(a) $k \geq 0$ *is the order of the zero of f at $z = 0$.*

(b) $P(z) = \displaystyle\prod_{n=1}^{\infty} E(z/z_n, h)$ *is the canonical product formed from the sequence $\{z_n\}$ of zeros of f distinct from $z = 0$. If $\{z_n\}$ is infinite, the exponent of convergence of $\{z_n\}$ is $\mu \leq \lambda$, and the order of P is μ. (h is defined by (6.1).)*

(c) g *is a polynomial of degree at most λ.*

Problems

1. Prove the formula

$$\frac{\sin \pi z}{\pi} = z \prod_{n \neq 0} \left(1 - \frac{z}{n}\right) e^{z/n}.$$

2. Show that a function of order $\frac{3}{2}$ must have infinitely many zeros. Generalize.

3. Suppose f is even $(f(z) = f(-z))$ and of finite order λ, where λ is not an even integer. Then f has infinitely many zeros. Same question for f odd. $(f(-z) = -f(z).)$

4. If f has order λ, $0 < \lambda < 1$, then f assumes every complex value an infinite number of times.

5. If f has order 0, then either f is a polynomial or else f assumes every complex value an infinite number of times.

6. The range of a nonconstant entire function of finite order omits at most one complex value.

7. An entire function of nonintegral order has infinitely many fixed points. (A *fixed point* z satisfies $f(z) = z$.)

8. Strengthen Problem 6. Show that with at most one exceptional value an entire function of nonzero order assumes every complex value an infinite number of times.

9. If $f_1, \ldots, f_n$ are nonconstant and of finite order, then $f(z) = f_n(f_{n-1}(\ldots (f_1(z))) \ldots)$ assumes with one possible exception every complex value. (CAREFUL: f need not have finite order.)

10. Let f be defined by any of the series of Problem 6, Section 4. For which of these can you prove that f has infinitely many zeros?

11. Suppose $p(t)$ is continuous on $0 \leq t \leq 1$. If $p \geq 0$, then

$$(*) \qquad f(z) = \int_0^1 e^{zt} p(t) \, dt$$

has infinitely many zeros.

12. Suppose $p(t)$ is continuous on $0 \leq t \leq 1$. If $\mu_n = \int_0^1 p(t) t^n \, dt$ is nonzero for infinitely many n, then the function defined by $(*)$ has infinitely many zeros.

10. The Gamma Function

Let $z_n = -n$ for each integer $n \geq 1$. The exponent of convergence of the sequence $\{z_n\}$ is 1, and therefore by Theorem 6.1 the canonical product

$$P(z) = \prod_{n=1}^{\infty} \left(1 + \frac{z}{n}\right) e^{-z/n}$$

is an entire function of order 1. For the value $z = 1$

$$P(1) = \lim_{N \to \infty} \prod_{n=1}^{N} \left(1 + \frac{1}{n}\right) e^{-1/n}$$

$$= \lim_{N \to \infty} (N + 1) e^{-\sum_{n=1}^{N} (1/n)}$$

$$= e^{-\gamma}$$

where $\gamma = \lim\limits_{N\to\infty} \sum\limits_{n=1}^{N} (1/n) - \log(N+1)$ is *Euler's constant*. The limit γ *exists* because $P(1)$ exists.

Define $Q(z)$ by $Q(z) = P(z-1)$. $Q(z)$ has order 1, and $Q(z)$ has $z = 0$ in addition to $\{z_n\}$ for its zeros. From the Hadamard product theorem follows the representation

$$P(z-1) = Q(z)$$
$$= e^{az+b}zP(z)$$

for certain constants a and b. We can determine a and b by computing $Q(1)$ and $Q'(0)$ as follows.

First,

$$P(0) = 1$$
$$= Q(1)$$
$$= e^{a+b}P(1)$$
$$= e^{a+b-\gamma},$$

and $a + b - \gamma = 2l\pi i$ for some integer l. Secondly, $Q'(0) = \lim\limits_{z\to 0} Q(z)/z = e^b$, and also $Q'(0) = P'(-1)$ which can be evaluated by

$$P'(-1) = \lim_{z\to -1} \frac{P(z)}{z+1}$$
$$= e \lim_{N\to\infty} \prod_{n=2}^{N}\left(1 - \frac{1}{n}\right)e^{1/n}$$
$$= e \lim_{N\to\infty} \frac{e^{\sum_{n=2}^{N} 1/n}}{N}$$
$$= e^{\gamma}.$$

Thus we can take $b = \gamma$, and $a = 2l\pi i$. Since $Q(z)$ is real for real z, the factor $e^{2\pi liz}$ must be real for real z, and this implies $l = 0$. We have obtained the formula

(10.1) $$P(z-1) = ze^{\gamma}P(z).$$

Definition 10.1.   The *gamma function*, $\Gamma(z)$, is defined for $z \neq 0, -1,$ $-2, \ldots$ by the equation

(10.2)
$$\Gamma(z) = \frac{1}{ze^{\gamma z}P(z)}.$$

$\Gamma(z)$ is meromorphic with simple poles at the negative integers and zero. If z is not one of the latter points, there is the reproducing formula

$$\Gamma(z + 1) = \frac{1}{(z + 1)e^{\gamma(z+1)}P(z + 1)}$$

(10.3)
$$= \frac{1}{(z + 1)\dfrac{e^{\gamma(z+1)}P(z)}{(z + 1)e^{\gamma}}}$$

$$= \frac{1}{e^{\gamma z}P(z)}$$

$$= z\Gamma(z).$$

By induction it is easily verified that for integers $n \geq 0$

$$\Gamma(n + 1) = n!.$$

$\Gamma(z)$ has residue 1 at $z = 0$ while at $z = -n$ the residue is, by the reproducing formula,

$$\lim_{z \to -n} (z + n)\Gamma(z) = \lim_{z \to -n} \Gamma(z)(z + n)\frac{z(z + 1) \cdots (z + n - 1)}{z(z + 1) \cdots (z + n - 1)}$$

$$= \lim_{z \to -n} \frac{\Gamma(z + n + 1)}{z(z + 1) \cdots (z + n - 1)}$$

$$= \frac{(-1)^n}{n!}.$$

We remark also that $1/\Gamma(z)$ is an entire function of order 1.

Problems

1. Prove $\Gamma'(1) = e^{-\gamma}$. (Consider $\Gamma'(z)/\Gamma(z)$ for $z = 1$.)
2. Let $a_1, \ldots, a_k$ and $b_1, \ldots, b_l$ be complex numbers.

(a) Prove

$$\prod_{n=1}^{\infty} \frac{(n - a_1) \cdot \cdot \cdot (n - a_k)}{(n - b_1) \cdot \cdot \cdot (n - b_l)}$$

is absolutely convergent if and only if $k = l$ and $a_1 + \cdot \cdot \cdot + a_k - b_1 - \cdot \cdot \cdot - b_l = 0$.

(b) Assume the product in (a) is absolutely convergent. Prove its value is

$$\prod_{j=1}^{k} \frac{\Gamma(1 - b_j)}{\Gamma(1 - a_j)}.$$

(Multiply each term by $1 = e^{(a_1 + \cdots + a_k - b_1 - \cdots - b_k)(1/n)}$.)

(c) Show that

$$\prod_{n=1}^{\infty} \frac{n(a + b + n)}{(a + n)(b + n)} = \frac{\Gamma(a + 1)\Gamma(b + 1)}{\Gamma(a + b + 1)}.$$

11. Standard Formulas

We shall establish some formulas concerning $\Gamma(z)$ which will be useful in Chapter 6.

For nonintegral z the equation

(11.1) $$\Gamma(z)\Gamma(1 - z) = \frac{\pi}{\sin \pi z}$$

is true. To see this we first substitute $z - 1$ for w in the relation $wP(w)P(-w) = (\sin \pi w)/\pi$ (Problem 1, Section 9) to obtain

$$P(1 - z) = \frac{\sin \pi(z - 1)}{\pi} \frac{1}{(z - 1)P(z - 1)}$$

(11.2) $$= \frac{\sin \pi(z - 1)}{\pi} \frac{1}{(z - 1)e^{\gamma z}P(z)}$$

$$= \frac{\sin \pi z}{\pi} \frac{1}{(1 - z)e^{\gamma z}P(z)}.$$

Equation (11.1) follows from (11.2) in view of the fact that $\Gamma(z)\Gamma(1 - z) = \{(1 - z)P(1 - z)e^{\gamma z}P(z)\}^{-1}$.

The value $z = \frac{1}{2}$, when substituted in (11.1), leads to the relation $\Gamma(\frac{1}{2})^2 = \pi$. Clearly, $\Gamma(\frac{1}{2}) > 0$, and therefore

(11.3) $\Gamma(\frac{1}{2}) = \sqrt{\pi}.$

The curious relation (11.3) is useful in proving

Theorem 11.1. (Legendre Duplication Formula) *If* $z \neq 0$, $-\frac{1}{2}$, -1, $-\frac{3}{2}$, . . . , *the equation*

(11.4) $\Gamma(z)\Gamma(z + \frac{1}{2}) = 2^{1-2z} \sqrt{\pi}\, \Gamma(2z)$

is true.

Proof.   Each of the functions $1/\Gamma(2z)$ and $(1/\Gamma(z))\,(1/\Gamma(z + \frac{1}{2}))$ is an entire function of order 1, and each vanishes at the points excluded in the statement of the theorem. The Hadamard product theorem implies for certain constants a and b that $1/\Gamma(z)\ 1/\Gamma(z + \frac{1}{2}) = e^{az+b}(1/\Gamma(2z))$. If $z = \frac{1}{2}$, then

$$\frac{1}{\Gamma(\frac{1}{2})} = e^{a/2+b}.$$

If $z = w + \frac{1}{2}$, then

$$\frac{1}{\Gamma(w + \frac{1}{2})} \cdot \frac{1}{\Gamma(w + 1)} = \frac{e^{aw+b}e^{a/2}}{\Gamma(2w + 1)},$$

or

$$\frac{1}{\Gamma(w)} \cdot \frac{1}{\Gamma(w + \frac{1}{2})} = \frac{e^{aw+b}e^{a/2}}{\Gamma(2w) \cdot 2},$$

where we have used (10.3). Therefore, $e^{a/2} = 2$ and $e^b = 1/(2\pi^{1/2})$. Equation (11.4) follows immediately upon inverting.

Theorem 11.2.   (Gauss) *If* z *is neither a negative integer nor zero, then* $\Gamma(z)$ *can be expressed as the limit*

(11.5) $\Gamma(z) = \lim_{n \to \infty} \dfrac{n!\,n^z}{z(z + 1)\, \cdots\, (z + n)}.$

Proof. By definition

$$\frac{1}{\Gamma(z)} = \lim_{N\to\infty} ze^{(1+\frac{1}{2}+\cdots+1/N)z-(\log N)z} \prod_{n=1}^{N}\left(1+\frac{z}{n}\right)e^{-z/n}$$

$$= \lim_{N\to\infty} ze^{-(\log N)z} \prod_{n=1}^{N}\left(1+\frac{z}{n}\right)$$

$$= \lim_{N\to\infty} \frac{z(z+1)\cdots(z+N)}{N^z N!},$$

and this relation when inverted is (11.5).

As a corollary to (11.5) we shall prove

(11.6)
$$\lim_{n\to\infty} \frac{\Gamma(z+n)}{n^z\Gamma(n)} = 1.$$

Verification is trivial upon noting that

$$\frac{\Gamma(z+n)}{n^z\Gamma(n)} = \frac{(z+n-1)\cdots(z+1)z\Gamma(z)}{n^z\Gamma(n)}$$

$$= \frac{n}{z+n}\frac{(z+n)\cdots(z+1)z\Gamma(z)}{n^z n!}.$$

Problems

1. If t is real, $|\Gamma(it)| = \left(\dfrac{\pi}{t \sinh t\pi}\right)^{1/2}$.

2. Prove Gauss's extension of Legendre's duplication formula. If $n \geq 2$

$$\Gamma(z)\Gamma\left(z+\frac{1}{n}\right)\cdots\Gamma\left(z+\frac{n-1}{n}\right) = (2\pi)^{(n-1)/2}\,n^{(1/2)-nz}\Gamma(nz).$$

(HINT: To evaluate $\Gamma(1/n)\cdots\Gamma((n-1)/n)$ square and pair the terms $\Gamma(k/n)$, $\Gamma(1-(k/n))$.)

12. The Integral Representation of $\Gamma(z)$

It will be necessary to have an integral-theoretic lemma.

Lemma 12.1. Let $\{\varphi_n\}$ be a sequence of nonnegative Riemann integrable functions defined for $0 \leq t < \infty$. If there exists a Riemann integrable function $\varphi(t)$ such that

(a) $\varphi_n(t) \leq \varphi(t)$ for all n, t, and
(b) For each δ, $0 < \delta < 1$, $\lim\limits_{n \to \infty} \varphi_n(t) = \varphi(t)$ holds uniformly for $\delta \leq t \leq 1/\delta$, then

$$\lim_{n \to \infty} \int_0^\infty \varphi_n(t)\, dt = \int_0^\infty \varphi(t)\, dt.$$

Proof.   Given $\epsilon > 0$ select δ, $0 < \delta < 1$, such that

(12.1)
$$\int_\delta^{1/\delta} \varphi(t)\, dt \geq \int_0^\infty \varphi(t)\, dt - \frac{\epsilon}{2}.$$

Next, choose N so large that if $n \geq N$, then

$$\max_{\delta \leq t \leq 1/\delta} |\varphi_n(t) - \varphi(t)| < \frac{\epsilon}{2} \cdot \frac{1}{1/\delta - \delta}.$$

For such n, we have

$$\int_0^\infty \varphi_n(t)\, dt \geq \int_\delta^{1/\delta} \varphi_n(t)\, dt$$

$$\geq \int_\delta^{1/\delta} \varphi(t)\, dt - \frac{\epsilon}{2}$$

$$\geq \int_0^\infty \varphi(t)\, dt - \epsilon.$$

Since also $\int_0^\infty \varphi_n(t)\, dt \leq \int_0^\infty \varphi(t)\, dt$, it follows that if $n \geq n_0$, then

$$\left| \int_0^\infty \varphi_n(t)\, dt - \int_0^\infty \varphi(t)\, dt \right| < \epsilon,$$

and the lemma is proved.

If Re $z > 0$, define

(12.2)
$$F(z) = \int_0^\infty t^{z-1} e^{-t}\, dt.$$

If $x = \text{Re } z$, then $|t^{z-1}| = t^{x-1}$, and from (12.2) it is clear that $|F(z)| \leq F(x) < \infty$. (The reader should check that this is so, even for $0 < x < 1$.)

If $0 < x_1 < x < x_2 < \infty$, then

$$|F(z)| \leq F(x)$$

$$= \int_0^1 t^{x-1} e^{-t}\, dt + \int_1^\infty t^{x-1} e^{-t}\, dt$$

$$\leq \int_0^1 t^{x_1-1} e^{-t}\, dt + \int_1^\infty t^{x_2-1} e^{-t}\, dt$$

$$\leq \int_0^\infty t^{x_1-1} e^{-t}\, dt + \int_0^\infty t^{x_2-1} e^{-t}\, dt$$

$$= F(x_1) + F(x_2).$$

Therefore, $F(z)$ is uniformly bounded in strips $x_1 \leq \operatorname{Re} z \leq x_2$. Also $F(z) = \lim_{n \to \infty} F_n(z)$, where $F_n(z)$ ($|F_n(z)| \leq F(x_1) + F(x_2)$) is the analytic function

$$F_n(z) = \int_{1/n}^n t^{z-1} e^{-t}\, dt.$$

By Vitali's theorem $\{F_n\}$ converges locally uniformly to F, and so F is analytic.

Lemma 12.2.   If x is real, and $x > 1$, then $F(x) = \Gamma(x)$.

Proof.   Fix x and for each n let

$$\varphi_n(t) = \begin{cases} \left(1 - \dfrac{t}{n}\right)^n t^{x-1}, & 0 \leq t \leq n \\ 0, & t > n. \end{cases}$$

If $0 < \delta \leq t \leq 1/\delta$, then $\lim_{n \to \infty} \varphi_n(t) = e^{-t} t^{x-1}$ holds uniformly. Furthermore, we claim $\varphi_n(t) \leq e^{-t} t^{x-1}$ for all n, t. If $t \geq n$ this is clear. If $t < n$, then

$$\log \varphi_n(t) = n \log \left(1 - \frac{t}{n}\right) + \log t^{x-1}$$

$$= -n \sum_{m=1}^\infty \frac{(t/n)^m}{m} + \log t^{x-1}$$

$$\leq -t + \log t^{x-1}$$

$$= \log e^{-t} t^{x-1}$$

implying $\varphi_n(t) \leq e^{-t}t^{x-1}$ as claimed. By Lemma 12.1

$$\lim_{n \to \infty} \int_0^\infty \varphi_n(t) \, dt = \int_0^\infty e^{-t}t^{x-1} \, dt.$$

However,

$$\int_0^\infty \varphi_n(t) \, dt = \int_0^n \left(1 - \frac{t}{n}\right)^n t^{x-1} \, dt$$

$$= \left(1 - \frac{t}{n}\right)^n \frac{t^x}{x} \bigg|_0^n + \frac{1}{x} \int_0^n \left(1 - \frac{t}{n}\right)^{n-1} t^x \, dt$$

$$= \frac{1}{x} \int_0^n \left(1 - \frac{t}{n}\right)^{n-1} t^x \, dt$$

$$= \frac{1}{x} \frac{1}{x+1} \frac{n-1}{n} \int_0^n \left(1 - \frac{t}{n}\right)^{n-2} t^{x+1} \, dt$$

(12.3)

$$\vdots$$

$$= \frac{1}{x} \frac{1}{x+1} \cdots \frac{1}{x+n-1} \frac{n-1}{n} \frac{n-2}{n} \cdots$$

$$\frac{1}{n} \int_0^n t^{x+n-1} \, dt$$

$$= \frac{1}{x} \frac{1}{x+1} \cdots \frac{1}{x+n} \frac{n!}{n^n} n^{x+n}$$

$$= \frac{n^x n!}{x(x+1) \cdots (x+n)}.$$

By Theorem 11.2 the limit as $n \to \infty$ of (12.3) is $\Gamma(x)$, and the lemma is proved.

Since $\Gamma(z)$ and $F(z)$ are analytic for Re $z > 0$, and since $\Gamma(x) = F(x)$ for $x > 1$, the uniqueness theorem for analytic functions implies

Theorem 12.1.   If Re $z > 0$, then

(12.4) $$\Gamma(z) = \int_0^\infty t^{z-1}e^{-t} \, dt.$$

Problems

1. If $-1 < \text{Re } z < 0$, prove that

$$\Gamma(z) = \int_0^\infty t^{z-1}(e^{-t} - 1) \, dt.$$

2. In general if $-k < \text{Re } z < -k + 1$

$$\Gamma(z) = \int_0^\infty t^{z-1}\left(e^{-t} - 1 - t - \cdots - \frac{t^{k-1}}{(k-1)!}\right) dt.$$

3. The *beta function* $B(p, q)$ is defined by

$$B(p, q) = \int_0^1 x^{p-1}(1 - x)^{q-1} \, dx.$$

(a) Prove $B(p, q) = B(q, p)$.
(b) Let $x^2 = u$, $y^2 = v$ in

$$\Gamma(p)\Gamma(q) = \int_0^\infty e^{-u}u^{p-1} \, du \int_0^\infty e^{-v}v^{q-1} \, dv$$

to obtain

$$\Gamma(p)\Gamma(q) = 4\int_0^\infty \int_0^\infty x^{2p-1}y^{2q-1}e^{-(x^2+y^2)} \, dx \, dy$$

for $\text{Re } p, q > \frac{1}{2}$.

(c) Using polar coordinates prove the integral in (b) equals $\Gamma(p + q) B(p, q)$. Thus

$$B(p, q) = \frac{\Gamma(p)\Gamma(q)}{\Gamma(p + q)}.$$

chapter 6

The Prime Number Theorem

1. Dirichlet Series

A *Dirichlet series* is a series of the form

(1.1)
$$\varphi(s) = \sum_{n=1}^{\infty} \frac{a_n}{n^s} \qquad (s = \sigma + it)$$

where $\{a_n\}$ is any sequence of complex numbers. In the present chapter various Dirichlet series will arise, but in each case (aside from the problems) $\{a_n\}$ will be such that $\sum_{n=1}^{\infty} |a_n|/n^\sigma < \infty$ for $1 < \sigma < \infty$. With this assumption it is a consequence of the Weierstrass M-test that since $|a_n/n^s| = |a_n|/n^\sigma$, φ is analytic for Re $s > 1$. Furthermore, φ' is given by a Dirichlet series with coefficients $-a_n \log n$. That is,

(1.2)
$$\varphi'(s) = -\sum_{n=1}^{\infty} \frac{a_n \log n}{n^s},$$

also for Re $s > 1$.

The symbol $d \mid n$, read "d divides n," means n/d is an integer. Thus $\sum_{d\mid n}$ denotes a sum over only those integers d, $1 \le d \le n$, which divide n. If $\varphi(s) = \sum_{n=1}^{\infty} a_n/n^s$ and $\psi(s) = \sum_{n=1}^{\infty} b_n/n^s$ are Dirichlet series, the product

200

of φ and ψ is given, at least formally, by

$$\varphi(s)\psi(s) = \sum_{k=1}^{\infty} \sum_{l=1}^{\infty} \frac{a_k}{k^s} \frac{b_l}{l^s}$$

(1.3)

$$= \sum_{n=1}^{\infty} \sum_{k \cdot l = n} \frac{a_k b_l}{n^s}$$

$$= \sum_{n=1}^{\infty} \frac{c_n}{n^s}$$

where c_n is defined by

$$c_n = \sum_{k \cdot l = n} a_k b_l$$

(1.4)

$$= \sum_{d \mid n} a_d b_{n/d}.$$

To justify (1.3) rigorously it is sufficient to know that the series defining φ and ψ converge absolutely (Problem 1).

Problems

1. Let $\{\alpha_n\}$ and $\{\beta_n\}$ be sequences of complex numbers, and suppose both sums $\sum_{n=1}^{\infty} |\alpha_n|$ and $\sum_{n=1}^{\infty} |\beta_n|$ are finite.

(a) Set $A = \sum_{n=1}^{\infty} |\alpha_n|$, $B = \sum_{n=1}^{\infty} |\beta_n|$, and define

$$\epsilon(M, N) = AB - \sum_{m=1}^{M} \sum_{n=1}^{N} |\alpha_m \beta_n|.$$

Observe that $\lim_{\substack{M \to \infty \\ N \to \infty}} \epsilon(M, N) = 0$.

(b) Let $m_1 n_1, m_2 n_2, \ldots$ be any ordering of the double indices mn, $1 \le m, n < \infty$. For every M and N prove that

$$\left| \sum_{k=1}^{\infty} \alpha_{m_k} \beta_{n_k} - \sum_{m=1}^{M} \sum_{n=1}^{N} \alpha_m \beta_n \right| \le \epsilon(M, N).$$

(c) Conclude for the ordering given in part (b)

$$\sum_{k=1}^{\infty} \alpha_{m_k} \beta_{n_k} = \sum_{m=1}^{\infty} \sum_{n=1}^{\infty} \alpha_m \beta_n.$$

(d) Use part (c) to prove (1.3), given the absolute convergence of the series for φ and ψ.

2. Assume $\{a_n\}$ is such that $\sum_{n=1}^{\infty} |a_n|/n^{\sigma} < \infty$ for $1 < \sigma < \infty$. Prove that for each $\sigma_0 > 1$

$$\lim_{N \to \infty} \sum_{n=1}^{N} \frac{a_n}{n^s} = \varphi(s)$$

exists uniformly in the half-plane $\{s \mid \operatorname{Re} s \geq \sigma_0\}$. Conclude that φ is analytic, and prove (1.2).

3. Let n and m be positive integers. Prove that

$$\lim_{T \to \infty} \frac{1}{T} \int_0^T \left(\frac{m}{n}\right)^{it} dt = 0$$

unless $n = m$.

4. Suppose $\{a_n\}$ is such that $\sum_{n=1}^{\infty} |a_n|/n^{\sigma} < \infty$, $1 < \sigma < \infty$. Prove that for each $m > 0$

$$\lim_{T \to \infty} \frac{1}{T} \int_0^T \varphi(2 + it) m^{it} \, dt = \frac{a_m}{m^2}.$$

Conclude that φ is identically zero only if $a_1 = a_2 = \cdots = 0$.

2. Number-theoretic Functions

In the study of number theory a sequence $f(1), f(2), \ldots$ of complex numbers is called a *number-theoretic function*. Just two of these functions will be of interest for our discussion, and these will be introduced shortly.

If $n > 1$ is an integer, the fundamental theorem of arithmetic asserts that n can be decomposed into a product of nonzero powers of distinct prime numbers. That is,

(2.1) $$n = p_1^{l_1} \cdots p_k^{l_k}$$

with $l_j > 0, 1 \leq j \leq k$. Furthermore, except for the ordering of $p_1, \ldots, p_k$ the representation is unique.

The first of our two number-theoretic functions is the *Möbius function*, $\mu(n)$. It is defined by

$$(2.2) \quad \mu(n) = \begin{cases} 1, & n = 1 \\ (-1)^k, & n > 1 \text{ and } l_1 = \cdots = l_k = 1 \text{ in } (2.1) \\ 0, & \text{otherwise.} \end{cases}$$

The Möbius function is well defined because of the uniqueness in (2.1). Notice that $\mu(n) = 0$ just when n is divisible by a perfect square other than 1.

Lemma 2.1.   If $n > 1$, then

$$(2.3) \qquad\qquad \sum_{d|n} \mu(d) = 0.$$

Proof.   To evaluate (2.3) it is sufficient to sum over those divisors of n for which $\mu(d) \neq 0$. If n is represented by (2.1), then unless $d = 1$, such a divisor must have the form

$$d = p_{i_1} \cdots p_{i_m}$$

for certain $i_1, \ldots, i_m$ with $1 \leq i_1 < i_2 < \cdots < i_m \leq k$. There are $\binom{k}{m}$ ways to choose $i_1, \ldots, i_m$, and for each choice $\mu(d) = (-1)^m$. Therefore,

$$\sum_{d|n} \mu(d) = 1 + \binom{k}{1}(-1) + \binom{k}{2}(-1)^2 + \cdots + \binom{k}{k}(-1)^k$$

$$= (1 + (-1))^k$$

$$= 0$$

and the lemma is proved.

REMARK.   Equation (2.3) can also be written as

$$(2.3') \qquad\qquad \sum_{d|n} \mu\left(\frac{n}{d}\right) = 0$$

since both d and n/d are divisors of n if either is.

Let f be a number-theoretic function, and associate with f a second such function, g, where g is defined by the formula

(2.4) $$g(n) = \sum_{d|n} f(d).$$

The *Möbius inversion formula* gives the inverse transformation to (2.4). More precisely,

Theorem 2.1.   *Let g be related to f by* (2.4). *Then for each n*

(2.5) $$f(n) = \sum_{d|n} g(d)\mu\left(\frac{n}{d}\right).$$

Proof.   Substituting the definition of g in the right side of (2.5) we see that

(2.6) $$\sum_{d|n} g(d)\mu\left(\frac{n}{d}\right) = \sum_{d|n} \sum_{m|d} f(m)\mu\left(\frac{n}{d}\right).$$

If m is a fixed divisor of n, the integers n/d which appear with m in (2.6) are just the divisors of n/m. Unless $m = n$, the contribution of these terms to the sum is

$$f(m) \sum_{\substack{\frac{n}{d}|n \\ d|\frac{n}{m}}} \mu\left(\frac{n}{d}\right) = 0$$

by Lemma 2.1. When $m = n$ the contribution is of course $f(n)$, and (2.5) obtains. The theorem is proved.

The second number-theoretic function we consider is $\Lambda(n)$, defined by

(2.7) $$\Lambda(n) = \begin{cases} \log p, & n = p^m, \ m > 0 \text{ and } p \text{ prime} \\ 0, & \text{otherwise.} \end{cases}$$

Let n be an integer greater than 1, and write $n = p_1^{l_1} \cdots p_k^{l_k}$ as in (2.1). Since $\Lambda(d) = 0$ unless d is a nonzero power of a prime number, we have

$$\sum_{d|n} \Lambda(d) = \sum_{j=1}^{k} l_j \log p_j$$
$$= \log n.$$

Therefore by Theorem 2.1

(2.8) $$\Lambda(n) = \sum_{d|n} \mu\left(\frac{n}{d}\right) \log d.$$

Formula (2.8) will be useful in Section 4 and beyond.

Problems

1. Let $d(n)$ denote the number of divisors of n. Prove that

$$\sum_{m|n} d(m)\mu\left(\frac{n}{m}\right) = 1.$$

2. Let $\sigma(n)$ denote the sum of the divisors of n. Prove that

$$\sum_{m|n} \sigma(m)\mu\left(\frac{n}{m}\right) = n.$$

3. Let $\varphi(n)$ be the number of integers less than n which are relatively prime to n (m is *relatively prime* to n if the greatest common divisor of m and n is 1). Prove that

$$\varphi(n) = \sum_{d|n} d\mu\left(\frac{n}{d}\right).$$

4. If $f(n)$ is a number-theoretic function, define

$$h(n) = \sum_{d|n} f(d)\mu\left(\frac{n}{d}\right).$$

Prove that

$$f(n) = \sum_{d|n} h(d).$$

3. Statement of the Prime Number Theorem

Denote by $\pi(x)$, $0 \leq x < \infty$, the number of primes less than or equal to x. While it was known to Euclid that there are infinitely many primes, i.e., that $\lim_{x\to\infty} \pi(x) = \infty$, it was not until the nineteenth century that mathematicians began to ask seriously about the rapidity of convergence of $\pi(x)$ to ∞.

It was conjectured by Gauss[1] on the basis of empirical evidence that for

---

[1] According to Gauss, formula (3.1) occurred to him in 1792 or 1793, roughly at the age of 15. (He was born in 1777.) An interesting history of the nineteenth century researches on the prime number theorem is to be found in Landau, *Handbuch der Lehre von der Verteilung der Primzahlen*, Chelsea, New York, pp. 3–55.

large values of x, $\pi(x)$ behaves like li x, where

$$(3.1) \qquad \text{li } x = \int_2^x \frac{du}{\log u}.$$

The sense of "behave like," though not spelled out, was undoubtedly the sense of asymptotic equality. In other words it should be true that

$$(3.2) \qquad \lim_{x \to \infty} \frac{\pi(x)}{\text{li } x} = 1.$$

Legendre also made conjectures concerning $\pi(x)$ for large x. Writing first in 1798 and then again in 1808, Legendre suggested that $\pi(x)$ could be represented as

$$\pi(x) = \frac{x}{A \log x - B},$$

where as functions of x, $\lim_{x \to \infty} A = 1$ and $\lim_{x \to \infty} B = 1.08366 \ldots$. To support his claim he offered data showing $\pi(x)$ to be in remarkably close agreement with $y(x)$, where

$$(3.3) \qquad y(x) = \frac{x}{\log x - 1.08366}$$

for values of x up to one million.

Using (3.3) as a guide Legendre also speculated that for large m and x, with m much less than x, the ratio of primes to integers in the interval $[x - m, x + m]$ is approximately $1/(\log x - 1.08366)$. Gauss's conjecture arose from taking this same density to be $1/(\log x)$. Thus Legendre and Gauss are not so far apart as it might at first appear.

While neither Gauss nor Legendre was able to prove his conjecture, each conjecture turned out to be true. (In Legendre's case 1.08366 . . . was wrong.) In 1896 J. Hadamard and C. de la Vallée Poussin, working independently, proved

$$(3.4) \qquad \lim_{x \to \infty} \frac{\pi(x) \log x}{x} = 1$$

which is known as the *prime number theorem*. Although (3.4) does not have the form of either Gauss's or Legendre's statement, it is very close. For example, since $\lim_{x \to \infty} (\log x \text{ li } x)/x = 1$ (Problem 1), (3.4) implies (3.2). As for (3.3), if we define $B(x)$ implicitly by

(3.5)
$$\pi(x) = \frac{x}{\log x - B(x)},$$

then by (3.4) the denominator of (3.5) is dominated by $\log x$; that is, $\lim_{x \to \infty} B(x)/(\log x) = 0.$[2]

The initial proofs of (3.4) used ideas put forth by Riemann in a short but widely celebrated article on the "zeta function," $\zeta(s)$, together with deep theorems from complex analysis, especially concerning $\zeta(s)$. As had been expected from the time of Riemann's paper (1859), the analytic properties of $\zeta(s)$ were seen to be at the heart of the matter, and this continued to be the case as the theorem aged and new proofs appeared. Most important to the theorem's development was the fact that the role played by $\zeta(s)$, while not diminishing in importance, became less and less difficult to describe. An important contributor to this process was Landau. However it was finally with the researches of Wiener on "Tauberian theorems" that both Wiener himself and later a student, S. Ikehara, were able to give proofs of (3.4) which stripped away all but one essential property of $\zeta(s)$. At once the picture became crystal clear and the proof (especially Ikehara's) relatively easy to understand. Indeed, thanks are due to Wiener and Ikehara for making accessible to the nonspecialist what Abel once called the "most remarkable theorem in the whole of mathematics."[3]

We shall conclude this section by reducing (3.4) to the statement

(3.6)
$$\lim_{x \to \infty} \frac{\psi(x)}{x} = 1,$$

where

(3.7)
$$\psi(x) = \sum_{n \le x} \Lambda(n).$$

The remainder of the chapter is then devoted to a discussion of $\zeta(s)$ and the machinery necessary for Ikehara's proof.

[2] From a more advanced version of (3.4) it follows that $\lim_{x \to \infty} B(x)$ exists, but the limit is 1, not 1.08366 . . . . As an approximation to $\pi(x)$, li x can be shown to be much better than $x/(\log x - 1)$. For proofs of these facts, see Ingham, *The Distribution of Prime Numbers*.

[3] In a letter in 1823. He was referring to the conjecture of Legendre.

Theorem 3.1.   *If*

(3.8)
$$\lim_{x \to \infty} \frac{\psi(x)}{x} = 1,$$

then

(3.9)
$$\lim_{x \to \infty} \frac{\pi(x) \log x}{\psi(x)} = 1$$

and

(3.10)
$$\lim_{x \to \infty} \frac{\pi(x) \log x}{x} = 1.$$

Proof.   Equation (3.10) is an obvious consequence of (3.9) and (3.8). Therefore we prove (3.9). In what follows p will denote a prime, and, for example, $\sum_{p \le x}$ will denote a sum over the primes less than or equal to x.

If $0 < x < \infty$, and if $p \le x$, let m be the integer such that $p^m \le x < p^{m+1}$. In the sum defining $\psi(x)$, $\log p$ occurs m times. Since $m \le (\log x)/(\log p)$, we have

$$\psi(x) \le \sum_{p \le x} \frac{\log x}{\log p} \log p$$

$$= \pi(x) \log x.$$

It follows that

(3.11)
$$1 \le \frac{\pi(x) \log x}{\psi(x)}$$

for $x > 0$.

Define $w_x = x/(\log^2 x)$ for $x > 1$. We will prove

(3.12)
$$\pi(x) \le w_x + \frac{\psi(x)}{\log w_x}$$

which in view of (3.11) implies

(3.13)
$$1 \le \frac{\pi(x) \log x}{\psi(x)} \le \frac{w_x \log x}{\psi(x)} + \frac{\log x}{\log w_x}.$$

Since obviously $\lim_{x \to \infty} (w_x \log x)/\psi(x) = 0$ and $\lim_{x \to \infty} (\log x)/(\log w_x) = 1$, (3.9) follows from (3.13).

To prove (3.12) write $\pi(x) = \pi(w_x) + \sum_{w_x < p \leq x} 1$, and then use the relations

$$\pi(w_x) \leq w_x$$

and

$$\sum_{w_x < p \leq x} \log p \leq \psi(x)$$

to obtain

$$\pi(x) = \pi(w_x) + \sum_{w_x < p \leq x} 1$$

$$\leq w_x + \sum_{w_x < p \leq x} \frac{\log p}{\log w_x}$$

$$\leq w_x + \frac{\psi(x)}{\log w_x}$$

as claimed. As we have observed, (3.9) follows, and the theorem is proved.

Problems

1. Prove

$$\lim_{x \to \infty} \frac{\text{li } x \log x}{x} = 1.$$

(HINT: Integrate by parts, and divide the interval $[2, x]$ into $[2, \log x]$ and $[\log x, x]$.)

2. Assume $\lim_{x \to \infty} ((\pi(x) \log x)/x) = 1$. If p_n denotes the nth prime, prove

$$\lim_{n \to \infty} \frac{p_n}{n \log n} = 1.$$

(HINT: Observe that $\lim_{x \to \infty} \log ((\pi(x) \log x)/x) = 0$, and prove

$$\lim_{x \to \infty} \frac{\log \pi(x)}{\log x} = 1.$$

Argue from there.)

3. Let $[y]$ denote the greatest integer less than or equal to y. Prove

$$\psi(x) = \sum_{p \leq x} \left[\frac{\log x}{\log p} \right] \log p.$$

4. Prove $\psi(x) \leq x \log x$.

5. Assume $\lim\limits_{x \to \infty} ((\pi(x) \log x)/x) = 1$. For every $\epsilon > 0$ there exists an integer n_0 such that if $n \geq n_0$, the interval $[n, (1 + \epsilon)n]$ contains a prime number.

4. The Riemann Zeta Function

The *Riemann zeta function*, $\zeta(s)$, is defined by the Dirichlet series

$$(4.1) \qquad \zeta(s) = \sum_{n=1}^{\infty} \frac{1}{n^s} \qquad (s = \sigma + it)$$

for Re $s > 1$. By Section 1 (with $a_n \equiv 1$) this function is analytic with derivative

$$(4.2) \qquad \zeta'(s) = -\sum_{n=1}^{\infty} \frac{\log n}{n^s}.$$

We will discuss first some of the elementary properties of $\zeta(s)$.

Take $a_n = \mu(n)$ in (1.1), where $\mu(n)$ is the Möbius function, and define $\varphi(s)$ by

$$(4.3) \qquad \varphi(s) = \sum_{n=1}^{\infty} \frac{\mu(n)}{n^s}.$$

Making use of formulas (1.3) and (2.3) we compute the product $\zeta(s)\varphi(s)$, getting

$$(4.4) \qquad \zeta(s)\varphi(s) = \sum_{n=1}^{\infty} \frac{1}{n^s} \sum_{d|n} \mu(d)$$

$$= 1.$$

It follows that $\zeta(s) \neq 0$ for Re $s > 1$, and $\varphi(s) = 1/\zeta(s)$.

Lemma 4.1. If Re $s > 1$, then

$$(4.5) \qquad \frac{\zeta'(s)}{\zeta(s)} = -\sum_{n=1}^{\infty} \frac{\Lambda(n)}{n^s}.$$

Proof. By (4.4) $\zeta'(s)/\zeta(s) = \zeta'(s)\varphi(s)$. Using (1.3) and (2.8) to evaluate $\zeta'(s)\varphi(s)$, we find

$$\zeta'(s)\varphi(s) = -\sum_{n=1}^{\infty} \frac{1}{n^s} \sum_{d|n} \mu\left(\frac{n}{d}\right) \log d$$

$$= -\sum_{n=1}^{\infty} \frac{\Lambda(n)}{n^s}$$

which implies (4.5). The lemma is proved.

It is equation (4.5) which provides the connection between number theory and complex analysis in the proof of the prime number theorem.

The zeta function was known to Euler for certain values of s, and his name is attached to a well-known formula containing it.

Theorem 4.1. (Euler Product Formula) *If* Re $s > 1$, $\zeta(s)$ *can be expressed as a product,*

(4.6) $$\zeta(s) = \prod_{n=1}^{\infty} (1 - p_n^{-s})^{-1}$$

where $\{p_n\}$ *is the sequence of prime numbers.*

Proof. For each n $(1 - p_n^{-s})^{-1} = \sum_{m=0}^{\infty} p_n^{-ms}$. Substituting this expression in the finite product $\prod_{n=1}^{N} (1 - p_n^{-s})^{-1}$ we find

(4.7) $$\prod_{n=1}^{N} (1 - p_n^{-s})^{-1} = \sum_{k=1}^{\infty} n_k^{-s}$$

the sum extending over those integers n_k whose prime decomposition contains only primes from the set $\{p_1, \ldots, p_N\}$. Because of unique factorization the coefficient of n_k^{-s} is 1 for each k.

Now let $N \to \infty$ in (4.7). The right-hand side approaches $\zeta(s)$ because (a) every integer eventually appears in the sum, and (b) (4.1) converges absolutely. Thus

$$\lim_{N \to \infty} \prod_{n=1}^{N} (1 - p_n^{-s})^{-1} = \zeta(s).$$

Since $\zeta(s) \neq 0$, the product is convergent in the sense of Chapter 5. This completes the proof.

REMARK.   It is unnecessary to know $\zeta(s) \neq 0$ for (4.6) because convergence is easy to verify directly. In fact the usual way of proving $\zeta(s) \neq 0$ for Re $s > 1$ is through (4.6).

Using the Euler product formula it is possible to prove $\sum\limits_{n=1}^{\infty} 1/p_n = \infty$.

Theorem 4.2.   *The sum of the reciprocals of the prime numbers is infinite. That is,*

$$\sum_{n=1}^{\infty} \frac{1}{p_n} = \infty.$$

Proof.   By Theorem 1.3 of Chapter 5 $\sum\limits_{n=1}^{\infty} 1/p_n = \infty$ if, and only if,

$$\sum_{n=1}^{\infty} \left| \log\left(1 - \frac{1}{p_n}\right) \right| = \infty.$$

Because $\log(1 - (1/p_n)) < 0$ for each n, it is sufficient to prove

$$-\sum_{n=1}^{\infty} \log\left(1 - \frac{1}{p_n}\right) = \infty.$$

Since the inequality

$$- \log\left(1 - \frac{1}{p_n}\right) \geq - \log\left(1 - \frac{1}{p_n{}^x}\right)$$

is true for $1 < x < \infty$, it follows from the Euler product formula that

$$(4.8) \qquad -\sum_{n=1}^{\infty} \log\left(1 - \frac{1}{p_n}\right) \geq -\sum_{n=1}^{\infty} \log\left(1 - \frac{1}{p_n{}^x}\right)$$

$$= \log \zeta(x).$$

As $x \to 1$, $\zeta(x) \to \infty$ and $\log \zeta(x) \to \infty$. The left side of (4.8), which is independent of x, must therefore be infinite. The theorem is proved.

Problems

1. Prove that $\zeta^2(s) = \displaystyle\sum_{n=1}^{\infty} \frac{d(n)}{n^s}$.

2. Prove that $\zeta(s)\zeta(s-1) = \displaystyle\sum_{n=1}^{\infty} \frac{\sigma(n)}{n^s}$.

3. Prove that $\dfrac{\zeta(s-1)}{\zeta(s)} = \displaystyle\sum_{n=1}^{\infty} \frac{\varphi(n)}{n^s}$.

4. Let $p_{n_1}, p_{n_2}, \ldots$ be a subsequence of the sequence of primes. Prove that if there exists a number $L < \infty$ such that every interval $(a, a + L)$ contains a number whose prime decomposition involves only primes from the given sequence, then $\displaystyle\sum_{i=1}^{\infty} 1/p_{n_i} = \infty$. (HINT: Let $m_1, m_2, \ldots$ be the integers expressible as products of powers of p_{n_1}, $p_{n_2}, \ldots$. Define $\tilde{\zeta}(s) = \displaystyle\sum_{k=1}^{\infty} 1/m_k{}^s$, note that $\tilde{\zeta}(1) = \infty$, and argue as in Theorem 4.2.)

5. Verify directly that $\displaystyle\prod_{n=1}^{\infty} (1 - p_n{}^{-s})^{-1}$ converges for Re $s > 1$.

6. Use the product formula for $\zeta(s)$ (better yet, $1/\zeta(s)$) to prove

$$\frac{1}{\zeta(s)} = \sum_{n=1}^{\infty} \frac{\mu(n)}{n^s}.$$

5. Analytic Continuation of $\zeta(s)$

We turn to the deeper analytic properties of $\zeta(s)$. It was proved by Riemann that $\zeta(s)$ can be analytically continued to a region much larger than is accounted for by (4.1). He proved

Theorem 5.1. *There exists an entire function g such that*

(5.1) $$\zeta(s) = \frac{1}{s-1} + g(s).$$

In other words $\zeta(s)$ can be defined to be analytic everywhere except $s = 1$ where there is a simple pole with residue 1.

In proving Theorem 5.1 and the functional equation (Theorem 6.1 of Section 6) we will follow the lines of (one of) Riemann's original arguments. Theorem 5.1 requires the three lemmas which follow.

Lemma 5.1.   Let $x^{s-1} = e^{(s-1)\ln x}$, $0 < x < \infty$. The integral

$$(5.2) \qquad f(s) = \int_0^\infty \frac{x^{s-1}}{e^x - 1}\, dx$$

defines an analytic function of s for Re $s > 1$.

Proof.   For any value of σ, $-\infty < \sigma < \infty$, the function $(x^{\sigma-1}/(e^x - 1))$ is integrable on the interval $[1, \infty)$. Being dominated by $x^{\sigma-2}$, it is also integrable on $(0, 1)$ if $\sigma > 1$. Thus letting $\sigma = $ Re s, (5.2) is convergent for Re $s > 1$.

We express f as a pointwise limit

$$f(s) = \lim_{\delta \to 0} \int_\delta^{1/\delta} \frac{x^{s-1}}{e^x - 1}\, dx$$
$$= \lim_{\delta \to 0} f_\delta(s)$$

of entire functions f_δ, $0 < \delta < 1$. The analyticity of f will follow from Vitali's theorem, Theorem 5.1 of Chapter 4, once we have shown that $\{f_\delta\}$ is locally bounded in the half-plane Re $s > 1$.

If $1 < \sigma_1 \leq$ Re $s \leq \sigma_2 < \infty$, then trivially

$$\left| \frac{x^{s-1}}{e^x - 1} \right| \leq \frac{x^{\sigma_1-1}}{e^x - 1} + \frac{x^{\sigma_2-1}}{e^x - 1}$$

on $(0, \infty)$. This implies

$$|f_\delta(s)| \leq f(\sigma_1) + f(\sigma_2),$$

and therefore $\{f_\delta\}$ is locally bounded. The lemma is proved.

Lemma 5.2.   If f is defined by (5.2), then $f(s) = \Gamma(s)\zeta(s)$. That is, for Re $s > 1$

$$(5.3) \qquad \int_0^\infty \frac{x^{s-1}}{e^x - 1}\, dx = \Gamma(s)\zeta(s).$$

Proof. By the uniqueness theorem it is enough to verify (5.3) for real values of s between 1 and ∞. Fixing such an s we set up the function

$$\varphi_n(x) = x^{s-1} \sum_{k=1}^{n} e^{-kx}$$

for each $n \geq 1$. It is easy to see that $\lim_{n \to \infty} \varphi_n(x) = (x^{s-1}/(e^x - 1))$ in such a way that the hypotheses of Lemma 12.1 of Chapter 5 are satisfied. Therefore

$$\int_0^\infty \frac{x^{s-1}}{e^x - 1} \, dx = \lim_{n \to \infty} \sum_{k=1}^{n} \int_0^\infty x^{s-1} e^{-kx} \, dx$$

$$= \lim_{n \to \infty} \sum_{k=1}^{n} \frac{1}{k^s} \int_0^\infty y^{s-1} e^{-y} \, dy$$

$$= \Gamma(s)\zeta(s)$$

which is (5.3). Applying the uniqueness theorem, (5.3) holds for complex s with Re $s > 1$, and the lemma is proved.

In order to define $\zeta(s)$ for Re $s \leq 1$ it would be enough to define the left side of (5.3) for Re $s \leq 1$. However $(x^{s-1}/(e^x - 1))$ is integrable near 0 only if Re $s > 1$. To avoid this difficulty at 0 we will replace $(0, \infty)$ with a contour whose points stay away from the origin.

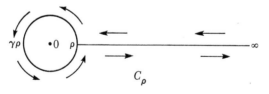

Figure 12.

Let C_ρ be the contour pictured in Figure 12, and denote by γ_ρ the circular portion of C_ρ. Notice that C_ρ traverses the interval $[\rho, \infty)$ twice, once from ∞ to ρ and once from ρ to ∞.

We define $\log z$ as follows on C_ρ. Let $\log z = \ln z$ on the upper branch of $[\rho, \infty), \log z = \ln \rho + i \arg z, 0 < \arg z < 2\pi$, on γ_ρ, and $\log z = \ln z + 2\pi i$ on the lower branch of $[\rho, \infty)$. Then we let $z^{s-1} = e^{(s-1)\log z}$ and set up the function

(5.4) $$I(s) = \int_{C_\rho} \frac{z^{s-1}}{e^z - 1} \, dz$$

where ρ is now taken to lie between 0 and 2π. So defined, $I(s)$ is entire. When the integral (5.4) is written as a sum of three integrals, one for each component of C_ρ, we find

(5.5) $$I(s) = \int_{\gamma_\rho} \frac{z^{s-1}}{e^z - 1}\,dz + (e^{2\pi i s} - 1)\int_\rho^\infty \frac{x^{s-1}}{e^x - 1}\,dx,$$

where in the second integral $x^{s-1} = e^{(s-1)\ln x}$. For later use we note that

(5.6)
$$I(1) = \int_{\gamma_\rho} \frac{dz}{e^z - 1}$$
$$= 2\pi i.$$

An important property of $I(s)$ is that it is independent of ρ, so long as $0 < \rho < 2\pi$. To prove this we fix ρ' and ρ with $0 < \rho' < \rho < 2\pi$, and let

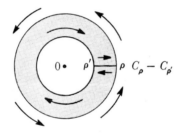

Figure 13.

$C_\rho - C_{\rho'}$ be the contour of Figure 13. It is easy to see that

(5.7) $$\int_{C_\rho - C_{\rho'}} \frac{z^{s-1}}{e^z - 1}\,dz = \int_{C_\rho} \frac{z^{s-1}}{e^z - 1}\,dz - \int_{C_{\rho'}} \frac{z^{s-1}}{e^z - 1}\,dz$$

and since the right side represents the difference between the definitions of $I(s)$ corresponding to ρ and ρ', our assertion will follow from the left side's being 0.

The contour $C_\rho - C_{\rho'}$ bounds a simply connected region (the shaded portion of Figure 13) in which $z^{s-1}/(e^z - 1)$ is an analytic function of z. Therefore by Cauchy's theorem (Problem 1)

$$\int_{C_\rho - C_{\rho'}} \frac{z^{z-1}}{e^z - 1}\,dz = 0,$$

and $I(s)$ is independent of ρ.

Lemma 5.3.   If Re $s > 1$, then

(5.8) $I(s) = (e^{2\pi is} - 1)\Gamma(s)\zeta(s).$

Proof.   Fix $\sigma = $ Re s, $\sigma > 1$. Since $e^z - 1 = zh(z)$, where h is continuous (in fact analytic) with $h(0) = 1$, there exists $\rho_0 > 0$ such that if $0 < |z| \leq \rho_0$, then

$$\frac{1}{|e^z - 1|} \leq \frac{2}{|z|}.$$

From this inequality it follows for $0 < \rho \leq \rho_0$ that

$$\left| \int_{\gamma_\rho} \frac{z^{s-1}}{e^z - 1}\, dz \right| \leq 2 \int_{\gamma_\rho} \rho^{\sigma-2}\, |dz|$$

$$= 4\pi\rho^{\sigma-1}$$

which tends to 0 with ρ. Therefore as $\rho \to 0$ in (5.5), we conclude from Lemma 5.2 that

$$I(s) = (e^{2\pi is} - 1)\Gamma(s)\zeta(s)$$

which was to be proved.

Proof of Theorem 5.1.   Equation (5.8) is true for Re $s > 1$, however both $I(s)$ and $(e^{2\pi is} - 1)\Gamma(s)$ are entire functions of s. (Poles of the gamma function cancel with zeros of $(e^{2\pi is} - 1)$.) Therefore $\zeta(s)$ can be *defined* by the equation

(5.9) $$\zeta(s) = \frac{I(s)}{(e^{2\pi is} - 1)\Gamma(s)}$$

for all values of s such that $(e^{2\pi is} - 1)\Gamma(s) \neq 0$.

Since $\Gamma(s)$ is never zero, and since $\Gamma(s)$ has simple poles at $s = 0, -1, -2, \ldots$, there are no zeros of $(e^{2\pi is} - 1)\Gamma(s)$, except $s = 1$, with Re $s \leq 1$. We know from the definition that $\zeta(s)$ is analytic for Re $s > 1$, and therefore it follows that $\zeta(s)$ is analytic for all values of s but $s = 1$. At $s = 1$ there is a simple pole with residue

$$\lim_{s \to 1} (s - 1)\frac{I(s)}{(e^{2\pi is} - 1)\Gamma(s)} = \frac{I(1)}{2\pi i\Gamma(1)}$$

$$= 1$$

by (5.6). The theorem is proved.

Problems

1. By adjoining intervals $re^{2\pi i/3}$, $\rho' \leq r \leq \rho$, and $re^{4\pi i/3}$, $\rho' \leq r \leq \rho$, to the contour $C_\rho - C_{\rho'}$, express the left-hand side of (5.7) as the sum of three integrals to each of which Cauchy's theorem for a disk applies.

2. Let the following formula of Jacobi be given for $0 < x < \infty$:

(5.10)
$$\sum_{n=-\infty}^{\infty} e^{-n^2\pi x} = \frac{1}{x^{1/2}} \sum_{-\infty}^{\infty} e^{-n^2\pi/x}.$$

Define $\psi(x) = \sum_{n=1}^{\infty} e^{-n^2\pi x}$

(a) Prove $\int_0^\infty x^{s/2-1}\psi(x)\,dx = \pi^{-s/2}\Gamma(\tfrac{1}{2}s)\zeta(s)$.

(b) Use (5.10) to show that
$$2\psi(x) + 1 = \frac{1}{x^{1/2}}\left\{2\psi\left(\frac{1}{x}\right) + 1\right\}.$$

(c) Separate (a) into two integrals, one from 0 to 1 and one from 1 to ∞. Substitute (b) for $\psi(x)$ in the first integral, and in so doing prove
$$\pi^{-s/2}\Gamma\left(\frac{1}{2}s\right)\zeta(s) = \frac{1}{s(s-1)} + \int_1^\infty \{x^{-s/2-1/2} + x^{s/2-1}\}\psi(x)\,dx.$$

(d) Prove that $\pi^{-s/2}\Gamma(\tfrac{1}{2}s)\zeta(s)$ is invariant under the substitution $s \to 1 - s$. This is Riemann's original form (and proof) of the functional equation.

3. The following is an alternative method for continuing $\zeta(s)$.

(a) Prove
$$\left(1 - \frac{1}{k^s}\right)\zeta(s) = \frac{1}{k^s}\sum_{j=1}^{k-1}\sum_{n=1}^{\infty}\frac{1}{n^s}\left(1 - \frac{j}{kn}\right)^{-s}.$$

(b) Set $z = -j/kn$ in the power series expansion of $(1 + z)^{-s}$ about 0 (Chapter 1, Section 1, Problem 3) to obtain

(5.10)
$$\left(1 - \frac{1}{k^{s-1}}\right)\zeta(s) = \frac{1}{k^s}\sum_{j=1}^{k-1}\sum_{n=1}^{\infty}\frac{1}{n^s}\sum_{i=1}^{\infty}\frac{(s+i-1)^{(i)}}{i!}\frac{j^i}{k^i n^i}$$

where $w^{(i)} = w(w-1)\cdots(w-i+1)$.

(c) Varying k where necessary show that (5.10) can be used to define $\zeta(s)$ for Re $s > 0$, $s \neq 1$.

(d) Observe that $\zeta(s) = A/(s - 1) + g(s)$, where g is analytic for Re $s > 0$ and $A = \lim_{s \to 1} (s - 1)\zeta(s)$. Thus

$$A \log k = \lim_{s \to 1} \left(1 - \frac{1}{k^{s-1}} \right) \zeta(s).$$

(e) Set $k = 2$ and $s = 1$ in the right-hand side of (5.10) to find $A = 1$.

(f) Finally, use (5.10) to define $\zeta(s)$ for Re $s \leq 0$.

4. Multiply both sides of (5.10) by k^{s-1} and assume Re $s < 1$. Observe that the right-hand side becomes an approximating sum for $\int_0^1 f(s, x)\, dx$, where

$$f(s, x) = \sum_{i=1}^{\infty} \frac{(s + i - 1)^{(i)}}{i!} \zeta(s + i) x^i.$$

Conclude that if the interchange of summation and integration is justified (which it is)

$$\zeta(s) = - \sum_{i=1}^{\infty} \frac{(s + i - 1)^{(i)}}{(i + 1)!} \zeta(s + i)$$

still for Re $s < 1$.

5. Using the definition $\Gamma(z) = \int_0^{\infty} t^{z-1} e^{-t}\, dt$, prove

$$\Gamma(z) = (e^{2\pi i z} - 1)^{-1} J(z)$$

where $J(z)$ is an entire function of z.

6. Prove from the definition that $I(n) = 0$, $n = 2, 3, \ldots$.

6. Riemann's Functional Equation[1]

Much of the analytic interest in the zeta function comes from *Riemann's functional equation*,

(6.1) $$\zeta(s) = 2^s \pi^{s-1} \sin \frac{\pi s}{2} \Gamma(1 - s)\zeta(1 - s)$$

[1] Section 6 and 7 are unnecessary for the prime number theorem.

which relates $\zeta(s)$ to $\zeta(1 - s)$. Equation (6.1) is the content of Theorem 6.1.

In order to resolve equation (6.1) with the analyticity of $\zeta(s)$ for $s \neq 1$, every pole of $\Gamma(1 - s)$, save $s = 1$, must be accompanied by a zero of either $2^s \pi^{s-1} \sin(\pi s/2)$ or $\zeta(1 - s)$. The poles occur when $s = 2, 3, \ldots$, and only those at $s = 2, 4, 6, \ldots$ are cancelled by $2^s \pi^{s-1} \sin(\pi s/2)$. We are forced to conclude that $\zeta(1 - s) = 0$ for $s = 3, 5, \ldots$. In other words, $\zeta(s) = 0$ when $s = -2, -4, \ldots$.

Since $\zeta(s) \neq 0$ for Re $s > 1$, another consequence of (6.1) is that every zero of $\zeta(1 - s)$ with Re $s > 1$ (i.e., Re $(1 - s) < 0$) must be accompanied by a pole of $2^s \pi^{s-1} \sin(\pi s/2)\Gamma(1 - s)$. Therefore, it follows that *the only zeros of $\zeta(s)$ with* Re $s > 1$ *or* Re $s < 0$ *are the points* $s = -2$, $-4, \ldots$. These are called the *trivial zeros*.

In the context of $\zeta(s)$ the strip $\{s \mid 0 \leq \text{Re } s \leq 1\}$ is called the *critical strip*. It was conjectured by Riemann that the zeros of $\zeta(s)$ inside the critical strip have real parts equal to $\frac{1}{2}$. While a great deal is known of these zeros, this assertion, the *Riemann hypothesis*, remains an open question.

A second computation of $I(s)$ follows. When the result is equated with (5.8), the functional equation will drop out rather easily.

Let C_n, $n = 1, 2, \ldots$, be the contour arising from taking $\rho = (2n + 1)\pi$ in Figure 12. Not only is $z^{s-1}/(e^z - 1)$ finite on γ_n, the circular portion of C_n, but also the number

$$(6.2) \qquad \sup_{n} \max_{z \in \gamma_n} \frac{1}{|e^z - 1|} = M$$

is finite (Problem 4).

In what follows we assume ρ to be a fixed number between 0 and 2π. For each n, $C_n - C_\rho$ is a contour whose definition is similar to that of $C_\rho - C_{\rho'}$ in Section 5.

Unlike Section 5 the function $z^{s-1}/(e^z - 1)$ is not analytic for fixed s in the region bounded by the curve $C_n - C_\rho$. However, it is meromorphic in this region with simple poles at the points $z = \pm 2k\pi i$, $k = 1, \ldots, n$ and residues

$$(2k\pi i)^{s-1} = -i(2\pi)^{s-1}k^{s-1}e^{is\pi/2} \quad \text{at } 2k\pi i,$$

$$(-2k\pi i)^{s-1} = i(2\pi)^{s-1}k^{s-1}e^{is3\pi/2} \quad \text{at } -2k\pi i.$$

By the residue theorem from the elementary theory (or a rather easy computation based on Cauchy's theorem, see Problem 3), the integral of

$z^{s-1}/(e^z - 1)$ over $C_n - C_\rho$ is $2\pi i$ times the sum of these residues. Thus

$$\int_{C_n - C_\rho} \frac{z^{s-1}}{e^z - 1} \, dz = (2\pi)^s e^{is\pi/2} \sum_{k=1}^{n} k^{s-1} - (2\pi)^s e^{is3\pi/2} \sum_{k=1}^{n} k^{s-1}$$

(6.3)

$$= -2i(2\pi)^s e^{i\pi s} \sin \frac{\pi s}{2} \sum_{k=1}^{n} \frac{1}{k^{1-s}}.$$

We now suppose Re $s < 0$. Letting $n \to \infty$ the right side of (6.3) tends to $-2i(2\pi)^s e^{i\pi s} \sin (\pi s/2)\zeta(1 - s)$, while the left, we claim, tends to

$$\int_{-C_\rho} \frac{z^{s-1}}{e^z - 1} \, dz = -I(s).$$

($-C_\rho$ is the contour C_ρ with the sense, i.e., arrows, reversed.) To prove our claim it is sufficient to note that by (6.2) the integral over γ_n in (6.3) is bounded by $2\pi M\{(2n + 1)\pi\}^{\text{Re } s}$ which tends to 0 as $n \to \infty$. We have proved

(6.4)
$$I(s) = 2i(2\pi)^s e^{i\pi s} \sin \frac{\pi s}{2} \zeta(1 - s)$$

for Re $s < 0$.

Theorem 6.1.   (Riemann) $\zeta(s)$ *satisfies the functional equation* (6.1).

Proof.   By the uniqueness theorem, (6.4) holds for all values of s. Equating (6.4) and (5.8) we find

(6.5)
$$(e^{2\pi i s} - 1)\Gamma(s)\zeta(s) = 2i(2\pi)^s e^{i\pi s} \sin \frac{\pi s}{2} \zeta(1 - s).$$

To prove (6.1) substitute the identities $e^{2\pi i s} - 1 = 2ie^{i\pi s} \sin \pi s$ and $\Gamma(s) = \pi/[\sin \pi s \Gamma(1 - s)]$ into (6.5). The theorem is proved.

Problems

1. Prove that $1/(e^z - 1)$ has a Laurent expansion

$$\frac{1}{e^z - 1} = \frac{1}{z} - \frac{1}{2} + \sum_{n=1}^{\infty} a_n z^n$$

in $0 < |z| < 2\pi$ with $a_{2k} = 0$, $k = 1, 2, \ldots$.

    (a) Evaluate a_1, a_3, and a_5.

    (b) In terms of (a) express $\zeta(2)$, $\zeta(4)$, and $\zeta(6)$. (In general $\zeta(2k)$ is easily found. None of the numbers $\zeta(2k + 1)$ are known.)

2. Let $P(z)$ be a polynomial of degree $n \geq 1$ with lead coefficient 1 and distinct roots $\alpha_1, \ldots, \alpha_n$. Prove

$$\sum_{i=1}^{n} \frac{\alpha_i^k}{P'(\alpha_i)} = \begin{cases} 0, & 0 \leq k \leq n - 2 \\ 1, & k = n - 1. \end{cases}$$

(HINT: Consider $\int_{\gamma_n} (z^k/P(z))\, dz$ for appropriate circles γ_n.)

3. By expressing the integral over $C_n - C_\rho$ as a sum of four integrals (new contours must be defined), prove (6.3) using only Cauchy's integral theorem and integral formula for disks.

4. Prove the number M in (6.2) is finite.

7. The Zeros of $\zeta(s)$ in the Critical Strip

We have seen as a consequence of the functional equation that those zeros of $\zeta(s)$ which lie outside of the critical strip are the trivial zeros $s = -2, -4, \ldots$. Inside the critical strip the situation is far more complicated, and the zeros are generally unknown. (Indeed the Riemann hypothesis would give only the x coordinates if it were true.) There are however many existence and nonexistence theorems, and it is the purpose of the present section to discuss one of them. Using the Hadamard product theorem it will be proved that $\zeta(s)$ vanishes infinitely many times in the critical strip.

We introduce auxiliary functions

(7.1) $$\xi(s) = \tfrac{1}{2}s(s - 1)\pi^{-s/2}\Gamma(\tfrac{1}{2}s)\zeta(s)$$

and

(7.2) $$\Xi(s) = \xi(\tfrac{1}{2} + s).$$

Since each pole of $\Gamma(\tfrac{1}{2}s)$ coincides with a trivial zero of $s\zeta(s)$, both $\xi(s)$ and $\Xi(s)$ are entire functions. Conversely, every trivial zero of $s\zeta(s)$ coincides with a pole of $\Gamma(\tfrac{1}{2}s)$. It follows from (7.1) that a zero of $\xi(s)$ corresponds to a zero of $\zeta(s)$ which is not one of the trivial zeros, that is, to a zero in the critical strip. Thus, if $\xi(s)$ (or $\Xi(s)$) has an infinite number of zeros, $\zeta(s)$ has an infinite number of zeros in the critical strip.

It is convenient to recall here the formulas

(7.3) $$\Gamma\left(\frac{s}{2}\right) = \frac{\pi}{\sin(\pi s/2)\Gamma(1 - s/2)}$$

and

(7.4) $$\Gamma(s)\Gamma(s + \tfrac{1}{2}) = 2^{1-2s}\pi^{1/2}\Gamma(2s)$$

which were proved in Section 11 of Chapter 5.

Theorem 7.1. *$\xi(s)$ and $\Xi(s)$ satisfy the relations*

(7.5) $$\xi(s) = \xi(1 - s)$$

and

(7.6) $$\Xi(s) = \Xi(-s).$$

Proof. Equation (7.6) is an obvious consequence of (7.5) and (7.2). To prove (7.5) first substitute in (7.1) the value of $\zeta(s)$ given by (6.1). We have

$$\xi(s) = \frac{1}{2}s(s - 1)\pi^{s/2-1}2^s\Gamma\left(\frac{1}{2}s\right)\sin\frac{\pi s}{2}\Gamma(1 - s)\zeta(1 - s).$$

Using (7.3) and (7.4) successively it follows that

$$\xi(s) = \frac{1}{2}s(s - 1)\pi^{s/2}2^s\,\frac{\Gamma(1 - s)}{\Gamma\left(1 - \dfrac{s}{2}\right)}\,\zeta(1 - s)$$

and

$$\xi(s) = \frac{1}{2}s(s - 1)\pi^{s/2-1/2}\Gamma\left(\frac{1 - s}{2}\right)\zeta(1 - s)$$

$$= \xi(1 - s)$$

which was to be proved.

Since $\frac{1}{2}s(s - 1)$ is invariant under the substitution $s \to 1 - s$, it is a consequence of Theorem 7.1 that $\pi^{-s/2}\Gamma(\frac{1}{2}s)\zeta(s)$ is invariant under the same substitution. This is Riemann's original formulation of the functional equation.

Our next task is to compute the order of $\xi(s)$. Because $\xi(s) = \xi(1 - s)$, the order is equal to

$$\lambda = \limsup_{\substack{|s| \to \infty \\ \mathrm{Re}\, s \geq \frac{1}{2}}} \frac{\log\log|\xi(s)|}{\log|s|}.$$

Lemma 7.1.   As $\sigma \to \infty$ through real values, we have

(7.7)
$$\limsup_{\sigma \to \infty} \frac{\log \log \Gamma(\sigma)}{\log \sigma} \leq 1$$

or equivalently

(7.8)
$$\limsup_{\sigma \to \infty} \Gamma(\sigma) e^{-\sigma^{1+\epsilon}} = 0$$

for every $\epsilon > 0$.

Proof.   Equation (7.7) is an easy consequence of (7.8). Let $M = \max_{\frac{1}{2} \leq \sigma \leq \frac{3}{2}} \Gamma(\sigma)$. If $\sigma > \frac{3}{2}$, choose an integer n such that $\frac{1}{2} \leq \sigma - n < \frac{3}{2}$. Using the reproducing formula for the gamma function n times we have

$$\Gamma(\sigma) = (\sigma - 1)(\sigma - 2) \cdots (\sigma - n)\Gamma(\sigma - n)$$
$$\leq (\sigma - 1)^n M$$
$$\leq \sigma^\sigma M.$$

Since $\sigma^\sigma = e^{\sigma \ln \sigma}$, and since $\sigma \ln \sigma - \sigma^{1+\epsilon} \to -\infty$ as $\sigma \to \infty$, (7.8) follows. The lemma is proved.

REMARK.   It can be shown (Problem 1) that

$$\lim_{\sigma \to \infty} \frac{\log \log \Gamma(\sigma)}{\log \sigma} = 1.$$

Let A be the set consisting of those points s such that Re $s \geq \frac{1}{2}$, $|\text{Im } s| \leq 1$, and $|s - 1| \geq \frac{1}{2}$ (Figure 14). B is defined to be the set consisting of those points s such that Re $s \geq \frac{1}{2}$ and $|\text{Im } s| \geq 1$ (Figure 15).

Figure 14.

We will prove $\xi(s)$ has order at most 1 by showing it has order at most 1 in the regions A and B. That is, we show

(7.9)
$$\limsup_{\substack{|s| \to \infty \\ s \in A}} \frac{\log \log |\xi(s)|}{\log |s|} \leq 1$$

and

(7.10)
$$\limsup_{\substack{|s| \to \infty \\ s \in B}} \frac{\log \log |\xi(s)|}{\log |s|} \leq 1.$$

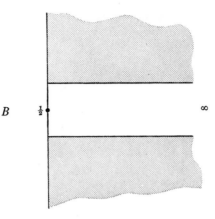

Figure 15.

To establish (7.9) we express $\xi(s)$ through its definition (7.1):

$$\xi(s) = \tfrac{1}{2}s(s - 1)\pi^{-s/2}\Gamma(\tfrac{1}{2}s)\zeta(s).$$

In A both $\zeta(s)$ and $\pi^{-s/2}$ are bounded, while $\tfrac{1}{2}s(s - 1)$ has order 0. Since $|\Gamma(\tfrac{1}{2}s)| \leq \Gamma(\tfrac{1}{2}\sigma)$ for $\sigma = \operatorname{Re} s$, Lemma 7.1 implies $\Gamma(\tfrac{1}{2}s)$ has order at most 1 in A. A finite product of functions of order at most 1 has order at most 1, and therefore $\xi(s)$ has order at most 1 in A.

To prove (7.10) we will need the representation

$$\zeta(s) = \frac{I(s)}{(e^{2\pi i s} - 1)\Gamma(s)}$$

from Lemma 6.3 to express $\xi(s)$ as

$$\xi(s) = \frac{\tfrac{1}{2}s(s - 1)\pi^{-s/2}\Gamma(s/2)I(s)}{(e^{2\pi i s} - 1)\Gamma(s)}.$$

Each of the functions $\tfrac{1}{2}s(s - 1)$, $\pi^{-s/2}$, $\Gamma(s/2)$, and $1/\Gamma(s)$ has order at most 1 in B. Furthermore $(e^{2\pi i s} - 1)^{-1}$ is *bounded* in B. Therefore we have only to prove $I(s)$ has order at most 1 in B.

Let ρ be a number between 0 and 2π. By (5.5)

$$I(s) = \int_{\gamma_\rho} \frac{z^{s-1}}{e^z - 1}\, dz + (e^{2\pi i s} - 1) \int_\rho^\infty \frac{x^{s-1}}{e^x - 1}\, dx.$$

If ρ has been chosen small enough, the first integral is bounded by $4\pi\rho^{\sigma-1}$. To estimate the second use the inequality

$$\frac{1}{e^x - 1} \leq \frac{e^{-x}}{1 - e^{-\rho}}$$

which is true for $\rho \leq x < \infty$ to obtain

$$\left| \int_\rho^\infty \frac{x^{s-1}}{e^x - 1}\, dx \right| \leq \int_\rho^\infty \frac{x^{\sigma-1}}{e^x - 1}\, dx$$

$$\leq \frac{1}{1 - e^{-\rho}} \int_0^\infty x^{\sigma-1} e^{-x}\, dx$$

$$= \frac{\Gamma(\sigma)}{1 - e^{-\rho}}.$$

Thus for $s = \sigma + it$

$$|I(s)| \leq 4\pi\rho^{\sigma-1} + \frac{|e^{2\pi is} - 1|\Gamma(\sigma)}{1 - e^{-\rho}}.$$

Since $e^{-|s|^{1+\epsilon}} \leq e^{-\sigma^{1+\epsilon}}$, it follows that

$$\limsup_{\substack{|s| \to \infty \\ s \in B}} |I(s)| e^{-|s|^{1+\epsilon}} = 0$$

for $\epsilon > 0$, and (7.10) obtains.

Collecting results, we have proved that $\xi(s)$ has order *at most* 1. We will now prove it has order *at least* 1 and from that conclude

Theorem 7.2. $\xi(s)$ *has order* 1.

Proof.   We have to prove $\xi(s)$ has order at least 1, for which it suffices to observe

(7.11)
$$\lim_{n \to \infty} \frac{\log \xi(2n)}{2n} = \infty.$$

By Definition (7.1) we have $\xi(2n) \geq \pi^{-n}(n - 1)!$ for $n > 0$. Expressing $(n - 1)!$ as

$$(n - 1)! = n^{n-1} \prod_{k=1}^{n-1} \left(1 - \frac{k}{n}\right)$$

and taking logarithms, we find

$$\frac{\log \xi(2n)}{2n} \geq -\frac{\log \pi}{2} + \frac{(n - 1)}{2n} \log n + \frac{1}{2n} \sum_{k=1}^{n-1} \log\left(1 - \frac{k}{n}\right).$$

The last sum on the right converges, by definition of the integral, to

$$\tfrac{1}{2} \int_0^1 \log(1 - x)\, dx = -\tfrac{1}{2}$$

as $n \to \infty$. Therefore since $\displaystyle\lim_{n \to \infty} \frac{(n-1)}{2n} \log n = \infty$, (7.11) follows, and the theorem is proved.

Theorem 7.3. $\Xi(s)$ *has infinitely many zeros.*

Proof. $\Xi(s)$ has order 1 because $\xi(s)$ does. $\Xi(s)$ is even, and therefore its power series expansion about 0 contains only even powers of s. It follows that $\Xi(s^{1/2})$ is entire and of order $\frac{1}{2}$. By the Hadamard product theorem an entire function of order $\frac{1}{2}$ cannot have a finite canonical product. In other words $\Xi(\sqrt{s})$ and *a fortiori* $\Xi(s)$ have infinitely many zeros. The theorem is proved.

As remarked earlier every zero of $\Xi(s)$ corresponds to a zero of $\zeta(s)$ in the critical strip. Thus we have proved

Theorem 7.4. $\zeta(s)$ *has infinitely many zeros in the critical strip.*

Problems

1. Prove $\displaystyle\lim_{\sigma \to \infty} \frac{\log \log \Gamma(\sigma)}{\log \sigma} = 1$.
2. Prove $\Xi(s)$ assumes every complex value an infinite number of times.

8. $\zeta(s)$ for Re $s = 1$

We will prove the theorem of Hadamard and de la Vallée Poussin which asserts that $\zeta(s) \neq 0$ for Re $s = 1$. Later on we will see that this theorem is actually *equivalent* with the prime number theorem (Problem 2, Section 9).

If f is analytic for $0 < |s - s_0| < r$, and if at s_0 f has either a pole of order $-k$, $k < 0$, or a zero of order k, $k \geq 0$, then

$$\lim_{s \to s_0} (s - s_0) \frac{f'(s)}{f(s)} = k$$

as the reader should check. Since k is real, it is also true that

$$\lim_{s \to s_0} \mathrm{Re}(s - s_0) \frac{f'(s)}{f(s)} = k.$$

Finally, if $s_0 = \sigma_0 + it_0$, and if $s \to s_0$ through values $s = \sigma + it_0$ of s with the same t coordinate, then $(s - s_0) = (\sigma - \sigma_0)$ is real, and

(8.1)
$$\lim_{\sigma \to \sigma_0} (\sigma - \sigma_0) \operatorname{Re} \frac{f'(s)}{f(s)} = k.$$

This fact will be used shortly.

From (4.5) it is immediate that

(8.2)
$$\operatorname{Re} \frac{\zeta'(s)}{\zeta(s)} = - \sum_{n=1}^{\infty} \operatorname{Re} \frac{\Lambda(n)}{n^s}$$

for $\operatorname{Re} s > 1$. If $s = \sigma + it$, a typical summand in (8.2) is

$$- \operatorname{Re} \frac{\log p}{p^{ms}} = - \frac{\log p}{p^{m\sigma}} \cos(mt \log p).$$

Therefore, it follows from the formula

$$3 + 4 \cos(mt \log p) + \cos(2mt \log p) = 2(1 + \cos(mt \log p))^2$$
$$> 0$$

that

(8.3)
$$3 \frac{\zeta'(\sigma)}{\zeta(\sigma)} + 4 \operatorname{Re} \frac{\zeta'(\sigma + it)}{\zeta(\sigma + it)} + \operatorname{Re} \frac{\zeta'(\sigma + 2it)}{\zeta(\sigma + 2it)} < 0.$$

Let t_0 be a nonzero real number. Because $\zeta(s)$ is analytic at both $1 + it_0$ and $1 + 2it_0$, (8.1) implies that the numbers

$$k = \lim_{\sigma \to 1} (\sigma - 1) \operatorname{Re} \frac{\zeta'(\sigma + it_0)}{\zeta(\sigma + it_0)}$$

and

$$l = \lim_{\sigma \to 1} (\sigma - 1) \operatorname{Re} \frac{\zeta'(\sigma + 2it_0)}{\zeta(\sigma + 2it_0)}$$

are nonnegative integers. Also because of the simple pole at $s = 1$, we have

$$-1 = \lim_{\sigma \to 1} (\sigma - 1) \frac{\zeta'(\sigma)}{\zeta(\sigma)}.$$

Combining the last three equations, we find

$$\lim_{\sigma \to 1} (\sigma - 1) \left\{ 3 \frac{\zeta'(\sigma)}{\zeta(\sigma)} + 4 \operatorname{Re} \frac{\zeta'(\sigma + it_0)}{\zeta(\sigma + it_0)} + \operatorname{Re} \frac{\zeta'(\sigma + 2it_0)}{\zeta(\sigma + 2it_0)} \right\}$$
$$= -3 + 4k + l$$
$$\geq -3 + 4k.$$

Since $\sigma - 1 > 0$ for $\sigma > 1$, this limit is ≤ 0 by (8.3). Therefore $4k \leq 0$ or $k = 0$. What is the same, $\zeta(1 + it_0) \neq 0$, and because t_0 is arbitrary, we have

Theorem 8.1.   (Hadamard-de la Vallée Poussin) $\zeta(s)$ *has no zeros for* Re $s = 1$. (*By the functional equation* $\zeta(s)$ *also has no zeros for* Re $s = 0$.)

9. Integral Representation of Dirichlet Series

Let $f(n)$ be a number-theoretic function, and define $S(x), 1 \leq x < \infty$, by

$$(9.1) \qquad\qquad S(x) = \sum_{n \leq x} f(n).$$

We will assume f and S are such that

$$(9.2) \qquad\qquad \lim_{x \to \infty} \frac{S(x)}{x^{1+\epsilon}} = 0$$

for every $\epsilon > 0$. Obviously, equivalent with (9.2) is the existence for every $\epsilon > 0$ of a constant $A_\epsilon < \infty$ such that

$$(9.3) \qquad\qquad |S(x)| \leq A_\epsilon x^{1+\epsilon}$$

for $1 \leq x < \infty$. This being so, the integral

$$(9.4) \qquad\qquad s \int_1^\infty \frac{S(x)}{x^{1+s}}\, dx = \lim_{T \to \infty} s \int_1^T \frac{S(x)}{x^{1+s}}\, dx$$

defines an analytic function of s in the half-plane Re $s > 1$.

Lemma 9.1.   With notations and assumptions fixed as above, the Dirichlet series

$$(9.5) \qquad\qquad \varphi(s) = \sum_{n=1}^\infty \frac{f(n)}{n^s}$$

converges for Re $s > 1$, and

$$(9.6) \qquad\qquad \varphi(s) = s \int_1^\infty \frac{S(x)}{x^{1+s}}\, dx.$$

Proof.   It is enough to prove

$$\varphi(s) = \lim_{T \to \infty} s \int_1^T \frac{S(x)}{x^{1+s}}\, dx.$$

To this end fix T, and use the definition of $S(x)$. We have

$$s \int_1^T \frac{S(x)}{x^{1+s}}\, dx = s \int_1^T \frac{\sum\limits_{n \le x} f(n)}{x^{1+s}}\, dx$$

$$= \sum_{n \le T} s \int_n^T \frac{f(n)}{x^{1+s}}\, dx$$

$$= \sum_{n \le T} \frac{f(n)}{n^s} - \frac{S(T)}{T^s}.$$

From (9.2) $\lim\limits_{T \to \infty} S(T)/T^s = 0$ for Re $s > 1$, and therefore (9.6) follows. The lemma is proved.

For example take $f(n) = \Lambda(n)$ and $S(x) = \psi(x)$, where Λ and ψ have been discussed earlier. By (3.11)

$$\psi(x) \le \pi(x) \log x$$

$$\le x \log x,$$

and so ψ satisfies (9.2). From (4.5) the Dirichlet series (9.5) sums to $-\zeta'(s)/\zeta(s)$, and therefore by (9.6)

$$(9.7) \qquad -\frac{\zeta'(s)}{\zeta(s)} = s \int_1^\infty \frac{\psi(x)}{x^{1+s}}\, dx$$

for Re $s > 1$.

An altered form of (9.7) will be easier to use. Define $F(u)$ for $0 \le u < \infty$ by

$$(9.8) \qquad F(u) = \psi(e^u)e^{-u}$$

and change variables in (9.7), letting $x = e^u$. That equation becomes

$$(9.9) \qquad s \int_0^\infty F(u)e^{-(s-1)u}\, du = -\frac{\zeta'(s)}{\zeta(s)}.$$

Lemma 9.2.   If $F(u) = \psi(e^u)e^{-u}$, then $\beta(s)$, defined for Re $s > 1$ by

$$(9.10) \qquad \beta(s) = \int_0^\infty (F(u) - 1)e^{-(s-1)u}\, du$$

is analytic, not only for Re $s > 1$, but also for Re $s = 1$.

Proof.   Using (9.9) and the equality

$$s \int_0^\infty e^{-(s-1)u} \, du = 1 + \frac{1}{s-1}$$

we can evaluate the integral (9.10), getting

(9.11) $$\beta(s) = -\frac{1}{s} \left\{ \frac{\zeta'(s)}{\zeta(s)} + 1 + \frac{1}{s-1} \right\}.$$

Naturally $\beta(s)$ is analytic for Re $s > 1$. If $s = 1 + it$, $t \neq 0$, $\zeta(s)$ is not 0, and therefore $\beta(s)$ is analytic. At $s = 1$, $\zeta'(s)/\zeta(s)$ has a simple pole with residue -1, and again $\beta(s)$ is analytic. The lemma is proved.

REMARK.   Since $\lim_{u \to \infty} F(u) = 1$ obviously implies $\lim_{x \to \infty} \psi(x)/x = 1$, the former equation also implies the prime number theorem.

Problems

1. Suppose $\varphi(s)$ is given by (9.5) and (9.6). If there exists a constant A such that $\varphi(s) - A/(s-1)$ is analytic for Re $s = 1$, prove a formula like (9.10).
2. Assume $\lim_{x \to \infty} \psi(x)/x = 1$, from which it follows that $\lim_{u \to \infty} F(u) = 1$. Following the outline below, prove that $\beta(s)$ is analytic for $s = 1 + it$, $t \neq 0$. (Naturally it follows that $\zeta(1 + it) \neq 0$.)

   (a) If $s_0 = 1 + it_0$, and if $s = \sigma + it_0$, then

   $$\lim_{\sigma \to 1} (\sigma - 1)\beta(s) = k$$

   is an integer ≥ 0 which represents the order of the zero of $\zeta(s)$ at $1 + it_0$.

   (b) Fix $t_0 \neq 0$ and let $\epsilon > 0$ be given. Choose T so large that $|F(u) - 1| < \epsilon$ for $u \geq T$. Prove

   $$|\beta(s)| \leq M + \frac{\epsilon}{\sigma - 1} \qquad (s = \sigma + it_0)$$

   where $M = M(T)$ depends only upon T.

   (c) Conclude that $\lim_{\sigma \to 1} (\sigma - 1)\beta(\sigma + it_0) = 0$, and therefore $k = 0$. Thus $\zeta(1 + it_0) \neq 0$.

10. Integral-theoretic Lemmas

In order to be able to justify certain manipulations and limit inter-changes with integrals we will present here some *ad hoc* results from the theory of integration. Since each result is a special case of a more general and well-known theorem, the reader who is familiar with the general theory of integration may proceed with Section 11. (In fact all readers may wish to read Section 11 before Section 10.)

Lemma 10.1. (Riemann-Lebesgue Lemma; Elementary Version) Let $f(t)$ be continuously differentiable on a finite interval $[a, b]$. Then

$$(10.1) \qquad \lim_{\alpha \to \infty} \int_a^b f(t) e^{i\alpha t}\, dt = 0$$

where α tends to ∞ through real values.

Proof. Assuming $\alpha \neq 0$, integrate by parts in (10.1) to obtain

$$(10.2) \qquad \int_a^b f(t) e^{i\alpha t}\, dt = \frac{f(b)e^{i\alpha b} - f(a)e^{i\alpha a}}{i\alpha} - \frac{1}{i\alpha} \int_a^b f'(t) e^{i\alpha t}\, dt.$$

Since f' is continuous on $[a, b]$, it is bounded there by a constant $M < \infty$. Thus both terms on the right of (10.2) tend to 0 with $1/|\alpha|$, and (10.1) follows. The lemma is proved.

The proof of the following corollary to Lemma 10.1 is left to the reader.

Lemma 10.2. Let $f(t)$ be continuously differentiable on intervals $[a, c]$ and $[c, b]$, where $-\infty < a \leq c \leq b < \infty$. Then (10.1) holds.

Lemma 10.3. Let $f(t)$, $0 \leq t < \infty$, be a nonnegative function which is bounded and integrable on every finite interval $[0, T]$. Suppose also that $\int_0^\infty f(t) e^{-t\epsilon}\, dt < \infty$ for every $\epsilon > 0$. If the limit

$$\lim_{\epsilon \to 0} \int_0^\infty f(t) e^{-t\epsilon}\, dt = A$$

is finite, then

$$\int_0^\infty f(t)\, dt = A.$$

Proof. By Lemma 12.1 of Chapter 5 we have for each $T < \infty$

$$\int_0^T f(t)\, dt = \lim_{\epsilon \to 0} \int_0^T f(t) e^{-t\epsilon}\, dt$$

and therefore since f is nonnegative

$$\int_0^T f(t)\, dt \leq A.$$

It follows that $\int_0^\infty f(t)\, dt = \lim_{T \to \infty} \int_0^T f(t)\, dt$ is not only finite, but it is bounded by A. On the other hand we have, again by the nonnegativity of f,

$$\int_0^\infty f(t)e^{-t\epsilon}\, dt \leq \int_0^\infty f(t)\, dt$$

for every $\epsilon > 0$. Letting $\epsilon \to 0$ gives

$$A \leq \int_0^\infty f(t)\, dt$$

and thus

$$A \leq \int_0^\infty f(t)\, dt \leq A$$

meaning $\int_0^\infty f(t)\, dt = A$. The lemma is proved.

In preparation of Lemma 10.4 note that the power series expansion of e^{ist} converges uniformly on any finite rectangle $a \leq t \leq b$, $c \leq s \leq d$. Therefore if $f(t)$, $a \leq t \leq b$, and $g(s)$, $c \leq s \leq d$, are bounded integrable functions, we have

$$\int_a^b \left\{ \int_c^d f(t)g(s)e^{ist}\, ds \right\} dt = \sum_{n=0}^\infty \frac{i^n}{n!} \left\{ \int_a^b f(t)t^n\, dt \right\} \left\{ \int_c^d g(s)s^n\, ds \right\}$$

$$= \int_c^d \left\{ \int_a^b f(t)g(s)e^{ist}\, dt \right\} ds.$$

Thus

$$(10.3) \qquad \int_a^b \int_c^d f(t)g(s)e^{ist}\, ds\, dt = \int_c^d \int_a^b f(t)g(s)e^{ist}\, dt\, ds.$$

Lemma 10.4. Let $G(t)$, $-\infty < t < \infty$, and $H(u)$, $0 \leq u < \infty$, be functions which are bounded and integrable on finite intervals, and suppose that both

$$\int_{-\infty}^\infty |G(t)|\, dt = A$$

and

$$\int_0^\infty |H(u)|\, du = B$$

are finite. Then

(10.4) $\displaystyle\int_{-\infty}^{\infty}\int_{0}^{\infty}G(t)H(u)e^{iut}\,du\,dt = \int_{0}^{\infty}\int_{-\infty}^{\infty}G(t)H(u)e^{iut}\,dt\,du.$

Proof.   We must first prove the integrals in (10.4) *exist*. To this end define $g(t)$, $-\infty < t < \infty$, by

$$g(t) = \int_{0}^{\infty}H(u)e^{iut}\,du$$

and note that $|g(t)| \le B$ because $|e^{iut}| = 1$. We claim g is continuous, in fact uniformly continuous. To this end let $\epsilon > 0$ be given and choose $T < \infty$ large enough that

$$\int_{T}^{\infty}|H(u)|\,du < \frac{\epsilon}{4}.$$

Then choose $\delta > 0$ so small that

$$\max_{\substack{0 \le t \le T \\ |\alpha| \le \delta}}|e^{i\alpha t} - 1| \le \frac{\epsilon}{2B}.$$

Using these inequalities we estimate $|g(s) - g(t)|$ for $|s - t| \le \delta$.

$$|g(s) - g(t)| = \left|\int_{0}^{\infty}H(u)(e^{ius} - e^{iut})\,du\right|$$

$$\le \frac{\epsilon}{2B}\int_{0}^{T}|H(u)|\,du + 2\int_{T}^{\infty}|H(u)|\,du$$

$$< \epsilon.$$

Thus g is continuous.

Because g is bounded and continuous, the function $G(t)g(t)$ is integrable on $-\infty < t < \infty$. Similarly, if $h(u)$ is defined by

$$h(u) = \int_{-\infty}^{\infty}G(t)e^{iut}\,dt,$$

then $H(u)h(u)$ is integrable on $0 \le u < \infty$. The integrals (10.4) exist.

For each pair S, T, $0 < S, T < \infty$, define

$$\epsilon(S, T) = AB - \int_{0}^{S}|H(u)|\,du\int_{-T}^{T}|G(t)|\,dt$$

and note by definition of A and B that $\displaystyle\lim_{\substack{S \to \infty \\ T \to \infty}}\epsilon(S, T) = 0$. For any such pair S, T it is clear that

$$\left| \int_0^\infty \int_{-\infty}^\infty G(t)H(u)e^{iut}\, dt\, du - \int_0^S \int_{-T}^T G(t)H(u)e^{iut}\, dt\, du \right|$$

$$\leq \epsilon(S, T).$$

Similarly,

$$\left| \int_{-\infty}^\infty \int_0^\infty G(t)H(u)e^{iut}\, du\, dt - \int_{-T}^T \int_0^S G(t)H(u)e^{iut}\, du\, dt \right|$$

$$\leq \epsilon(S, T).$$

Since

$$\int_0^S \int_{-T}^T G(t)H(u)e^{iut}\, dt\, du = \int_{-T}^T \int_0^S G(t)H(u)e^{iut}\, du\, dt$$

by the remark preceding the lemma, it follows that

$$\left| \int_{-\infty}^\infty \int_0^\infty G(t)H(u)e^{iut}\, du\, dt - \int_0^\infty \int_{-\infty}^\infty G(t)H(u)e^{iut}\, dt\, du \right|$$

$$\leq 2\epsilon(S, T).$$

Letting S and T tend to infinity (10.4) obtains, and the lemma is proved.

11. Weak Limits

Let $h(t)$, $-\infty < t < \infty$, be a continuous function such that

(a) $h(t) = 0$ for all t outside of a finite interval.

(b) $\hat{h}(\alpha) = \int_{-\infty}^\infty h(t)e^{i\alpha t}\, dt \geq 0$ for $-\infty < \alpha < \infty$.

(c) $\int_{-\infty}^\infty \hat{h}(\alpha)\, d\alpha = 1$.

If $0 < \lambda < \infty$, define h_λ by the equation

(11.1) $$h_\lambda(\alpha) = \lambda \hat{h}(\lambda\alpha), \quad -\infty < \alpha < \infty.$$

By a change of variables in (c) it is true for each $\delta > 0$ that

(11.2) $$\lim_{\lambda \to \infty} \int_{-\delta}^\delta h_\lambda(\alpha)\, d\alpha = \lim_{\lambda \to \infty} \int_{-\lambda\delta}^{\lambda\delta} \hat{h}(\alpha)\, d\alpha$$

$$= 1.$$

Example. Set $c = \int_{-\infty}^\infty (\sin^2 \alpha)/\alpha^2\, d\alpha$, and define $h(t)$ as

(11.3) $$h(t) = \begin{cases} \dfrac{1}{2c}\left(1 - \dfrac{|t|}{2}\right), & |t| \leq 2 \\ 0, & |t| > 2. \end{cases}$$

Leaving the computation to the reader (Problem 1) we find $\hat{h}(\alpha)$ to be

(11.4)
$$\hat{h}(\alpha) = \frac{\sin^2 \alpha}{c\alpha^2}$$

and therefore h and $\hat{h}$ are functions satisfying (a)–(c). In what follows h and $\hat{h}$ will be given by (11.3) and (11.4). However the only essential properties to be used are (a)–(c) and (11.2).

Let us return to the situation discussed in Section 9, particularly as it pertained to $\psi(x)$. There it was proved that if

$$F(u) = \psi(e^u)e^{-u}, \quad 0 \le u < \infty$$

and

$$\beta(s) = -\frac{1}{s}\left\{\frac{\zeta'(s)}{\zeta(s)} + 1 + \frac{1}{s-1}\right\}, \quad \mathrm{Re}\ s \ge 1,$$

then

(11.5)
$$\int_0^\infty (F(u) - 1)e^{-(s-1)u}\, du = \beta(s)$$

for $\mathrm{Re}\ s > 1$.

Fix ϵ and λ with $\epsilon > 0$ and $0 < \lambda < \infty$, and consider $\beta(1 + \epsilon + i\lambda t)$ for $-\infty < t < \infty$. Lemma 10.4 allows us to interchange the order of integration in

$$\lambda \int_{-\infty}^\infty h(t)\beta(1 + \epsilon + i\lambda t)e^{i\alpha\lambda t}\, dt$$
$$= \lambda \int_{-\infty}^\infty h(t)e^{i\alpha\lambda t}\int_0^\infty (F(u) - 1)e^{-u\epsilon}e^{-iu\lambda t}\, du\, dt$$

to obtain

(11.6)
$$\lambda \int_{-\infty}^\infty h(t)\beta(1 + \epsilon + i\lambda t)e^{i\alpha\lambda t}\, dt$$
$$= \int_0^\infty (F(u) - 1)e^{-u\epsilon}\int_{-\infty}^\infty \lambda h(t)e^{it(\lambda\alpha - \lambda u)}\, dt\, du$$
$$= \int_0^\infty (F(u) - 1)e^{-u\epsilon}h_\lambda(\alpha - u)\, du.$$

Since $\lim_{\epsilon \to 0} \beta(1 + \epsilon + i\lambda t) = \beta(1 + i\lambda t)$ uniformly for $-2 \le t \le 2$ by uniform continuity, and since $h(t) = 0$ for $|t| > 2$, it follows that

$$\lim_{\epsilon \to 0} \lambda \int_{-\infty}^\infty h(t)\beta(1 + \epsilon + i\lambda t)e^{i\alpha\lambda t}\, dt = \lambda \int_{-\infty}^\infty h(t)\beta(1 + i\lambda t)e^{i\alpha\lambda t}\, dt.$$

Also by Lemma 12.1 of Chapter 5

$$\lim_{\epsilon \to 0} \int_0^\infty e^{-u\epsilon}h_\lambda(\alpha - u)\, du = \int_0^\infty h_\lambda(\alpha - u)\, du.$$

These facts combine with (11.6) to yield

$$\lim_{\epsilon \to 0} \int_0^\infty F(u)e^{-u\epsilon}h_\lambda(\alpha - u)\, du = \int_0^\infty h_\lambda(\alpha - u)\, du$$
$$+ \lambda \int_{-\infty}^\infty h(t)\beta(1 + i\lambda t)e^{i\alpha\lambda t}\, dt,$$

and therefore by Lemma 10.3

(11.7)
$$\int_0^\infty F(u)h_\lambda(\alpha - u)\, du = \int_0^\infty h_\lambda(\alpha - u)\, du$$
$$+ \lambda \int_{-\infty}^\infty h(t)\beta(1 + i\lambda t)e^{i\alpha\lambda t}\, dt.$$

Next, we let $\alpha \to +\infty$ in (11.7). Because $\lambda h(t)\beta(1 + i\lambda t)$, which is effectively a function on $[-2, 2]$, is continuously differentiable on $[-2, 0]$ and $[0, 2]$, the second term on the right tends to 0 by Lemma 10.2. As for the first, a change of variable shows it tends to 1. We have proved

Theorem 11.1. *If $0 < \lambda < \infty$, then $\int_0^\infty F(u)h_\lambda(\alpha - u)\, du$ exists, and furthermore*

(11.8)
$$\lim_{\alpha \to +\infty} \int_0^\infty F(u)h_\lambda(\alpha - u)\, du = 1.$$

REMARK.   For each λ, $0 < \lambda < \infty$, define F_λ by

$$F_\lambda(\alpha) = \int_0^\infty F(u)h_\lambda(\alpha - u)\, du.$$

If $F(u)$ is extended to be zero for negative values of u, then by a change of variables

(11.9)
$$F_\lambda(\alpha) = \int_{-\infty}^\infty F(u)h_\lambda(\alpha - u)\, du$$
$$= \int_{-\infty}^\infty F(\alpha - u)h_\lambda(u)\, du.$$

Since $\int_{-\infty}^\infty h_\lambda(\alpha)\, d\alpha = 1$, F_λ is seen to be an average or "expected value" of $F(\alpha - u)$ with respect to the mass distribution whose density is $h_\lambda(u)\, du$. Theorem 11.1 asserts that the averaged function $F_\lambda(\alpha)$ tends to 1 as $\alpha \to +\infty$.

The prime number theorem has been reduced to proving the existence of the "unaveraged" limit

(11.10)
$$\lim_{\alpha \to +\infty} F(\alpha) = 1.$$

The connection between (11.8) and (11.10) is best seen through (11.2).

For using that equation it is not difficult to prove that

$$\lim_{\lambda \to \infty} F_\lambda(\alpha) = F(\alpha)$$

holds at each point of continuity of F. Therefore the problem (roughly) is to justify the interchange of $\lim_{\alpha \to \infty}$ and $\lim_{\lambda \to \infty}$ in

$$\lim_{\alpha \to \infty} F(\alpha) = \lim_{\alpha \to \infty} \lim_{\lambda \to \infty} F_\lambda(\alpha)$$

(11.11)
$$= \lim_{\lambda \to \infty} \lim_{\alpha \to \infty} F_\lambda(\alpha)$$

$$= 1.$$

Since the interchange in (11.11) is not valid in general, it is necessary to make use of the special nature of F in order to justify it. A Tauberian theorem is in order, and this is the subject of Section 12.

Problems

1. Prove

$$\frac{\sin^2 \alpha}{c \alpha^2} = \int_{-\infty}^{\infty} h(t) e^{i\alpha t} \, dt$$

where $h(t)$ is defined by (11.3).
2. Assume $F(u)$ (defined for $-\infty < u < \infty$) is bounded. (It is as we will see.) Prove: $\lim_{\lambda \to \infty} F_\lambda(\alpha) = F(\alpha)$ whenever F is continuous at α.
3. Place Theorem 11.1 in the context of Problem 1, Section 9.

12. A Tauberian Theorem

The prime number theorem has been reduced to proving that $\lim^1 F(\alpha) = 1$ follows from $\lim_{\alpha \to \infty} F_\lambda(\alpha) = 1$. For this purpose it is necessary to have a Tauberian theorem (Chapter 3, Section 13), a theorem which uses the second equality together with a special (Tauberian) condition on F to conclude the first. In the present situation the Tauberian condition is

$$F(u)e^u \le F(v)e^v$$

which is valid for $u \le v$. This inequality is trivial because by definition $F(u) = 0$, $u \le 0$, and $F(u) = \psi(e^u)e^{-u}$, $u > 0$.

---

[1] It will be understood that $\alpha \to \infty$ means $\alpha \to +\infty$.

Theorem 12.1.   *Let* $\{h_\lambda\}$, $0 < \lambda < \infty$, *be a family of functions on the real line such that*

(a) $h_\lambda(\alpha) \geq 0$, $-\infty < \alpha < \infty$.

(b) $\int_{-\infty}^{\infty} h_\lambda(\alpha) \, d\alpha = 1$.

(c) $\lim_{\lambda \to \infty} \int_{-\delta}^{\delta} h_\lambda(\alpha) \, d\alpha = 1$, $\delta > 0$.

Suppose $F(u)$ is a nonnegative function on $(-\infty, \infty)$ such that $F(u) = 0$ for $u < 0$ and

$$\lim_{\alpha \to \infty} F_\lambda(\alpha) = A$$

exists for each λ, where

$$F_\lambda(\alpha) = \int_{-\infty}^{\infty} F(\alpha - u) h_\lambda(u) \, du.$$

If in addition

(12.1) $$F(u)e^u \leq F(v)e^v$$

for $u \leq v$, then

$$\lim_{\alpha \to \infty} F(\alpha) = A.$$

Proof.   Fix $\delta > 0$. For each $\alpha > 0$

$$F_\lambda(\alpha + \delta) = \int_{-\infty}^{\infty} F(\alpha + \delta - u) h_\lambda(u) \, du$$

(12.2)

$$\geq \int_{-\delta}^{\delta} F(\alpha + \delta - u) h_\lambda(u) \, du$$

since the integrand is nonnegative. For $|u| \leq \delta$ it follows from (12.1) that

$$F(\alpha + \delta - u)e^{\alpha + \delta - u} \geq F(\alpha)e^\alpha$$

or

$$F(\alpha + \delta - u) \geq F(\alpha)e^{u - \delta}$$

$$\geq F(\alpha)e^{-2\delta}.$$

Substituting this inequality in the integrand of (12.2) gives rise to

$$F_\lambda(\alpha + \delta) \geq F(\alpha)e^{-2\delta} \int_{-\delta}^{\delta} h_\lambda(u) \, du$$

$$= \rho(\lambda, \delta) F(\alpha).$$

Letting $\alpha \to \infty$ we find therefore that

$$\rho(\lambda, \delta) \limsup_{\alpha \to \infty} F(\alpha) \leq \lim_{\alpha \to \infty} F_\lambda(\alpha + \delta)$$

$$= A.$$

Since by assumption (c) $\lim\limits_{\delta \to 0} \lim\limits_{\lambda \to \infty} \rho(\lambda,\, \delta) = 1$, it follows that

(12.3) $$\limsup\limits_{\alpha \to \infty} F(\alpha) \leq A.$$

With the help of (12.3) we will next prove $\liminf\limits_{\alpha \to \infty} F(\alpha) \geq A$, and from this the theorem will follow.

By (12.1) $F(u)$ is bounded on finite intervals $[0,\, T]$, $T > 0$. Also by (12.3) $F(u)$ is uniformly bounded for large u. Since $F(u) = 0$ for $u < 0$, it follows that

$$\sup\limits_{-\infty < u < \infty} F(u) = M$$
$$< \infty.$$

M is fixed in what follows.

If $\delta > 0$ is fixed, write

(12.4)
$$F_\lambda(\alpha - \delta) = \int_{-\infty}^{\infty} F(\alpha - \delta - u) h_\lambda(u)\, du$$
$$= \int_{-\delta}^{\delta} F(\alpha - \delta - u) h_\lambda(u)\, du + R(\lambda,\, \delta,\, \alpha)$$

where

$$R(\lambda,\, \delta,\, \alpha) = \int_{-\infty}^{-\delta} F(\alpha - \delta - u) h_\lambda(u)\, du + \int_{\delta}^{\infty} F(\alpha - \delta - u) h_\lambda(u)\, du$$
$$\leq M \left(1 - \int_{-\delta}^{\delta} h_\lambda(u)\, du \right)$$
$$= M\epsilon(\lambda,\, \delta).$$

Of course, by assumption (c) $\lim\limits_{\lambda \to \infty} \epsilon(\lambda,\, \delta) = 0$.

Using (12.1) for $|u| \leq \delta$, we have

$$F(\alpha - \delta - u) e^{\alpha - \delta - u} \leq F(\alpha) e^\alpha$$

or

$$F(\alpha - \delta - u) \leq F(\alpha) e^{2\delta}.$$

Substitution of this inequality in the integrand of (12.4) gives

(12.5) $$F_\lambda(\alpha - \delta) \leq F(\alpha) \rho_1(\lambda,\, \delta) + \epsilon(\lambda,\, \delta)$$

where

$$\rho_1(\lambda,\, \delta) = e^{2\delta} \int_{-\delta}^{\delta} h_\lambda(u)\, du$$

satisfies $\lim\limits_{\delta \to 0} \lim\limits_{\lambda \to \infty} \rho_1(\lambda, \delta) = 1$. Letting $\alpha \to \infty$ in (12.5) we see

$$\rho_1(\lambda, \delta) \liminf_{\alpha \to \infty} F(\alpha) + \epsilon(\lambda, \delta) \geq \lim_{\alpha \to \infty} F_\lambda(\alpha - \delta)$$

$$= A.$$

The desired relation

$$\liminf_{\alpha \to \infty} F(\alpha) \geq A$$

follows when $\lambda \to \infty$ and $\delta \to 0$. The theorem is proved.

Applying Theorems 3.1, 11.1, and 12.1 we can state

Theorem 12.2.   (Prime Number Theorem)

$$\lim_{x \to \infty} \frac{\pi(x) \log x}{x} = 1.$$

Problem

1. (Ikehara's Tauberian theorem.) Let $\psi(x)$ be nonnegative and non-decreasing on $0 \leq x < \infty$, and suppose that $\phi(s) = s \int_0^\infty \psi(e^u) e^{-su} \, du$ is analytic for Re $s > 1$. If A is a constant such that $\phi(s) - A/(s - 1)$ is continuous for Re $s = 1$, then

$$\lim_{x \to \infty} \frac{\psi(x)}{x} = A.$$

Bibliography

Ahlfors, L. V. *Complex Analysis. An Introduction to the Theory of Analytic Functions of One Complex Variable*, Second Edition. McGraw-Hill Book Co., New York, 1966.

Behnke, H., and Sommer, F. *Theorie der analytischen Funktionen einer komplexen Veränderlichen*. Springer-Verlag, Berlin, 1955.

Bieberbach, L. *Conformal Mapping* (translated by F. Steinhardt). Chelsea Publishing Co., New York, 1953.

Carathéodory, C. *Conformal Representation*. Cambridge University Press, London, 1952.

Carathéodory, C. *Theory of Functions*, Volumes I and II (translated by F. Steinhardt). Chelsea Publishing Co., New York, 1958.

Cartan, H. *Elementary Theory of Analytic Functions of One or Several Complex Variables*. Addison-Wesley Publishing Co., Inc., Reading, Mass., 1963.

Churchill, R. V. *Complex Variables and Applications*, Second Edition. McGraw-Hill Book Co., New York, 1960.

Frost, R., *Complete Poems of Robert Frost*. Holt, Rinehart and Winston, New York, 1964.

Goluzin, G. M. *Geometrische Funktionentheorie*. VEB Deutscher Verlag der Wissenschaften, Berlin, 1957.

Heins, M. *Selected Topics in the Classical Theory of Functions of a Complex Variable*. Holt, Rinehart and Winston, New York, 1962.

Hille, E. *Analytic Function Theory*, Volumes 1 and 2. Ginn & Co., Boston, 1963.

Hoffman, K. *Banach Spaces of Analytic Functions*. Prentice-Hall, Inc., Englewood Cliffs, N.J., 1962.

Ingham, A. E. *The Distribution of Prime Numbers*. Stechert-Hafner Service Agency, Inc., New York, 1964.

Julia, G. *Leçons sur la représentation conforme des aires multiplement connexes*. Gauthier-Villars, Paris, 1934.

Knopp, K. *Theory of Functions*, Volumes 1 and 2. (Translated by F. Bagemihl) Dover Publications, New York, 1947.

Landau, E. *Handbüch der Lehre von der Verteilung der Primzahlen*, Second Edition. Chelsea Publishing Co., New York, 1953.

Levin, B. Y. *Distribution of Zeros of Entire Functions* (translated by R. P. Boas, Jr., *et al.*). American Mathematical Society, Providence, R.I., 1964.

Markushevich, A. I. *Theory of Functions of a Complex Variable*, Volumes I and II (translated by R. A. Silverman). Prentice-Hall, Inc., Englewood Cliffs, N.J., 1965.

Montel, P. *Leçons sur les familles normales de fonctions analytiques et leurs applications*. Gauthier-Villars, Paris, 1927.

Nevanlinna, R. *Eindeutige Analytische Funktionen*. Springer-Verlag, Berlin, 1936.

Newman, M. H. A. *Elements of the Topology of Plane Sets of Points*. Cambridge University Press, London, 1939.

Osgood, W. F. *Functions of a Complex Variable*. (Bound in one volume with *Functions of Real Variables*, by the same author.) Chelsea Publishing Co., New York, 1958.

Saks, S., and Zygmund, A. *Analytic Functions* (translated by E. J. Scott). Nakładem Polskiego Towarzystwa Matematycznego, Warsaw, 1952.

Titchmarsh, E. C. *The Theory of Functions*, Second Edition. Oxford University Press, London, 1939.

Titchmarsh, E. C. *The Theory of the Riemann Zeta-Function*. Oxford University Press, London, 1951.

Weyl, H. *The Concept of a Riemann Surface* (translated by G. R. MacLane). Addison-Wesley Publishing Co., Inc., Reading, Mass., 1964.

Whittaker, E. T., and Watson, C. N. *A Course of Modern Analysis*, Fourth Edition. Cambridge University Press, London, 1963.

Zygmund, A. *Trigonometric Series*, Volumes I and II, Second Edition. Cambridge University Press, London, 1959.

Index